ZELENKO

(1973-2022)

How To Decapitate The Serpent

Zelenko

1973-2022

How to Decapitate the Serpent

Zev Zelenko, MD & Brent Hamachek

PIERUCCI
PUBLISHING
Elevating World Consciousness
Through Books.

Pierucci Publishing books may be purchased in bulk at special discounts for sales promotion, corporate gifts, fund-raising or educational purposes. Special editions can be created to specifications. For details, contact the Sales Department, Pierucci Publishing, PO Box 8067, Aspen, CO 81612 or publishing@pieruccipublishing.com.

Visit our website at www.pieruccipublishing.com

Print ISBN: 978-1-956257-59-5
Ebook ISBN: 978-1-956257-58-8
Hardcover: 978-1-956257-60-1
Audio: 978-1-956257-61-8

Cover Design by Alyssa Yanto
Edited by Jill McKlellan and Dale Chaplin

Proudly printed in the United States of America.

Dedication

For all who lost a friend or loved one to the COVID-19 bioweapon so that they might come to understand that their death was needless, and that in remembrance, they will pledge to employ their reason, skepticism, and resolve to thwart future attempts at genocide.

Never again!

Publisher's Note

PLEASE READ:

This book details the author's personal experiences and opinions about general health, prevention of disease, nutritional supplements, and/or exercise. The author is not your healthcare provider. The Zelenko Labs Team as well as Brent Hamachek are providing this book and its contents as a story on an "as is" basis with no representations or warranties of any kind with respect to this book or its contents. The authors and publisher disclaim all such representations and warranties including, for example, warranties of merchantability and healthcare for a particular purpose. In addition, the authors and the publisher do not represent or warrant that the information accessible via this book is accurate, complete or current.

The statements made about products and services have not been evaluated by the U.S. Food and Drug Administration. They are not intended to diagnose, treat, cure, or prevent any condition or disease. Please consult with your own physician or healthcare specialist regarding the suggestions and recommendations made in this book. Except as specifically stated in this book, neither the authors, nor Zelenko Labs, LLC, nor any contributors or other representatives will be liable for damages arising out of or in connection with the use of this book. This is a comprehensive limitation of liability that applies to all damages of any kind, including (without limitation) compensatory; direct, indirect or consequential damages; loss of data, income or profit; loss of or damage to property and claims of third parties.

Understand that this book is not intended as a substitute for consultation with a licensed healthcare practitioner, such as your physician. Before you begin any healthcare program, or change your lifestyle in any way, you should consult your physician or another licensed healthcare practitioner to ensure that you are in good health and that the examples contained in this book will not harm you. This book provides content related to physical and/or health issues. As such, use of this book implies your acceptance of this disclaimer.

Other Important Notes

In this book we choose to use the term vaccine in parentheses when referring to the COVID-19 injection. This investigative vaccine does not work in the same way as conventional vaccines in that it does not prevent the illness, its intention is to reduce the symptoms. In addition, it has not undergone the rigorous testing of conventional and effective vaccines. For these and other reasons, we have chosen to change the term to Investigational Gene-Based Treatments in certain applicable instances or simply "vaccine."

A Foreword by Dr. David E. Martin

In Shakespeare's Julius Caesar, Mark Antony laments at the funeral, "the evil that men do lives after them; the good is oft interred with their bones."

To know Dr. Vladimir Alexandrovich 'Zev' Zelenko is to know a man acquainted with the nuance of mortality. Like many of you, I became acquainted with Zev during the global madness marketed as COVID-19. At our very first meeting he approached me and embraced me with a confident hug.

"I thank G-d that he's kept me alive to meet you," he stated with a hushed certainty.

At the time, I had no idea what gravity that sentence had to either of us. Standing behind him, Moshe gave me a nod and a smile as though to reinforce the importance of Zev's greeting. He motioned us to three vacant chairs where we sat so Zev could begin his passionate inquiry into the two decades of work I had done to bring the bioterrorism of coronavirus to the public's attention. We discussed the sinister acts of Dr. Anthony Fauci at the National Institute of Allergy and Infectious Diseases (NIAID) and his funding of lethal Gain-of-Function research with Dr. Ralph Baric at the University of North Carolina Chapel Hill. We discussed the patents that had been filed since 1990 on the coronavirus "vaccine," and I pleaded with him to join me in my efforts to break the pattern of calling mRNA a "vaccine" as it neither protected anyone from infection or transmission of any pathogen.

Called away for my speech, I had no idea that this momentary collision of our lives would turn into the collaboration that included frequent conversations, e-mails, a lunch with a governor, and conclude with a May fourteenth, 2022 virtual presentation at the Church of Glad Tidings in Yuba City California, an event during which Zev delivered a benedictory address reminiscent of Moses in Deuteronomy Thirty-Three.

You are holding *ZELENKO: How To Decapitate The Serpent* and are about to embark on a journey that will instruct you with a first-hand account of the historic events. It will illuminate one man's story of his own wandering through the wilderness of self-esteem, professional celebrity and vilification, faith, compassion, and inspiration. His final destination?

On the way to a heavenly mountaintop overlooking a promised land into which Zev could look – a land of Liberty from Tyranny – that would remain elusive during his sojourn on Earth. You will be sitting with a great and honest man, listening to his epic journey to the Source of his passion – his unflagging conviction that he was placed on this Earth for this time to accomplish precisely this mission ordained by G-d.

Reading *ZELENKO: How To Decapitate The Serpent*, I found myself frequently lost in the feeling that we were still sitting on those chairs at our first meeting. Sometimes chasing a tangential thought; sometimes in the meticulous flow of precise inquiry; ever enthusiastic to fully wring from each moment all the wisdom and insight within our reach.

Brent Hamacheck has masterfully preserved the authentic cadence of Zev's conversation so much so that, if you close your eyes every now and then, you can almost hear the melodic syncopation of Zev's voice.

In Exodus Seventeen, the mystery is told of the Israelites fighting the Amalekites. Descendants of Esau, the Amalekites were known to be fierce enemies of Israel using their spears and arrows to deliver death and destruction to the Jewish people. Imagine that! People who would use sharp pointy objects to deliver death to others! Surely no one would do that these days, would they? When the Israelites entered into battle, they were losing… until Moses held up his hands. With this act, he turned the tide of battle. But his arms grew weary and when they dropped, the enemy would win. That's when Aaron and Hur decided to take rocks, prop up Moses' elbows, and hold his hands up so that the battle and the day could be won.

Ultimately, the Amalekites, through their being steeped in evil, allowed forces of evil to guide them and take them over. They became willing pawns for the forces of the Primordial Snake, the embodiment of Satan. Repeatedly, Amalek is defeated, yet, as was seen in the last World War, the Nazis, the most recent widely accepted manifestation of Amalek, rose again, but thankfully was defeated.

The US Government facilitated Operation Paperclip, relocating over 200 Nazi officers, scientists, and engineers. The United States government gave these demons new identities and rewarded them with anonymity and a good "American life" in the State of New Jersey. Many attribute Operation Paperclip as the origins of the Deep State which plagues us to this very day.

In a small way, this book is a metaphor for each of us to continue to hold up the arms of a great man – Dr. Zev Zelenko – and, like Aaron and Hur, keep his arms lifted in the battle against the terrorists disguised in lab coats, infiltrating government agencies, non-profit organizations, and atrociously corrupt for-profit corporations. By continuing to hold up Dr. Zelenko's spiritual arms through our dedication to advocating truth until We The People can win the battle, and the day, for a brighter future for humanity. Antony ends his tribute to Caesar with his lament:

O judgment, thou art fled to brutish beasts
And men have lost their reason!
Bear with me;
My heart is in the coffin there with Caesar
And I must pause till it come back to me.

The good that Zev unleashed on this world will long live after him. The multitude of lives he's saved will forever be a tribute to his life and conviction. And while our hearts still feel the loss of a friend and colleague, we've got a battle on our hands. No pausing!

There's a Serpent to decapitate.

So Be Strong!

Be Courageous!

Hold up his arms through our dedication, loyalty and action. Stand with Zev and decapitate the Snake.

Dr. David E. Martin
September, 2022

Table of Contents

Part One
Where I'm Coming From

Chapter One

These People Are Much More Dangerous Than Any Animal

O n an early autumn morning in 2021, I was awakened by a phone call from my friend, the medical activist and founder of the Alliance for Human Research Protection, Vera Sharav. Vera is a Holocaust survivor, and she had invited me to be a guest on a podcast with her and Robert Kennedy Jr. some months prior. Vera broke the calm of this cool autumn morning to tell me that both she and I had been placed on an assassination list by a radical group based in Germany. This list was located inside the body of an intercepted email, written in German. On it were the names of people "guilty" of the crime of telling the truth about COVID-19 and speaking out against what I had labeled the kill-shot "vaccine" or, later, the "poison death shot."

My first macabre question to her was, "Whose name is higher on the list? Mine or yours?" Despite my always wanting to be humble before G-d, I certainly didn't want to be just some afterthought on a list of the people singled out for opposing the international handling of the pandemic. As it turned out the list was in first-name alphabetical order, with the word "doctor" being treated as a first name. As such, I did come ahead of Vera.

Because of connections I had made as a result of my activism up until that time, I was able to have some very qualified folks check out the veracity of the list and assess the threat. The report concluded that the threat was, in fact, very real—a memo truly was being circulated that encouraged the assassination of myself and other, more prominent, figures.

I am reprinting the entire email here, translated from its native German (so please forgive any awkward grammar), and offering it as a sort of (forgive me) proof of life. While the language is slightly awkward, and the threat seems a bit vague, I can assure you qualified experts verified this as being a carefully worded "hit list." It has since been shared with me that ANTIFA was behind it:

Von: The double vaccinated <address>

Gesendet: Thursday, 23. September 2021 10:21

Subject: The 250 Misanthropes

This is the list of the 250 biggest misanthropes. I'll tell you honestly: for many of them, only a removal would actually help. That's what you do with dangerous animals that get too close to settlements. These people are much more dangerous than any animal. Tens of thousands more people will die because of their propaganda. Would it really be a crime to take out 250 people to save tens of thousands? Of course, this is a purely hypothetical question, because I don't want to incite anyone to do anything, because that would be punishable by law. But how many people would not have died in World War II if the 250 worst Nazis had been taken out in time? In the coming weeks and months, however, these people will realize that you can cause them big problems even without physical violence. All it takes is a notebook.

Internationally there are also a few dangerous corona deniers who should not remain unmentioned. But they are difficult to eliminate from Germany. Here are just a few of them:

21 International Misanthropes – Beginning
Chet Hanks
Donald Trump
Donald Trump Jr.
Doug Ducey
Doutzen Kroes
Dr. Robert O. Young
Dr. Roger Hodkinson
Dr. Vladimir Zelenko
Eric Clapton
Gisele Bündchen
Greg Abbott
Greg Locke
Jair Bolsonaro
Mike Yeadeon
Nicki Minaj
Rand Paul
Rob Schneider
Robert Kennedy Jr.
Ron DeSantis
Tucker Carlson (Fox News)
Vera Sharav
In addition there are Telegram channels, Twitter accounts, and other "sources" listed to support this message whose base source is apparently Antifa. To those of us who didn't get distracted with

expressing our views despite the bombardments of contrary comments and beliefs, good for standing up and expressing your need for the truth or at minimal, not making your decisions based on fear (more on that in Chapter 4.)

Yet, there are also bright spots. These are only 150 of countless German and international celebrities who had themselves vaccinated and at the same time publicly called to do the same. In addition some landlords, who do not want to entertain unvaccinated people and doctors, who do not want to treat unvaccinated people. If you look at this list, you'll quickly see that there are a lot cooler people on it than on the list of 250 misanthropes. David Hasselhoff is on the right side of history. So is Patrick Stewart, Samuel L. Jackson, The Weeknd, and Arnie.

Many of the people on the list have even donated big bucks to vaccination campaigns, Bill Gates and George Soros being two examples. Jennifer Aniston has decided to remove all unvaccinated people from her life. We should all follow her example. Mark Zuckerberg has made sure that contrarian propaganda and criticism of vaccination are immediately removed from Instagram and Facebook when reported. Christoph Waltz, Nora Tschirner, Harrison Ford, Anthony Hopkins, Dwayne Johnson, Leonardo DiCaprio, Morgan Freeman, Julia Roberts and Tom Cruise are openly messing with the film industry, which is dripping with corona deniers, even if it means they risk never being cast again for a film by Til Schweiger. Annalena Baerbock and Robert Habeck made it clear that there could be compulsory vaccination in the fall, even if this statement will cost them quite a few votes.

About me: I can't tell you who I am, because then I'll get in a lot of trouble from some weird lawyers in this wixland (German obscenity). To be on the safe side, I fled abroad to take it down a bit and cure my back problems. But of course, at some point I have to go back. I used to be friends with some of the misanthropes, but looking back, they all just f**ked me. Those people should be ashamed of themselves. I wonder who I trusted all this time. I couldn't stand it in Germany anymore, because there I see my life threatened by the corona deniers, whose secrets I will help to publish in the near future.

To all of you, whose email address I could determine, I sent this mail as well. Thereby I give you the possibility to change to the light side of the power. Any of you who in the next two weeks advocate vaccination, mask wearing and harsh sanctions against the unvaccinated will be forgiven after all. Just as a former Nazi can get back on the path of virtue, so can covidiots like you. Think twice about which side you want to be on. Either delete your Telegram channels or - even better - use them to show the world how dangerous the virus is and how safe the vaccinations are.

DEADLINE: THIS EMAIL MUST NOT BE MADE KNOWN TO A WIDER PUBLIC BEFORE THE POLLS CLOSE (SEPTEMBER 26, 2021, 6PM), OTHERWISE THERE IS A RISK THAT IT WILL INFLUENCE THE ELECTION IN FAVOR OF THE QUERDENKER (Own Name) AND CORONA DENIERS!

They Worship the G-d of Expediency

One could ask why a group like ANTIFA - a group dedicated to worldwide anarchy - would have any sort of vested interest in matters related to a "vaccine?" After all, they are supposed to be anti-fascist (a perversity on its face), so why wouldn't they be opposed to a fascist-like policy of coerced vaccinations?

The answer lies in their commitment to chaos and their willingness to partner with any group or align themselves with any cause that expedites the creation of that chaos. They worship the G-d of expediency. In this case, partnering with globalists provided them the opportunity to keep the pandemic fear alive. People like me posed a threat to their ability to create fear and thereby enable its ensuing chaotic consequences. I was a voice of reason, trying to tell people to stay calm because there was a simple, effective, and affordable treatment for this virus.

ANTIFA's primary goal is to take down the United States as a world economic and military superpower. That also just happens to be the goal of the World Economic Forum (WEF). In this, they are kindred spirits and tacit allies. ANTIFA wanting to target people who stand in the way of those objectives, therefore, made perfect sense.

Once I learned that the threat was indeed real, I took immediate steps to protect my family and myself from a security perspective, even going so far as to arrange private air transportation to avoid the risk of being too easily targeted in large crowds. I also made certain to have a private security detail so that my family members would be safe.

Taking action to create a secure personal perimeter was an obvious necessary step; it is almost therapeutic. It makes you feel like you are doing something; like you have stepped on enough toes and generated enough waves to be seen and noticed. That said, finding myself on an assassination list did create a moment of introspection for me as it related to my outspoken activism during the spread of COVID-19.

First and foremost, it made me realize that I no longer operated with any sense of fear. Fear has been extricated from my psyche because of my medical history. I have been living with the knowledge that my end could be at any moment since I received my cancer diagnosis in 2018. How a person faces that news and processes it depends to a large extent on their spirituality, and also on their psychology. If you accept that your end is imminent, you stop worrying about things that are out of your control. Sure, I did my due diligence and took precautionary security measures, but I wasn't going to let my being an assassination target affect my activities, my activism, my research, my advocating for people's health, and my fighting against tyranny. I was in an acceptance phase. I enjoyed both the energy and the peace that accompanies being in such a state.

People Fear Uncertainty

People fear uncertainty, and the greatest of all uncertainties for many people relates to death. I, however, had the unique perspective of having processed the certainty of my own mortality for three years since my diagnosis. I had already been preparing myself to meet G-d, a fact that is immensely sobering to say the least. I had come to accept that when G-d wants to take me, He will. That holds true whether it comes from pulmonary sarcoma, a traffic accident, or an assassin's bullet. The only certainty is that I will be taken one day. Being on that list made me aware of just how far I had come in terms of that stark understanding; of being surrendered to the certainty of my own mortality and the uncertainty that came with each new day, year after year.

The list was not without consequence, though. It did cause me to take a step back and ask myself the questions: *What is truly motivating my activism? Am I doing it altruistically? Am I doing it to fulfill some type of narcissistic or existential need?* I questioned my motives, and in doing so, I wondered if I could have perhaps used a different tone of rhetoric to accomplish the same thing without being unnecessarily inflammatory.

Ultimately, I decided to not judge myself too harshly. I probably did invite the assassination threat in some way, but that's who I am. That's my style. I'm not really interested in rewriting my personality and temperament in order to avoid or obtain a place on any particular list. I will refine myself only because I need to be refined. I will tweak my delivery style for the purpose of conveying my message more clearly in a way that opens up the mind, not closing it down against my work.

I will not, however, change who I am out of fear. I am not fear-driven. That is a gift from G-d.

The people that decided to target me for possible assassination were likely hoping that the threat would be enough to silence me, that they would not actually need to kill me. After all, if they killed me, they would make me a martyr. If they could just make me frightened enough, then maybe I'd decide to lie low and step out of the fight. That might well have worked had I not been someone who had been given the gift of terminal cancer by G-d, helping a fearless persistence emerge in my work and life.

That list did appear at the very moment I was contemplating writing this book. While it is not responsible for my decision, it certainly did help strengthen my resolve. This is my legacy to share with you, and knowing that whether it was by cancer or an assassin, I might depart this world ahead of an actuary's schedule, and that meant that I'd best get started in crafting my legacy.

I'm Always Learning

When a rockstar creates the setlist to open a concert, they have to decide if they are going to open soft or with an explosion of sound. I elected for the explosion. I decided to open this book with an assassination story because I thought that might get you, the reader, right up out of your seat. Now, let's settle back and share an acoustic set while I share with you just a little bit about myself and why I'm writing this book.

I want this book to be informative, spiritual, antagonizing, and motivational–a rather ambitious goal, I must admit. Many books are written aiming to trigger just one of those reactions. I'm aiming for all four. In addition, I want people to get to know me as a person. Prior to the spring of 2020, I was just a family physician living a blessed normal life and enjoying the same sort of things that many Americans do. Really, I'm no different than any of you; I just had myself placed into a very different and unique set of circumstances.

Over these past few years, I have found myself yearning for calm. On a weekly basis, I find it in my commitment to honoring the Sabbath. From sundown Friday evening to sundown on Saturday, I unplug and enjoy a meditative and spiritual experience in a sort of digital detox.

When Friday arrives, I shower and put on festive clothing. The children are dressed up and happy. Candles are lit and the house is bathed in the fragrance of good food cooking. It is a real contrast to the rest of the week. I will enjoy a good book for an hour or so–usually something mystical or relating to metaphysics. I allow myself to go into an almost hypnagogic state.

When my health was better, I enjoyed regular walks in the woods. I found that time allowed me to reflect and be in closer touch with G-d. I can experience the same sort of tranquility sitting in front of a warm fire, which has become easier for me to do these days than it once was. I love writing, especially the kind of writing that allows for spiritual and philosophical reflection. These simple pleasures are great pleasures. The simpler the pleasure, the closer I come to G-d.

I enjoy movies–especially war movies. My favorite is *Saving Private Ryan*, where I can repeatedly watch the iconic opening scene as they land on the beaches of Normandy. For reasons that are hard to explain to others, that type of movie makes me feel relaxed. What I don't like to watch are movies that feature non-actualized love. I cannot bear the story of *Romeo & Juliet*, where two people who are meant to be together simply cannot.

When it comes to the "telly," I've always enjoyed science-fiction and grew up watching *Battlestar Galactica*. I also played catch-up and became a *Star Trek* fan. Today, I find myself drawn to documentaries. I'm always learning.

My favorite reading, as you would expect given my Orthodox Jewish faith, comes from Scripture. I do, however, find myself reading a good deal of non-fiction as of late to continue trying to satiate that endless quest for knowledge that I thrive on. Beyond that, two books come to mind that have had a sustained impact on me. The first is Michael Morpurgo's *Lord Of The Flies*, which showed how quickly a man, or indeed a boy, can devolve into an animal. I didn't realize it when I first read it, but that book has been distinctly prophetic when viewed in the context of what we have seen during the pandemic. Another book I enjoyed was *The Count of Monte Cristo*. I romanticized the journey from redemptive revenge to forgiveness and then finally to peace. There is much to be learned in that story for all of us.

When it comes to music, as a youth, I enjoyed listening to The Doors, whose music resonated with me because of the chaos I found myself living in throughout my formative years. I also enjoyed the sounds of Sting with The Police. Today, I've mellowed, and when I sit back to listen to the stereo, I prefer the classic sounds of Chopin, Dvorak - especially his *From The New World* symphony - and then Beethoven's Fifth & Ninth Symphonies. And yes, I've seen *A Clockwork Orange*—I wasn't always religious!

I love single-malt scotch. Red or white wine are both enjoyed but they need to be expensive—I am not a Ripple in a brown paper bag sort of wine drinker. Thin-crust pizza is the real deal. Please, no minivan, I drive a Mercedes GT sports car. I love to go to a new fine-dining restaurant and experience their new foods. I prefer mountains to shorelines, and I choose coffee over tea. And to answer the most important question of all personal questions… It's Mary Ann over Ginger!

The Middle-Aged Zev Has Gone Truth-Telling

For somewhat obvious reasons, my cancer has had a profound impact on every aspect of my life. For a start, it has compelled me to reexamine my priorities. It is important for each of us to examine and reassess our priorities at regular intervals in our lives because, quite simply, different phases require different priorities. You need to determine if the way in which you are spending your time and your resources is the best way to address your circumstances.

In early 2022, Turning Point USA founder Charlie Kirk invited me to be a guest on his podcast and afterward was kind enough to write an opinion piece about getting to know me.

It opened as follows:

Years ago, Country & Western megastar Tim McGraw had a hit song titled Live Like You Were Dying. The song's story is that of someone in their early 40's who received a very bad medical prognosis. McGraw asks the man, "how it hits you, when you get that kind of news?" The ill-fated character's famous lyrical response was that he "went skydiving, Rocky Mountain climbing." He also reportedly rode 2.7 seconds on a bull named "Fu Manchu" (presumed mechanical). The protagonist's message was simple: Someday, I hope you get the chance to live like you were dying.

Dr. Vladimir Zelenko, the courageous doctor who has successfully treated over seven thousand Chinese coronavirus patients and who pioneered the use Hydroxychloroquine (HCQ) and zinc as an early-stage enemy of the pandemic, is now living like he is dying but not in lyric; in reality. Dr. Zelenko, or "Zev" as he likes to be called, has a rare and now-inoperable form of cancer. He has defied odds for four years in surviving, but eventually with cancer, like with the house in Vegas, the odds have a way of prevailing.

What has Zev done since he got "that kind of news?" Well, he didn't go skydiving. Instead, the doctor who has saved lives all around the globe through his treatment protocols and who, as a result, has become a nemesis of politicians, big pharma, health agency bureaucrats, and even his fellow physicians, has chosen a different activity in which to engage while he lives as he is dying.

In his early autumn, the middle-aged Zev has gone "truth telling," and Americans who are living in a potentially terminally sick republic should be taking notes.

Those words are kind and humbling, and also accurate. In this moment of my life, I have decided to launch a no-holds-barred attack on the lies and purely evil behavior of our world leaders. I have spent my time relentlessly truth-telling, and this book serves as a continuation and extension of that process.

Each one of us needs to be dynamic, nimble, and resilient. We have to be able to make both big changes in our lives and to adjust through little tweaks along the way. What we cannot do is ever allow ourselves to become locked into one lane, trapped there indefinitely. Changing lanes and shifting directions is necessary because we can never quite predict what is going to happen. You have to allow yourself to be fluid, flexible, and reactionary. Nobody expects the Spanish Inquisition, and I certainly did not expect a terminal cancer diagnosis or the COVID-19 pandemic. The only thing anyone can ever predict is that things will change. As they change, you should adjust to handle that change in the best possible way. The only certainty of life is uncertainty.

There Are No Celebrities During a Pandemic

One of the great lessons I've gained from the pandemic is understanding public figures. Prior to the pandemic, my exposure to celebrities and other well-known people had been minimal. In truth, I often knew them only from the silver screen or the flat screen, and I occasionally pondered what they were really like–just like most people do.

Since the pandemic, I've become highly visible for having discovered a successful treatment and for being outspoken about it. My encounters with the "rich and famous" have been numerous, and from these encounters, one lesson is simply yet prevalent: Famous people are just people, fellow human beings, and they get just as scared of the unknown in the same way that everyone else does. When they have reached out to me, I have listened to them, informed them, and treated them (medically and personally) no differently than I have any other patient. In turn, I have not noticed them behaving any differently than any other patient.

There are no atheists in foxholes, and there are no celebrities during a pandemic, just scared patients.

That said, there have been celebrities who have used their status during the pandemic either to show great courage or, conversely, to join in with the propaganda effort to help promote genocide. I have great respect for people like Nicki Minaj, Matthew McConaughey, and Evangeline Lilly, who have taken public stands against the kill-shot "vaccine." I have the same respect for politicians, like Florida Governor Ron DeSantis, who have taken leadership roles while in office to resist imposing totalitarian-like restrictions on citizens and their health choices.

Then there are the others, the ones that have used their positions of celebrity or political status to help facilitate global chaos. Some have done so unwittingly, but many - I boldly suggest most - have done so deliberately. To me, the poster child for this is Dr. Sanjay Gupta, who sank so low as to appear on Sesame Street and encourage children to get the "vaccine." Keep in mind that children have no reason to fear COVID-19, but they have every reason to fear the effects of the mRNA vaccination. Gupta is a doctor, meaning he knows the "science," and he knows well that there is no need for children to be vaccinated.

Why does he encourage it? You'd have to ask him, but my belief is that he simply wants mass conformity and if that means children dying unnecessarily, then so be it.

After all, it is for the greater good.

How I Chose to Act

I'd like to offer a few more thoughts to set the table as we launch our journey together through the pages of this book.

I decided that when I received my terminal cancer diagnosis back in 2018, I had best write my life's story up to that point. I came to this decision so that my children would have a permanent source of reference about who their father was, what he had done during his time on this Earth, and what he had taken away from that life in terms of thoughts and ideas. That is why I took the time to write both my autobiography, *Metamorphosis*, and *Essence to Essence*, which are my reflections on both philosophy and theology—those defining interactions between G-d and Man.

What I could not have imagined is that I would still be here over four years later and that during those four years, I would be placed at the center of the most devastating man-made pandemic in all of human history.

It became clear to me that my life story had to be updated and that this time, a new audience would be garnered that expanded beyond my children. I have been at the cold face of the fight against the Primordial Serpent that has sought to destroy humanity and I have developed a significant following along the way. While I have made more public appearances than I can count to share my views, I felt it was time to pull them all together in one place.

I also wanted to tell the story of what it has been like to be part of the story, because I never could have imagined this happening. I'm guessing that those who read this still have a hard time imagining it in their lives at times, yet, here we are, and what has happened with this pandemic demonstrates how there are some moments that define us by the circumstances they present us with and how we choose to act.

This story shares how I chose to act.

I am reminded of a famous anecdote told about a reporter asking the late John F. Kennedy how he managed to show such courage and bravery after the PT-109 torpedo craft he was commanding was hit by a Japanese destroyer. Kennedy's simple response is said to have been, "Somebody sunk my boat." Kennedy didn't wake up that morning wanting to be a hero, but circumstances were presented and he acted.

I didn't ask to be fixed in the center of an international viral storm starting back in 2020. I was just a family doctor treating patients. My patients were getting sicker, and I wanted to figure out how to help them. Now, here we are.

My simple goal with this book is to first give you a sense of who I am by sharing my life's journey prior to the onset of COVID-19, a sort of Reader's Digest version of my prior book, *Metamorphosis*. I will then share my battle with cancer, which has both prepared me for performing G-d's work during the pandemic and has hampered me while in His service because of a hamster wheel of complications that have arisen from the disease.

After regaling you with my personal Zelenko life facts, I will give you a taste of the life theory that has come from living through those facts. This will be another Reader's Digest version of a prior work, in this case, *Essence to Essence*, but it will also be distinctly different because much has been revealed to me about mankind during the pandemic. Therefore, some of my "takes" on who we are as people and the evolution of where we stand in our relationship to G-d have been modified, adjusted, and grown upon.

This journey through the COVID-19 pandemic is not for the faint of heart. I will share the journey chronologically for the most part, while taking detours along the way to share my thoughts on topics like villains (Andrew Cuomo, Bill Gates, Klaus Schwab, etc.), heroes, and relevant side-stories. No matter the detour, we will always return to the COVID-19 storyline because I know that is why most of you want to read this book.

To that end, I have inserted three argumentative chapters that I think will be the three that everyone will want to read twice and reference often. They are:

The case for a man-made virus;

The case for treatment, and;

The case against the "vaccine."

I feel that each of these topics deserves its own special self-contained discussion for the reader's convenience, but as you would imagine, each of the three will also be mentioned within the story of the past two years.

How could it possibly be otherwise? After all, this was a virus that was deliberately engineered by men, released into the general population without treatment being permitted, and ultimately used as a way to force an unproven and unhealthy "vaccine" upon billions of people. That is the story, and it is worthy of its place in the pantheons of a great tragedy, worthy of Sophocles, Aeschylus, and Euripides, the great Greek tragedy playwrights.

I am going to use very direct language in this text. An old saying about someone who is very direct is that they don't call a spade a spade; they call it a G-ddamn shovel. I will do exactly that.

You will see words and terms like genocide, mass murderer, satanic cult, slave masters, and Primordial Serpent (I love Primordial Serpent); terms that upset the brigade. I use none of these terms metaphorically. Nor do I use them lightly. I am not a fear merchant, I'm a realist, and these terms are all quite literal descriptions of the kinds of acts and people that we have seen surface throughout the pandemic. We have witnessed the acts of true monsters. Again, not a metaphor.

I will use the term COVID-19 as an abbreviation for Chinese coronavirus. While the Spanish Flu had nothing to do with Spain, this disease has everything to do with China and with its genocidal accomplices in the World Economic Forum, the United States government, and elsewhere throughout the world. It is not a racist term. The term "Chinese" is not referred to as a race. It is a term designated to reflect the origin of the virus both geographically and creatively.

I have created the content for this book by sitting through hours of interviews spanning a period of several months. For me, the process has been both spiritual and cathartic. It has given me an opportunity to reflect, vent, and organize thoughts that had been many and mixed. Through that interview process, I was forced to put these thoughts together in a way that would make sense both to me and, most importantly, to you.

So, please join me on this journey through another metamorphosis. This is one where both an entire world and a lone family medical practitioner have both been transformed.

Perhaps for the better?

Perhaps for the worse?

Definitely for good.

Chapter Two

From Humble Origins: An Ordinary Life With Extraordinary Moments

Everyone is familiar with the common story of the rock band from the 1970s that announces a "farewell tour," goes on that tour, and then five years later announces another farewell tour. Then, they repeat this process twenty years later, and so on…

This book feels a bit like that for me insofar as I had already written an autobiographical book titled *Metamorphosis* back in 2018 upon my terminal cancer diagnosis. That book, intended to be left for my children as the story of their father's life, was supposed to be my "farewell tour."

Yet, here I am again in 2022, embarking on yet another literary road show. Since I have already shared in detail the story of my life up to 2018 in *Metamorphosis*, I'll simply provide some of the highlights of my life that I feel a new reader should know about me. It will help with the processing of the experiences I'll share, and my responses to those experiences, on the pages that follow.

To understand me, you need to know me. Let's get acquainted.

I was born on November 27, 1973, in Kiev, Ukraine. My parents gave me the name Vladimir Alexandrovich Zelenko. This is not to be confused with Vladimir Alexandrovich Zelensky, the President of Ukraine–this happens more often than you might imagine. Being Jews in Europe in the Twentieth Century, I had numerous family members imprisoned and killed during the Holocaust and under the Pogroms of Soviet totalitarianism prior to my birth. My family understands tyranny firsthand and thus, a healthy respect for the savagery of men is part of my DNA.

At the age of four, I came to America with my parents circa 1978. We settled in Brooklyn, New York, after a circuitous journey that took us through both Vienna in Austria and Rome, Italy. At the time, that was the route that Jews were embarking upon when they were permitted to leave the Soviet Union. It is ironic to think that back then, Russia and Ukraine were both part of the USSR. After the Iron Curtain was lifted, Ukraine became its own distinct nation and now Russia is attempting to conquer them again. It is one of the reasons we are fond of the term "The Ukraine," which was a term used to denationalize a country and turn it into a region of the greater Soviet empire.

I have no memories of my life in Ukraine. Interestingly enough, my memories do not truly start until I got to the United States. I find this peculiar and interesting because so many people I know have memories from an earlier age. I'm pretty intelligent, but life prior to four is a mystery and a blank space in my mind. I do know that my parents left to pursue a better life, which to them meant the chance to acquire material possessions and to escape persecution for being Jewish. It was difficult to be Jewish in the USSR, and even though my parents were secular in their living, they still found themselves dirt poor, sleeping on a mattress that they had found lying on the street. To them, coming to America felt like making a journey to the promised land.

Once they arrived in New York, my mother found a job working as a secretary, and my father started driving a Yellow taxicab. To illustrate what a product we become of our conditioning, my father tells the story of being pulled over by a member of the NYPD only a week or two after he started working. At the time, my father spoke only broken English, understanding very little, so when the police officer came to his window and sounded like they were asking him for something, my father tried to hand him a ten-dollar bill. That was the way things were done in Russia. The police officer refused the money and said, "So, you're new here. Here's a piece of advice, don't do this again."

Eventually, my mother went to school and became a computer programmer. She worked for a home insurance company, working her way to a prominent position at Morgan Stanley, where she worked for many years. In mid-life, she developed colon cancer and left her job during her treatment and convalescence. When she resumed her professional career, she did so first as a consultant, and then eventually she joined me to help me run the business side of my medical practice.

Going back to my youth, one thing I remember about myself is the perpetual feeling that I was stupid, ugly, and insecure. My default position was the fetal position, and I would often find myself simply curling up as if attempting to revert to non-existence. Part of why I felt this way was made clear to me many years later when, through therapy, I was able to recall an event from my childhood that deeply traumatized me. It is the kind of thing that as even an only partially well-adjusted adult, you would laugh at and dismiss. For me, as a child, however, it had a profound effect.

Look at that Ugly Kid!

In 1979, I would have been in public elementary school. It was a time made difficult enough by the fact that Americans, generally speaking, didn't like Russians--a byproduct of that decades-long stand-off we call the Cold War. By default, being Ukrainian was tantamount to being Russian, and being "Russian" worked against me. In addition to that, at this time I could justifiably be referred to as "funny looking." My ears were the same size that they are today, whilst my head was half the size. I resembled a non-animated version of Dumbo. The funny-looking kid from Russia, therefore, was bullied a great deal. I didn't enjoy grade school, yet despite it all, that funny-looking kid ended up being valedictorian of my sixth-grade class.

Anyway, let's track back to that traumatic incident that shaped so much of my childhood. I began attending therapy at around the age of forty. This was largely because I was searching for a way to better understand myself. I was subjected to a method referred to as EMDR (Eye Movement Desensitization and Reprocessing). EMDR induced a sort of hypnagogic state and made it easier to talk about things that I normally would suppress. Through EMDR, I was able to recall an incident that occurred when I was about five or six years old.

It was summertime, and I was in the driver's side back seat of my parent's Oldsmobile. We were in Brooklyn, on Ocean Parkway to be precise, heading towards Manhattan. I recall that we stopped at a traffic light, in the middle lane, and a car with a man and a woman pulled up alongside of us on our left. The windows were down, and the woman said loudly to her right, "Look at that ugly kid!"

Now, to you and me, at the ages we are now, this seems small. But to a five or six-year-old whose world is considerably smaller than ours, this wedge itself in my brain and had a severe impact on the way I interacted with the world. When my therapist helped me to recall this incident, it brought into stark contrast things about myself and how I had felt emotionally through my youth and adulthood up to that point. Consider my defenseless, already insecure five-year-old self being called ugly, and obviously not having the skill-set to process that in the right way. That event left an imprint that I had never been able to see and, as a result, could never push away. It had always been there and probably fueled a lot of my spirits.

As a forty-year-old going through that experience and reprocessing it as an older person with a different emotional mentality, I was finally able to overcome that demon. I was able to carve it out of me and put it on a shelf. It shaped me, but it could no longer hold me back.

It certainly held me back as a youth, especially with girls. I never felt comfortable with the female gender and didn't have my first girlfriend until I was in the 11th grade.

I attended a high school that was near Brooklyn College called Medical Science Institute. I was in a gifted program, but I really didn't apply myself. Filled with self-doubt and insecurities, I had a hard time staying motivated and finding my way. After high school, I enrolled at Hofstra University to study chemistry. There, I did find my way academically. I eventually graduated *summa cum laude*, but not after almost transferring to the University of Colorado after my freshman year, simply out of restlessness. Hofstra countered my notion of transferring by offering me a partial scholarship. Up to that point I had been commuting each day from Brooklyn to Long Island which was a good deal in terms of room and board, but difficult from a daily travel perspective. The scholarship from Hofstra made staying there make sense.

My considering transferring after a very successful first year was just another symptom of the restlessness and insecurity with which I'd been dealing most of my young adult life. While my personal demons had stopped me from applying myself during high school, those same demons manifested themselves in a different way once I started succeeding academically. It was as if the success was a drug to which I got addicted and I just couldn't get enough to sustain the high. It is said that addicted people are restless, irritable, and discontent by nature. While I may not be an addict today, I certainly was behaving like one then. I used my personal appearance with torn jeans and long hair as a way to partly rebel and partly to draw attention, but it most likely made some sort of undefined statement.

In deciding to stay at Hofstra I had the good fortune to study under, and be mentored by, my first-semester organic chemistry teacher, Dr. Rosen. He took me under his wing and made me believe in myself. Because of his influence, I moved from being an above-average student exerting only the necessary effort to a stellar student showing lots of effort. I owe him a debt of gratitude. Later on, when I was applying to medical schools, I interviewed at Harvard. Dr. Rosen flattered me when he wrote me a letter of recommendation, saying that I was one of the top students he had taught during his career and he wished there was an A+ grading system so that he could properly distinguish my work.

Dr. Rosen did much to build the self-esteem that I had never truly had but for which I had clearly been searching. I am extraordinarily grateful to him, and today I can fully appreciate through the accumulation of a greater total sense of life awareness just how important he was to me professionally as well as with my spiritual development. He has since passed away, but I hope he left this Earth knowing just how important he was to me.

Unfortunately, at the time, he still wasn't enough to get my head completely into the right place.

Education

I didn't end up at Harvard, but I was accepted into medical school with a scholarship at SUNY-Buffalo in just my third year at Hofstra. For most people, that would bring a sense of joy, but for me, it brought depression. This depression arose because I had accomplished what I wanted, which left me feeling empty. It's a big feat to get a medical scholarship early, but instead of feeling joy, for me it exposed a sense of emptiness. At that point, I still had no sense of who I was. I knew I was "Russian" and an American. I knew I was Jewish but had no ties to my faith. I had no clear understanding of what any of it meant.

Because of my early acceptance to medical school, I had my fourth year at Hofstra free to explore realms that I probably wouldn't have explored otherwise. Having been accepted, all the academic pressure for me had been removed. Therefore, I started studying philosophy and I took a class in classical music, which did instill in me an appreciation for that genre which I have maintained to this day. It was the philosophy classes, though, that revealed something more interesting to me. I was drawn to Nietzsche and

Sartre and their dark G-ds; brilliant but dark. Through their darkness, I started to find revelation.

What stands out especially is Sartre's one-act play, *No Exit*. The premise of *No Exit* is that three people find themselves entering Hell together. In Hell, each of the play's three protagonists expects to be punished with fire and brimstone. Instead, they simply find themselves locked in a room with one another. There are interesting nuances to their mutual imprisonment, with one being that there is food in the room but they cannot bend their elbows, so the only way to eat is to feed each other. After colorful discussions, confessions, attempts to escape, and even an attempt by one to kill another (you can't kill someone who is already dead), they come to the conclusion that Hell is other people. Coming to this conclusion with resignation, the play ends with one of the characters simply saying, "Oh well, let's get on with it."

As a theological atheist at the time, this story seemed to resonate with me and fit my worldview at that time. This play boldly claimed that conflict was the essence of all human relationships, and that Hell was other people. My G-d, then, what was science and empirical evidence? I believed what I could actually see. As for people, well, associating with them up to that point in my life had not gone well. There was no pleasure. Was I perhaps living a bit of Hell on Earth?

I graduated from Hofstra with a 3.99 GPA in Chemistry and a collection of accolades and awards. Prior to medical school starting, I was presented with the opportunity to travel to Israel for a month. This was a birthright-type trip, free for Jewish college students who had never been to Israel before. They had a big financial sponsor and so I went along with a bunch of other Jewish college students from the New York area. Far from looking for a spiritual awakening, I just really went in the hope of meeting girls, and not necessarily nice Jewish girls…

While that might have been my intention, that was not the outcome. Instead of meeting nice girls, I ended up meeting G-d and myself. The trip transformed me, and I encountered my true essence–I discovered that I have a soul. That seems so obvious to so many people, but it wasn't obvious to me. I would just look at the body as a biomedical machine, and so I came to understand that the machinery was simply a housing unit for so much more than just chemicals and electricity.

The trip was laden with a variety of unique and life-changing experiences, and there are several that stand out above others. One was at Wailing Wall during the holiday of Shabbos, which is when we commemorate the giving of the Torah to Moses on Mount Sinai. There were tens of thousands of people there, a mass of humanity, and we were all in prayer and with a fervor that was like something in which I had zero experience. In this environment, I was clueless. That wavelength simply didn't exist for me. Having an analytical mind, I found myself trying to reverse engineer what was going on and reconcile it with my prior belief (or lack of belief) systems. I just didn't know. It was quite an experience.

Another special moment came when I was invited for a Sabbath meal by a local Hasidic family in Sharon Maor, which is an ultra-religious neighborhood in Jerusalem. I still have pictures of myself on that day. I was wearing a green linen Armani suit, hair in a ponytail, and no Yamaka. This was not an Orthodox outfit! I found the apartment and I rang the doorbell (another Sabbath no-no) and one of the children came to answer. Not knowing what to say, I simply said, "I was sent here to eat." Fortunately for me, the family was an American family who had moved to Israel, so they were quite forgiving of my sort of "ugly (Jewish) American" behavior.

They were also seemingly poor, with ten kids. No matter, the ambience, the spirit, the energy that was there, all of it was perfect. It was very ordered. Everyone was dressed the best that they could, the food looked regal, candles were lit, and the smells in the home were simply delicious.

Those were the physical observations, but the dynamics of the meal fascinated me. The father was the king, the mother the queen. The children surrounded the table and the father engaged with each of them, asking what they had learned that week. Each conversation was geared to the level of the child's development, and I found it to be so "beautiful" to witness. I thought to myself, *this is something I want*. I grew to understand how this kind of life could fill something in me that I previously didn't even realize was empty. I stayed in Israel another three weeks after that special evening and perhaps would have stayed longer but I had run out of money, and it was time to start medical school.

The sum of all the experiences I had during my trip to Israel helped me arrive at a higher plane of existence. I have never stopped striving to continue climbing to higher levels of existence ever since.

Hi, Rabbi!

Once I returned to Buffalo, I still wasn't what you consider to be "religious." After a month or two, when I had settled into med school and got used to the routine, I felt something telling me that I wanted to reconnect to the wavelength I had been on in Israel. In an effort to explore this, I found a synagogue and decided to attend services. Still the most "unorthodox" of Jews, I drove there on the Sabbath, which is not what Orthodox Jews do–I didn't even know that much. I pulled into the parking lot and shouted, "Hi, Rabbi!" which is something else that isn't meant to be done. I wasn't trying to be disrespectful; I just didn't know the proper decorum. I didn't even know enough to think maybe I should park a block away and walk in so as not to make people uncomfortable.

I was so innocent and uninformed at that point, but the members of the congregation were receptive to me and wanted to help. As I slowly got to know these families (some of whom basically adopted me), I became the project of the Jewish Community Center. Because there wasn't a big Jewish community in Buffalo in the first place, and not too many, or none at all at the time, who were interested in learning more about Judaism, I benefited from a wealth of support and love. It was at that point that I started wearing a yamaka and began learning about, and settling into, my faith.

Perhaps the most profound experience - definitely an inflection point - I had in developing my deep belief and trust in G-d came in January 1996 when there was a historic blizzard in the Northeast, one that led to over four feet of snow blanketing the area. In the midst of this snowstorm, I called my father in Brooklyn to say hello. When he answered the phone, I immediately noticed he did not sound right.

"What's wrong?" I asked, concern heavy in my voice.

"I was just outside shoveling snow off the car and started feeling sick, so I came back in just as you rang. I'm sure it's just the cold." This is a skill that many men have - particularly from my father's generation - of brushing of illness.

Knowing this, I asked, "What do you mean? What are you feeling?"

"Just a bit of pain in my chest, and a bit of trouble breathing."

"Dad," I said as calmly but urgently as I could, a sudden awareness coming to me, "you may be having a heart attack, you need to call an ambulance." My urgency seemed to register. He put the phone down and called 911.

A few minutes later, I called him back. He was feeling worse and growing more anxious and afraid. I asked him to say a prayer with me–a prayer that at that time was the only one I knew by heart from Jewish tradition. My father repeated it, word-for-word. To my knowledge, that was the first time my father prayed. The ambulance arrived within five minutes of his call, and he was taken to Coney Island Hospital.

As he was being wheeled into the emergency room, his heart went into ventricular fibrillation and he clinically died. However, since he was in the emergency room, the doctor was able to shock his heart and give him the appropriate medications. His heart started to beat normally again, and thankfully, he was revived. My father had, in fact, experienced a serious heart attack and he was transferred to the cardiac care unit.

While this was all happening, I was sitting alone in Buffalo, completely unaware of his condition. I could not reach any relatives for an update and felt helpless.

This was the first time in my life that I sincerely and heartfully prayed. I was four hundred miles away and could do nothing except beg the Creator that my father should live. And beg I did.

After a few days, my father was discharged from the hospital in a stable condition and told to follow up with an interventional cardiologist at New York University Medical Center. My father had a cardiac catheterization the following week, and the results showed that he would need to have open-heart surgery to repair the blocked arteries.

He was sent home and began to prepare for what needed to be done prior to surgery. The next day, however, the doctor called him and said that there had been a mistake and a mix-up with the results. He did not need surgery, instead only requiring medicine to control his condition. It all seemed a bit miraculous, and I was deeply affected by what had happened to my father. For the first time in my life, I was given a true sense that G-d had answered my prayers. My father's heart attack had solidified my faith in G-d and heightened my desire to live according to Jewish law.

My parents reacted to my zealous conversion in a very interesting way. My entering into a religious sort of lifestyle was, shockingly, very difficult for them to process. Things like wearing a yamaka, growing a beard, wearing tallit katan (fringed garment associated with Orthodox observance), and anything external that made me look more Jewish was clearly disturbing to them.

I couldn't understand or appreciate their reaction. After all, it wasn't as though I had converted to Scientology. While it was frustrating to me at the time, and while it led to some very tough exchanges with my parents over my embrace of Judaism (I remember once arguing with my mother and warning her not to make me choose between her and G-d), I have come to understand their reaction over time with my increased level of awareness and maturity.

You see, for the past seventy years up to that point, my family had been experiencing the sort of hatred and persecution that had been common for people of our faith dating back thousands of years. Whether it had been at the hands of the Nazis or the communists, the observance of our traditions had been routinely interrupted with exile, imprisonment, and murder. For my family, and for others in post-war Russia, their Judaism was not something that was spoken about, and it certainly wasn't something associated with positive energy. This history had taught them that it was necessary to hide it. Having a son who was reconnecting to the tradition that had not been outwardly enjoyed since the days of my great-grandfather was very difficult for them.

As my Judaism developed, I started learning more. I found that my appetite for knowledge and understanding was almost insatiable. I took myself through the cycle of Jewish life, the celebrations and observances throughout the year, and I even started to enjoy Jewish "fashion." My need for immersion grew so intense that I took a leave of absence from medical school for a year. In that gap year, I went to live in Israel and I studied in a Jewish school, a Yeshiva, for eighteen hours a day. It was the most difficult of learning and the most rigorous intellectual endeavor I had ever experienced. I was surrounded by brilliant minds and keeping pace required tremendous discipline. I made the effort because I was determined to acquire the skill set.

Judaism is very much rooted in the study and learning of and from ancient texts in the original language, including Aramaic and Hebrew, so there was a lot to acquire in terms of skills before I could even begin to navigate the content. It was imperative to me to gain a complete understanding because I knew that I wanted to get married and live my life a certain way; a life that would be rooted in the Torah, observance of the Commandments, and guided by divine wisdom.

Within the Torah there are many subjects, the ones that resonated in my soul and drew my attention the most were mysticism and metaphysics, so I committed to their study and in turn, my life has been guided by these divine principles.

I left Israel after my completed studies and, in a sense, never looked back at the life that preceded them, save for perhaps that moment in therapy I described earlier.

As I have come to understand the interconnections between events and the progressive path toward G-d's revelations, I perhaps should be grateful to those two anonymous people who remarked upon the ugliness of a child. Without that moment, I might not ever have found my way to G-d. It is certainly easier for me to forgive them and to thank them than it is for me to carry the resentment.

Those were the key moments from my young life that helped to shape the man I have become. From the point of my return from Israel, my life could be considered quite ordinary by any outside party, but it has been anything but ordinary to me.

Jumping ahead twenty-six years, I have eight beautiful children, I have written books about my life and my spiritual journey, and I have had the opportunity to develop close and meaningful relationships with thousands of patients where my form of family practice has made me practically feel like a member of my patients' families.

All of what I have done has been accompanied and aided by the writing in ancient texts that have made me resilient, providing me with both spiritual and emotional restoration on a continuous basis. These texts energize me and keep me balanced. They have taught me to persevere like the great King David because, while my journey has not been easy, it has been guided, like David's, by G-d. I have been forced to confront my own brutal demons, and, over the past two years, the demons among us who serve the Beast. I now have come to terms with who I am and what to expect, and indeed not to expect, from the temporal life.

Back to Nietzsche: I haven't been destroyed by my life, I have been made stronger.

Cain and Abel

The history of humanity is best characterized in the Biblical story of the two brothers, Cain and Abel. Both brought offerings to G-d. Abel's was accepted, and Cain's was not.

G-d's refusal of Cain's offering led to a depression in Cain, and G-d came to him and asked, "Why are you depressed? Simply improve yourself and I will accept your offering as well."

What did Cain do? Did he rise to G-d's challenge? No, in spite, jealousy, and anger, Cain killed his brother.

Cain's actions serve as a metaphor of human history, a history in which the typical response is that "I'd rather kill the competition that makes me feel inadequate over taking personal responsibility for the things that are not yet perfect in my life and fix them."

My life's journey has led me to the exact opposite conclusion. I have learned that you need to force yourself to acknowledge that perhaps you are the source of whatever is wrong in your life. Your life is the sum total of the choices that you have made and the way that you think. You need to constantly analyze situations, process them, and then perhaps restructure the way you approach life or take ownership of your situations. You have to stop blaming others, and that is not an easy thing to accomplish. It requires you to be brutally honest with yourself and before G-d. My path to self-discovery and developing my relationship with G-d has not been linear. I've had many setbacks along the way - some self-inflicted - but today in my life I truly love G-d and I'm grateful to Him for giving me consciousness and the ability to even ponder life's great questions.

He has sent me messages along the way in life, one of which is to be careful about what you say. Years ago, I was sitting at a dining room table in a chair made of the highest quality; quite heavy and sturdy. Someone at the table said something that irritated me, and I responded with a flippant, disparaging remark. The instant the words left my lips, a leg on that brand new, heavy-duty chair in which I was sitting snapped and I slammed my head on the table, almost losing consciousness in the process.

Thanks, G-d. Got it.

I recall another incident, one which happened when I was in my first year of residency. Each month, we would rotate into a new area of practice, and I was just finishing my internal medicine rotation—one of the more difficult areas to master. The process of leaving your rotation and helping transition in the next rotation is called "signing out." I was signing out and going through the patient list with a new entrant to the internal medicine rotation and he expressed to me that he was a bit overwhelmed at the size of the list. In an attempt to be glib and demonstrating poor timing for a "joke," I looked at the list and said to him, "This patient here, he's not so interesting. You can maybe just cross him off the list." At that very instant, our pagers went off and that patient was coding; he suffered a cardiac arrest and died.

That resident was afraid of me for the next two years.

So, G-d has taught me to be careful with what I say, alongside a great many other things, as well. All of these lessons have come to serve me well and they continue to be given as G-d continuously reveals Himself to me.

Like everyone, I have some regrets in my life. I try not to dwell on them, but it is important to be aware of them and acknowledge them. For example, I feel that I worked too much during the formative years of my children's lives. I realized that when my seventh child was born; Shira, my wife, and I got sick, diagnosed with cancer ten days later, and I was homebound for a year and a half. In this time, I saw her in stages of development that I had never experienced with my other children. I was changing diapers and doing the feedings. I was present for the gentle "coos" and for the innocent smiles. I had missed these milestones in the past. I can remember noticing suddenly that one of my children had a mouth filled with teeth and I couldn't even remember any of them coming originally.

I have some regrets when it comes to family. I wish I had made different choices and reallocated time and energy more toward family, and less on my career. I have made changes in that regard. Recently, my second son was approaching his Bar Mitzvah, and concurrently I was presented with the opportunity to make an important presentation with regard to my

COVID-19 treatment protocol that would have been delivered to someone in a position to take action. In contrast to so much of mine and my childrens' lives, I chose the Bar Mitzvah. For me, that was growth, because it wasn't always that way. As I faced my mortality, not knowing how many more opportunities I'd have to spend precious time with them, I found myself making different and better choices. I see each one of my children as being like their own separate world, each one like a unique winning lottery ticket for me. They have been through so much these past few years, first with my cancer, then with my unintended celebrity (and the controversy) arising from the pandemic, and now with my cancer once again.

I've been at death's door eight times in the past four years. They have gone through that with me and stayed with me. They are my greatest accomplishment, and I simply love them and thrive in their presence. It was hard when, during the early days of the pandemic, I wasn't able to see my children because I was committed to finding a way to defeat the virus. My explanation to them is that their father was away from them so that he could find a way for other fathers to be able to be with their children; they accepted that for the most part. When I finally did get a chance to sit down with them, I often found that I couldn't even talk; there was a raw emotion that had overcome me, and all I wanted to do was to sit on the couch and embrace all of them. When I was back with them, I was filled with love.

It is with that love that I carry the worry of how my children will make their way in this world without me. My cancer makes it likely that they will face a world without their father's mentorship sooner than most other children do. While that frightens me somewhat, I take comfort in knowing that G-d loves my children more than I. I cannot worry about things I can't control. They will find their own unique path to G-d–that's the logical, intellectual approach that I adhere to and usually it works. However, sometimes what the mind understands and what the heart feels operate on a different beat. And yet, I know my children will be well, just as I know they will be missed deeply by me.

For today, I still stand. Through G-d's grace and with the help of prayers of hundreds of thousands of people around the world I am still here and I am still working more than years past what the medical community had considered my best case hopes in 2018. It is now time to share that cancer story with you so that you can carry it along as you travel with me throughout the rest of the book. So much of what I have been able to do in fighting back against those who imposed COVID-19 upon us has been a result of the gift of cancer that G-d has given to me.

Without it, I would never have been able to persevere.

There's Nietzsche again.

Chapter Three

Battles, Blessings, and Revelations; My Personal Journey Through Cancer

I t all started with a cough.

Anyone who has been diagnosed with cancer can always tell you when they got the first sign something was wrong. For some, it is a dramatic moment, like finding a lump during an otherwise refreshing shower. A friend once shared the story of someone who was walking down an office hallway only to have his ankle break during a normal stride. That turned out to be the first sign of an advanced spread of melanoma.

For me, it was simply a cough and some shortness of breath that became a nuisance in early 2018. In response, I did what every good doctor knows better than to do, but typically always does, and I treated myself. A few doses of antibiotics and I felt a little better, but I noticed there was still a wheezing caused by bronchospasms (tightening of the lungs). In response, I tried an inhaler which, again, helped a little bit, but my wife noticed I was getting progressively shorter of breath, and it got to a point where I had trouble breathing when completing menial tasks, like taking the garbage out. It then became my wife, not her husband the physician, who decided it was time to get a "second opinion" as to what was going on.

To be frank and reveal my human hypocrisy, I hate doctors. Well, going to them at least. This makes me representative, I suspect, of the general population. Most people don't like going to the doctor–some are even phobic about it. For me, however, as a member of the profession, I know I should probably have a more receptive and positive attitude about the matter, yet I don't. That position has only worsened over the past few years as I have watched my colleagues' deliberate lack of response to COVID-19. In early 2018, that was still over two years away on the horizon. My distrust for my profession was prescient.

My wife took me to her primary care doctor, Lara Zilberstein, in Englewood, New Jersey. I found her to be a very pleasant, competent doctor, and when she examined me, she said the only thing of concern that she saw was that my heart rate was a little abnormally rapid. With that noted, and because of my history, she sent me for a chest X-ray.

The next day I heard back from her, and she said that, "There's something on the chest X-ray, and I want to get a better picture." She ordered a CAT scan and, conveniently, I was at work in my office in Monroe, New York, where we had a radiology center on the first floor. As I wandered down a flight of stairs, I had no idea how many stairs were about to be presented to me that would need to be climbed.

When the doctor reached out to me after the CAT scan results were read, the news wasn't good. After asking me how I was feeling, perhaps with fingers crossed given the news, I was told I had a very large saddle pulmonary embolism. A pulmonary embolism (PE) is a blockage in one of the arteries of the lungs. A saddle PE is when a large blood clot gets stuck where the main pulmonary artery, traveling from the heart, bifurcates and goes to the right and left lung. This is always bad news because here, it obstructs blood flow to both lungs. In most cases, the death rate for a saddle pulmonary embolism is over 50 percent. And I thought that was the problem. Little did I, or my doctors, truly know…

I was sent to Lenox Hill Hospital because that's where my colleagues and I had developed a professional rapport over a ten-year period. They repeated the imaging and confirmed the embolism. I was brought to the ICU for a heparin treatment (blood thinning) using IVs. After a few days, I was transitioned to an oral anticoagulant, or blood thinner. Afterward, I was sent home and told to follow up in three to four weeks to reassess how the blood clot was hopefully dissolving. All of this was taking place in the weeks and days leading up to the birth of my daughter, Shira, who entered this world on February twenty-seventh, 2018

As is customary, we had an event on the Sabbath at our synagogue to commemorate her birth. To get to the synagogue that day, I had to walk down a long hill. That was fine, but what goes down must eventually come back up, and after the ceremony I had to climb that hill. That hill may as well have been Everest. The walk was tortuous, and by the time I got home, I was coughing up blood. My lungs were filling, and I was drowning. I called the EMS system team which I ran at the time, and they came and took me back to the hospital.

A new CAT scan showed that the clot was getting worse, not better, and it was more pronounced, intrusive. I was presented with two choices. Option number one was to use a clot-busting drug called TPA, which would be injected proximate to the clot and upstream from it, kind of like putting Drano into your sink. The hope is that, like its chemical sink-cleaning sister, it would dissolve the clot and effectively reopen blood flow. Option number two was open heart surgery. Here they would open my chest, enter the pulmonary artery, and physically remove the clot.

I understood that the clot-busting drug seemed much more attractive because they didn't have to crack open my chest, but I also understood the theoretical risks of breaking off micro-pieces and effectively seeding my lungs with new blood clots. One of the things that I've been able to do as a physician over the years, and it has impacted my overall method of thinking, is to suppress my emotions and make a risk versus benefit analysis, allowing me to come to a conclusion. For better or worse, but using that approach, I decided to choose open heart surgery. I did so objectively, without letting my feelings get in the way.

On the day of my procedure, March 11, 2018, I went under anesthesia, believing that I was about to undergo a serious operation to remove a blood clot.

A few days later, I woke up in the ICU. I had been heavily sedated and fitted with a breathing tube. I was told that I had been quite combative with regard to the breathing tube (apparently a permanent condition for me) and kept pulling it out, despite being sedated. They eventually acquiesced and removed the tube, leaving me sedated, but breathing on my own. When they brought me out of sedation, almost everything was blurry, but I distinctly recall seeing my wife, my parents, and my eldest son. I was surrounded by love and family.

It's a good thing they were there; I would need that support for the news I was about to receive.

That news was that, when they opened the chest and went into the artery, it was not a blood clot they found. It was a large tumor.

From that moment, the timeline went something along these lines:

They did a tissue biopsy right immediately. By removing a section of the tumor, they could get to a preliminary diagnosis. It looked like a pulmonary artery sarcoma. It had also spread to my right lung and had completely destroyed it. This was playing out while I was on the operating table. My lead doctor, a cardiothoracic surgeon by the name of Dr. Derek Brewster, realized that the lung was going to need to be removed. He brought in a second surgeon, Dr. Richard Lazaro, who was an expert in pulmonary surgery. Together, they approached my parents, wife, and son in the surgical waiting room and asked for consent to do radical right pneumonectomy (remove my right lung), excise the tumor that was in the right pulmonary artery, along with a small portion in the main pulmonary artery, and then repair the pulmonary artery with bovine pericardium because otherwise, I wouldn't be able to pump blood into my remaining lung.

Obviously, my family gave consent. There really wasn't much of a choice.

When Dr. Lazaro told me I had pulmonary artery sarcoma, I had, in truth, never even heard of it. In fact, most people have never heard of it. On average, there are only about ten cases of it per year globally, and those are typically diagnosed at autopsy. That's because it is typically misdiagnosed as a pulmonary embolism.

Think for a moment about what you would do if you went to sleep believing you were to have a blood clot removed, only to wake up several days later and learn you had terminal cancer and was missing a lung. That is what happened to me and it felt surreal… only it was completely real, completely urgent.

I Have Been at War With Serpents Among Us

There are reasons for telling you my cancer story as its own distinct chapter in this book, as well as at this early stage in it before we get to what might be most interesting to a reader, which is my very public journey through the COVID-19 travesty. Everything that follows in this book, everything that I've been able to accomplish - or at least try to accomplish - in terms of fighting against the institutional terrorism that has seen fit to let millions of people needlessly die worldwide, is all directly related to my battle with cancer.

The experience of looking imminent death in the eye and being forced to come to terms with my own likely mortality years in advance of what would be a normal life span has created a sort of personal immunity to the trials and tribulations of this life. It has brought me even closer to G-d than I could have hoped, and I was already exceptionally close prior to my illness.

I am, indeed, walking through the valley of the shadow of death and I am not afraid because I know He is with me.

There is a line in the Stephen Ambrose book, *Band of Brothers*, written about soldiers fighting in World War Two and further immortalized in the HBO miniseries of the same name. It reads:

The only hope you have is to accept the fact that you're already dead. The sooner you accept that, the sooner you'll be able to function as a soldier is supposed to function: without mercy, without compassion, without remorse. All war depends upon it.

I have embraced that notion since the onset of COVID-19 and I firmly believe that I have been at war with satanic forces; Serpents among us committed to evil. They don't frighten me. I'm already dead.

The other reason is to share my cancer journey and its emotional experiences. This is common to many, I know, but if a single person can find value in what I write, that is one person that might not have done so otherwise. The miracle is that I am writing these words in the late spring of 2022, years after that bleak winter 2018, in which I received my diagnosis. Since then, I have had improvements and setbacks, and have been subjected to experimental treatments in the US and in Europe. I have become both a vilified and admired public figure. I have treated thousands of patients and have moved from one pole of our country to the other. I have been the recipient of tens of thousands of prayers from well-wishers, and I have had people take to social media to wish me nothing but the very worst.

Through it all, I am just a man with a family I love very much and children who I wish to see grow up into adulthood and realize the philosophers' "good life." I am just a man facing the same ravages of cancer as do so many other men and women.

I am not alone. You are not alone.

Breaking Down, Building Back Up

Post-surgery, I was littered with staples that held my chest together and I was plagued with a chronic neurogenic cough that lasted a year. Every time I would cough, my chest would stretch and the pain would be almost unbearable; a ten out of ten on the proverbial doctor's subjective pain scale. I was afraid to breathe, but if I didn't breathe, my remaining lung would not expand and adapt the way it needed to. I was given narcotics and they helped, but I was afraid of becoming addicted, so I resisted their use. Finally, the doctor said to me "I'd rather you get addicted than die," so I used the medication as sparingly as I could and upon being discharged, it took me upwards of eight weeks to recuperate enough to walk about twenty feet.

That day when I arrived back home after the surgery, a nineteen-day-old daughter was waiting for me. As I held her for the first time, the emotion I had been repressing finally overwhelmed me, and finally, I broke down under the weight of it all. There was this precious life in my arms, dependent upon me, in part, to manage her needs, and I myself was in such a struggle. It was intense to process, but I knew I had no choice but to live as best as I could with the days allotted to me.

Once I got myself back into motion, I began the search for a cancer treatment specialist. I was referred to three who were widely regarded as the best in the world. In fact, two of them had been students of the third. I decided to go to the professor: Dr. Gary Schwartz of Columbia Presbyterian Hospital.

Prior to finding Dr. Schwartz, I was performing my own research online and what I found was dismal. For my rare form of cancer, the five-year survival rate was less than 5 percent, and even that data only existed for tumors that were *similar* to mine. As I mentioned, my tumor was incredibly rare, so no real data existed. If it did, I'm guessing that the five percent number would have looked good in comparison. I was in uncharted territory.

As I trawled through page after page of research, I did manage to come across one study that was performed in a different context. This particular study was performed with patients that were in stage four cancer with a metastatic form of differing sarcomas. The common element was that they were all deemed terminal. Here, treatment consisted of a standard drug, doxorubicin, together with a monoclonal antibody called Olara. The study showed longer survival rate io its patients, to the tune of a year, and I found that both interesting and worthy of further inquiry.

When I got to my first meeting with Dr. Schwartz, I asked him about the study. He said to me, "You do realize that I was part of the team that developed that study and that my name is on the paper?" Truth is, I hadn't realized that. I asked him if he would be willing to treat me using the protocol in the study as a sort of prophylactic. While my cancerous tumor had been excised, I was obviously concerned about recurrence, given the grim statistics surrounding this form of cancer. Dr. Schwartz indicated that the study was not set to start for about a year or so and that the results wouldn't be known for three years. I told him I'd like to still be around in three years, and I volunteered to become patient number one. Dr. Schwartz agreed.

In actuality, Dr. Schwartz was excited at the prospect because he considered this treatment protocol his "baby," and now he had a chance to get started sooner rather than later. In the weeks that followed, I commenced the treatment and was on it for approximately a month. I started losing all the hair on my body, which was interesting because I hadn't seen my chin in over twenty years. Since my hair was coming out in clumps, I elected to give myself a Marine Corps haircut, just to get ahead of the process.

The treatment seemed to be working. My follow-up imaging showed no recurrence and I steadily started feeling incrementally better. This brought me stability for almost a year, and it was during this time that I wrote the aforementioned books, *Metamorphosis* and *Essence to Essence*.

I slowly transitioned myself back into work throughout the fall of 2018. Although I wasn't seeing my normal number of patients, I was happy to be back to work and I gradually built back my stamina. By the time we reached March 2020, just before the onset of the COVID-19, I was seeing twenty to twenty-five patients per day; still not close to my old routine, but a vast improvement from where I started post-arrival of a terminal form of cancer.

When COVID-19 did hit, I found myself working six days a week, up to twenty-one hours per day from March until June. Initially, I was providing patient care directly, then I made the transition to telemedicine, and ultimately, owing to sheer case numbers, my role migrated to one of supervising my team, completing research, and compiling data. My success with the treatment led me to work on publishing a paper and to try to influence and teach other physicians. My results had been remarkable, and I wanted to spread the word as aggressively as possible.

June 2020, however, had other plans for me: The cancer that had been put behind me for over a year tapped me on the shoulder. A routine scan revealed a recurrence of my cancer in my pulmonary artery and found evidence that the cancer had metastasized and spread to my left hip. I went into surgery on July 20, 2020, and had the tumor removed and my heart valve replaced.

A few weeks later, I went for follow-up stereotactic radiation to the hip. There were three treatments, which I found to be painless. After that, I saw a new oncologist, one who was very experienced, and in September 2020, he put me on a very difficult regimen of chemo—a blend of different drugs. I had two rounds of that treatment before I developed cardiomyopathy, or inflammation of the heart. My heart's ability to pump blood was reduced to 35 percent, which is the same level you would find in someone who has suffered a massive heart attack. When that happens, when the heart stops pumping effectively, and it backs up with fluid. This is what happened to me, and I developed congestive heart failure.

My lung was once again drowning, so I was promptly admitted to the hospital and given diuretics to clear out the fluid. I was placed on a regimen of heart failure drugs and told I would have to discontinue chemotherapy. The new chemo regimen I had been placed on simply was being rejected by my body and it would not be a part of my healing process this round.

After a few months, I felt better, despite residual symptoms. It had been over two years since my original diagnosis and my heart was, amazingly, pumping normally again. The cancer, though, still needed to be treated, so I went back to the oncologist in December 2020, and he put me on what even he described as a horrible drug: An oral version of chemotherapy called sutent. I commenced the protocol and was fine for a while, but then I began feeling extremely weak. In early April 2021, I went into my own office and had a complete blood count test (CBC) done, and it revealed a worryingly low white blood cell count. This meant that my bone marrow, my immune system, had been suppressed by the sutent. It was also during that time that I contracted COVID-19 for the first time. Now, I was in the uniquely compromising position of suffering from metastatic cancer, with a low white blood cell count, and missing a lung while facing a disease that actively attacks the lungs. If ever anyone would fall into the "high risk" category of COVID-19 patients, it was me. I ended up in the hospital for a week and, while I can't prove it, I believe it was the fact that I had been pre-treating myself for the virus that allowed me to survive.

My oxygen level was low, in the seventies, and there were discussions about placing me on a respirator. I told them, "No thanks. I'll die this way." Eventually, the steroids kicked in and I slowly got better. I was finally discharged from the hospital in the last week of April 2021 with my intellect and will intact, but they were residing in what was now a very broken body. I was physically exhausted while simultaneously mentally driven to be of service to others who viewed the pandemic from a different lens than institutions like the National Institute of Health (NIH) and the Centers for Disease Control (CDC).

It was when I arrived home from that hospital stay that I had a late-night encounter, one in which I felt G-d's presence and I heard Him talk to me. The message to this humble and broken servant was clear.

G-d told me to get up.

Florida-Bound

At that moment, a decision was made that my family needed to move to Florida. It was time for a fresh start; a pressing need to escape the hell-hole that had once been known as New York could no longer be ignored.

We moved on the first of May, 2021. The escape from New York was necessary for a variety of reasons, yet it created one not-so-insignificant problem: I didn't have a team of doctors in Florida to treat my cancer. How was I going to manage that when I had no connections?

Well, as it happens, that's not exactly true. I did have one connection, and it was a remarkably good one. Early on in the COVID-19 wars, I had been contacted by a Dr. David Galbut, one of the country's top cardiothoracic surgeons, who resided in the greater Miami area. Dr. Galbut was around seventy years old, and wanted to start operating again. He first reached out to me to learn what sort of precautionary treatments he could take to protect himself from COVID-19, which I was glad to be able to help him with. Through this, we had developed a sort of friendship, so when it was my turn to call on him and let him know about my problematic set of cancer issues and that I was coming to Florida, he stepped in to help me. He put together a top-tier team for me that collaborated and worked together on my case. For me, I knew I needed that level of skill to even understand the complexity of my situation. G-d bless him for how he shepherded me through making all of the connections that became relevant and necessary after my arrival in Florida.

By now, it was August 2021, and time for another CT scan—another disappointing scan that revealed another pulmonary artery sarcoma. This one was located in a place where it was, in essence, inoperable. Any operation would have involved an exceedingly high risk of death on the operating table—not in recovery, but during the procedure itself. I was not willing to take that risk. Conversely, chemo wasn't going to be strong enough. We were looking for alternatives, and so Dr. Galbut connected me with the CEO of the Miami Cancer Institute (MCI), who then arranged for me to see their top radiation oncologist.

It is important that I pause here and recognize not only Dr. Galbut, not only the people at the Miami Cancer Center, but all of the people along this cancer journey of mine who have gone out of their way, above and beyond, to try to give me the most specialized and highest quality of care for which any patient could wish. All along the way, I have been given this sort of red-carpet treatment without ever feeling as though I was entitled to it. I certainly didn't expect it. I have been blessed, almost beyond words, for the love and concern that has been shown to me as a patient. After all of the attacks my family and I have endured, I realize that to some large extent I have benefited from those attacks; for every assault made upon me, there have been acts of kindness and love revisited tenfold.

The MCI's radiation oncologist made the decision to irradiate this tumor. The tricky part was that the pulmonary artery pulsates, which means any tumor located here moves. Traditionally, in order to erase the entire tumor, you would need to irradiate the entire field in which the tumor could be during movement. The problem with that is there is a lot of collateral damage and I only had one lung. I didn't have much lung tissue to spare. No matter what decisions I made for treatment there was ample opportunity for new risks to arise.

There was good news, bad news, then good news. The first bit of good news was that there was a new modality called M R. Linear Accelerator, or MRI- LINEC. The advantage of this machine is that, with a high degree of precision, it could track the tumor and radiate only on the tumor and its immediate area. As a result, it minimizes the margins, reducing or eliminating any collateral damage. The bad news was there were only two machines in the country, one of which was in Michigan and used only for research. Finally, the next piece of good news, however, was the other machine was at the Miami Cancer Institute, which is used in patient care.

Amazed at this stroke of good news, and the luck that I had found myself in the only place I could access this treatment, I went through that radiation process in September, 2021. It was painless, and, to some extent, effective. I wasn't done, though, and in early October my search for outside-the-box treatments led me to traveling to Europe along with my dear friend Moshe Knobel to see the now late Dr. Ralph Kleef. Options were limited, but Dr. Kleef was a pioneer in two such options: Immunotherapy and hyperthermia therapy. In his forty years of experience, I saw potential.

Immunotherapy and Heat

To explain these concepts, it is helpful for me to provide an overview:

Back in 1891, Dr. William Coley had a theory as to how to activate the body's natural immune systems to treat cancer. As described on the NIH website:

> *In 1891, William B. Coley injected streptococcal organisms into a patient with inoperable cancer. He thought that the infection he produced would have the side effect of shrinking the malignant tumor. He was successful, and this was one of the first examples of immunotherapy. Over the next forty years, as head of the Bone Tumor Service at Memorial Hospital in New York, Coley injected more than 1,000 cancer patients with bacteria or bacterial products. These products became known as Coley's Toxins. He and other doctors who used them reported excellent results, especially in bone and soft-tissue sarcomas.*

Despite his reported good results, Coley's Toxins came under a great deal of criticism because many doctors did not believe the validity of his results. This criticism, along with the development of radiation therapy and chemotherapy, caused Coley's Toxins to gradually disappear from use. However, the modern science of immunology has shown that Coley's principles were correct and that some cancers are sensitive to an enhanced immune system. Because research is very active in this field, William B. Coley, a bone sarcoma surgeon, deserves the title "Father of Immunotherapy."

I was drawn to this research and Dr. Kleef's dedication to further studying it.

It is widely believed that the success of his work was buried by the excessively powerful masters of the universe of their day, people whom we would consider earlier versions of Klaus Schwab and Bill Gates, because they didn't want the information to get out; doing so would have eliminated a profit center for those who controlled the population's access to medicine. Hopefully you are connecting the dots between this and the later similarities present in the COVID-19 pandemic, which we shall address later.

When Dr. Kleef, who ultimately opened medical centers in Vienna, Austria, and Budapest, Hungary, was completing his graduate work at Sloan Kettering in Manhattan, where he met Dr. Coley's daughter, who was a very elderly woman at that time. In that meeting, she shared with him her father's writings and he became inspired, taking that research and cultivating it over the past four decades.

Dr. Kleef has also specifically focused on using body temperature as a modality to mitigate cancer recurrence and/or prolong life. In this, he achieved a twenty to thirty percent success rate in stage four cancer. That's not great, but it's better than nothing.

To understand how this works, it is important to identify how the delivery of heat to combat cancer is performed in three ways. One is whole body hyperthermia. To induce whole body hyperthermia, the patient is placed into what is best compared to a sauna, where the patient's body is heated to up to forty degrees Celsius (104 Degrees Fahrenheit). Another method is to focus heat onto just the area of the tumor. The third method, and to me the most interesting, was the use of an IV to administer interleukin two, which is associated with the human fever response. In this process, the patient is titrated and maintained at a specific fever, if you can tolerate it, for two hours.

By accepting this treatment, I was going outside-the-box and into a hot-box.

Dr. Kleef also used other modalities, including checkpoint inhibitors, ozone, vitamin C, alpha lipoic acid, and various other unconventional processes. While I was there, Dr. Kleef told me that he had a colleague who was working on Coley's observation—specifically the use of bacteria to invoke an immune response with the potential to allow that system to finish the job of killing cancer when combined with the induced fever. He felt that the combination represented a likely cure for cancer.

Dr. Kleef also shared with me another crucial bit of information: The problem with Coley's Toxins was that many patients died as a result of this practice because he was giving them live bacteria that was at full strength. What he and his colleague were doing now is using attenuated, weakened bacteria as is done in certain "vaccines". By making the necessary adjustments, and combining it with heat, it was believed that the treatment, and the bacteria is far less likely to be fatal, instead invoking an immune response that is site-specific. For example, bacteria like Klebsiella will invoke an immune response in the lungs, whereas certain staphylococcus can invoke an immune response in the skin of tissue and bone. E-Coli can invoke an immune response in the digestive tract. This list is not exhaustive.

The treatment in Europe seemed to have had some degree of success. I returned home and had a follow-up imaging done, which showed that my inoperable pulmonary artery tumor had, in fact, decreased in size. Unfortunately, though, there was something small found in my left hip. A decision was made to wait two months and have another image taken.

Tragically, I learned shortly thereafter that Dr. Kleef had died from COVID-19.

For those two months in between scans, I underwent a form of immunotherapy (a hybrid of the treatments used by Dr. Coley and Dr. Kleef) which involved a subcutaneous injection every other day. This therapy was supposed to actually increase the size of my pulmonary artery tumor because, as the immune response occurs, white blood cells infiltrate the tumor causing an inflammatory reaction. As a result, there is an initial increase in tumor size, which hopefully, begins to decrease. Another scan completed on April 10, 2022, showed that the pulmonary artery tumor was not active in a PET scan, meaning that it was dead or dormant. It was still around the same size, but it didn't "light up" on the PET.

That was good news. For now at least

A recurring theme in this cancer odyssey through which I've traveled is that, like Newton's Third Law of Motion, for each action there is an equal and opposite reaction. In this case, when my cancer seemed beaten, it pushed back. In this instance, the pressure from the tumor created a compression fracture at my L3 vertebrae, leaving the bone destroyed. I also had a large area of activity or lesion in my hip. My conclusion was that site-specific immunotherapy actually worked because it kept the lung cancer at bay, but like a version of metastatic Whac-A-Mole, a new problem had emerged.

I was then sent to Dr. Gary Onik. Dr. Onik is interesting in that he is an interventional radiologist who had his own bout with stage four prostate cancer that also involved metastatic bone lesions. In response, he created his own treatment, which was administered by a colleague, utilizing five different checkpoint inhibitors. Tumors are smart; they are able to make themselves invisible to the immune system by creating a sort of cloak so the immune system cannot detect them. If the immune system cannot detect them, then it cannot attack them. Checkpoint inhibitors remove the cloak, making the tumor visible, which spurs the immune system into action. After consultation, Dr. Onik and I decided to proceed with that treatment.

We started the process in early May 2022. It had been decided that we would leave the L3 tumor alone because of concerns for its instability, which could result in a neurosurgical emergency. What we did was focus on my hip. Holes were drilled right into the tumor in my left hip and it was injected with large doses of checkpoint inhibitors. I also took daily shots that would raise my white blood cell count, because, in military terms, if we're sending soldiers to the frontline, you want to have a lot of soldiers.

As was the case with my prior immunotherapy, he warned me that if the process is working, then the tumor is going to grow, and the symptoms are going to get worse. He even told me that if the tumor in a month was shown to be bigger, don't call him—it's working. Even for a man of science, these types of realities are hard to easily accept, especially when it is a question of your own mortality.

Problems arose, however, after the third week, when I started to suffer from a severe shortness of breath. This shortness of breath meant that I couldn't walk up a flight of steps. At rest my oxygen level was ninety-seven, but if I climbed one flight of steps, it dropped into the seventies. In response, we took a follow-up image of the original pulmonary artery tumor and it had almost disappeared. It seemed that the radiation did the job. This begged the question though: What was causing the shortness of breath? I took yet another CAT scan, and in a fresh sucker punch, a new tumor had emerged in the right ventricle with a large blood clot on top of it, partially obstructing the flow of blood from the right ventricle to my remaining lung.

I was admitted into the hospital with what was apparently bad news, but what could also have been very good news. It could mean that Dr. Onik's treatment was working. It increased tumor sizes as predicted, and in the process, allowed us to pick up the tumor in my right ventricle, which had not previously shown up on the CAT scan.

The question was, what now? If the clot were to break off, that would punch me an instant ticket to Heaven. While it had been nice to have so many people tell me that they knew I was Heaven-bound after I left this life, I was still up for the fight, armed with the hope that is where I'd be going. Most people cannot feel so confident and certain about themselves. If they do, they have a big problem because they are probably not repenting the way they should. I'm left to hope and pray that what people say about my post-temporal existence comes true, but for now, I'm doing what I can to preserve this life to permit for a bit more prayer and preparation.

In consulting with the doctors while I was in the hospital, I knew I generally had a decently high risk tolerance. I wanted them to go in through the veins or arteries and try to suck out the blood clot; a sort of all-or-nothing procedure. My team of doctors, the ones that Dr. Galbut helped me to assemble, convinced me that a regimen of heavy blood thinners for a few weeks could weaken the clot enough that the tumor could be radiated through what remained. We could then resume a regimen after receiving some proof that the concept of radiation combined with Dr. Onik's checkpoint inhibitors was working.

If all of that isn't enough for you, there is more. We had one last option available to us, which was to go to Dallas for a type of hyperthermia treatment like Dr. Kleef's, but with a whole new level of intensity. There is a team there that has been pushing the edges of human physiology. They've discovered that tumors die at forty-three degrees Celsius, but unfortunately, so does the person.

The solution? Raise the body temperature to 42.5 degrees. This is done in the operating room under full anesthesia and a respirator. They route the blood through a machine, like a sort of bypass process, and they heat it in a controlled fashion to raise the body temperature to that 42.5-degree threshold. Then, they keep the patient at that temperature for a few hours in the operating room.

The risks are tremendous because what they found was that as the tumor dies, it releases toxins through tumor necrosis that can cause the cardiovascular system to collapse. This is in addition to other issues like electrolyte abnormalities. The bottom line is that humans are not meant to live at those body temperatures. They try to counter this by having full teams of people standing by, each dedicated to the micromanagement of any one of the possible complications that can arise.

If a person can survive the procedure (they have only done about fifty of these at the time of writing), the results are remarkable. They have seen people who were previously on hospice care out routinely jogging again. I wasn't living in a fantasy, but I did appreciate the thoughts of being one of these people who were able to jog again, and I wasn't even a jogger.

Here in early June, 2022, my game plan was to continue blood thinners for another few weeks, with the logic that, hopefully, they would take care of the blood clot. Then, there would be imaging to assess the effect of Dr. Onik's checkpoint inhibitor treatment. Next, I was to undergo radiation treatment to hopefully finish off the tumor in my right ventricle. Finally, I would likely then go to Dallas and nuke any cells leftover, a sort of scorched-earth policy for anything not already eliminated by prior processes.

This is the story of my cancer journey right up until this stroke on the keyboard. Perhaps I should have waited to write this chapter until the book's final conclusion so as to have been able to give a sort of "final" report. The problem, as you can clearly discern from reading all that has preceded, is that I really have no way of knowing how or when this journey will end. If my blood is heated to 42.5 degrees Celsius, that end could come quite quickly and surreptitiously on an operating room table.

There is a chance you will know the end of my cancer story before you ever read this.

Best for me to tell the story now.

Running Into Battlefields

This journey through cancer started when I had just turned forty-four, had been recently divorced from my first wife with whom I had six children, and just prior to the birth of my first child (seventh overall) with my new wife. It has lasted through the birth of child number eight (my daughter Liba, born August 7, 2019) and the greatest manmade onslaught of disease the world has ever seen; a pandemic that has altered the course of history and one for which I discovered the first effective treatment, despite being vilified and persecuted for having done so. As they say, history will eventually reveal the truth.

I have been asked by some people how I have been able to continue through this process without just finally saying "enough." I'll answer the "not giving up" question in a moment, but first I want to share what this gift - yes, I said gift - of cancer that G-d has given me has done for me.

By viewing cancer as a gift, I am reminded of something that a mentor of mine told me a long time ago. He had been to prison, and whilst he said that he never wanted to go and would never want to return, he also said that he would not trade the fruits of that experience for anything. It is a variation on the overused Nietzsche line of "what doesn't kill you makes you stronger."

As I mentioned earlier, this experience, this journey, has prepared me in a way that nothing else could have to get through the COVID-19 pandemic. Of course, I would have preferred to not have developed terminal cancer. Perhaps a healthy Zev might have still done just fine, but if everything were different, nothing would be the same. The fact is that I do have terminal cancer and it has made me a better person.

The main fruit of this cancer battle is how I have come to terms with facing - and no longer fearing - uncertainty and the unknown. I can only speak for myself, but I think it is true for most people that uncertainty leads to anxiety. This anxiety stems from having an unhealthy relationship with uncertainty. A healthy relationship with uncertainty allows you to understand that it is a divine mechanism put into place to facilitate the growth of consciousness, the growth of perception and intimacy, and the ever-expanding potential to have a relationship with the Creator.

When I encountered my cancer, an unknown, I encountered one of the many anomalies of life in which I didn't know what to do next. It was like stepping onto a battlefield and I found myself having my relationship with the Creator intensifying and growing. Now, I find myself running toward fear. I run toward anxiety. I run toward situations that may induce anxiety and the mysterious because it's in those battlefields that I discovered that for which I had been looking.

Allow me to define life and death in terms by which I have come to understand them—it's counterintuitive to what you may think. I'm a doctor and have been trained to perceive what is life and what is death, but as a Jew and spiritually-oriented person, I define it in a completely different way using two statements. First, *the wicked are called dead, even when they're alive.* Conversely, *the righteous are called alive even when they're dead.* If we define G-d as the life of life, then the relative proximity to the life of life is what makes someone alive. That does not involve being in a body. The opposite is also true as you distance yourself from the Creator. The more distant you are, the more dead you also are. In that context, I have a very loosey-goosey relationship with my body.

Referring back to my *Band of Brothers* comment earlier, when I say that I'm already dead, what I mean is that I am ready to allow this body to go into the ground and to be liberated from its mundane constraints. I'm not going to be proactive about it, because I believe G-d has set a mission for me. There's a saying that goes, "Against your will, you live." In many ways I find that to be true. I want my soul to bask in the glory of the Divine, rather than have to deal with this world. That, to me, is a no-brainer. At the same time, there is a difference between what I want and what G-d wants. It seems to me to be proof that since I woke up this morning, He wants to remind me that He is in command. So, it's against my will that I live because I accept the yoke of hope. That brings me to the concept of surrender. Surrender, not by giving up but by surrendering to the will of G-d, who will do with me as He wishes.

That is the answer to the question of why I continue to pursue such aggressive and extreme experimental forms of treatment. It is not because I am afraid to physically die, it is because I feel G-d's presence urging me on to physically live. He is not done with me here on Earth, and until He is done with me, I will do all that I can to continue to fight and carry out His work. Whenever he is ready for me to transition, I will be ready almost by definition.

Having been diagnosed with incurable cancer and being told there were really no effective treatments drove me to look for answers on my own. I had skin in the game when it came to finding some way to extend my own life. What was born out of necessity and desperation - the search for answers not readily available - has quickly become a habit that has served me, and all of those that have been treated using my protocol, well over the past couple of years.

At the beginning of the COVID-19 pandemic, when there were no answers, I was already predisposed to searching for answers no one else had. I had been neural pathing to not accept the statement, "There's nothing we can do." My thought pattern was *there must be. I just have to find it.* So, I searched and started on a path, the documenting of which will be the subject of most of this book.

When I was thrust into the epicenter of the COVID-19 pandemic, I came under great personal and professional attack. My enemies, the enemies of humanity who have resisted letting people be treated and who have forced a "kill shot" disguised as a "vaccine," sought to vilify and intimidate me so that I might self-silence.

They made a serious miscalculation. It is just the reality that when someone believes that they are on the way out and are about to stand in front of G-d for final judgment, there isn't much that any man or men can do to intimidate them.

When you're in that mindset, you stop being afraid of human beings. I wasn't in that mindset in 2018 and 2019, but by 2020, I most certainly was. I realized that, although I had been prepared to die, G-d had said, "I don't want to see Zev yet. He still has a few more things to do." I was steeled and prepared to be put on a direct collision with the Primordial Serpent and his tentacles that had slithered in, masked as our leaders in government and medicine.

People who have been responsible for my security joke with me that they don't want to give me a Kevlar vest because then I'll really let loose. Over time, my rhetoric has become stronger, and I have become even more outspoken. I call a murderer a murderer. I speak of genocide. I call out the influence of Satan among our global leaders. I taunt them. There is no truth I'm unwilling to tell.

I repeat, though I walk through the valley of the shadow of death, I fear no evil, for Thou art with me.

So, what are we dealing with when it comes to the man-made COVID-19 pandemic? I believe that this is war. The consequence of losing this war is the death of G-d consciousness in society and ensuing global tyranny and enslavement. There is everything to lose, to be blunt. While I want to be able to be here to experience every milestone in my children's lives as would any father, it doesn't appear likely that I will get that chance. What I can do is teach them one of life's most important lessons which is to do what's right, not what's easy.

My relationship with G-d has become quite intimate and emotional over these past several years. Each day, whether I am battling cancer or the Serpent that has deliberately unleashed COVID-19 upon humanity, I engage in battle knowing that G-d is my shield. Cancer cannot cause me to die, and men cannot remove my joy in living. This is the *how* and the *why* in my journey through cancer. It has made me clearer in my mind and brought me nearer to my G-d.

Now let me share how it has shaped my thinking on the relationship between G-d and Man, and where we stand today as His children.

Chapter Four

Reflections From The Messenger

*W*hen Zev and I originally outlined this book, Zev's intention was to have three chapters open the book that would give readers a glimpse into who Zev is before launching into his harrowing account of the pandemic. It is through understanding his family, faith, and most importantly, the surrender with which he lived his life since being steeled with a terminal cancer diagnosis, that you can appreciate his daring courage during the pandemic.

Since Zev passed away prior to being able to revise and extend his remarks, this chapter is as close as we can get to directly lifting his original words from a series of recorded interviews prior to his passing. The minimal alterations I've made are simply for the purpose of framing, and to make the transition from the purely conversational to the written.

Brent Hamachek, July 2022

Pausing to Behold Divine Providence…

The story of my life over the past four years is so latent with Divine Providence and the hand of G-d that it illustrates itself. My intuition is that what seems to be a series of single, random, and unconnected events, when taken together and viewed panoramically, will be seen by anyone who is willing to acknowledge the hand of G-d that He has been present throughout all of it and guiding my way.

Of course, they can't see that unless I share the experience with them. And, so, I write.

Another reason I write this book is that the process is incredibly cathartic for me. I've written two previous books, and I have to say that the process of going through the self-reflection that writing compels allows me to integrate events and process their meaning better. It also has a healing and restorative effect. I've been through many trials in the last few years. I say to people, "Don't let this calm demeanor fool you." The best way I can describe my feelings is metaphorically by expressing myself as if I am coming off the frontlines of battle having witnessed carnage for over two years. Writing this book allows me to take a step back, to breathe in and process what I have experienced. In doing so, I am helping myself and I believe I can help others.

I've had issues my entire life with what is referred to today as "self-esteem." As earlier chapters have suggested, I have carried the feelings of being stupid and ugly with me most of my life, but through these past two years, whatever I might think about myself or my shortcomings, I am certain that I have been thrust by G-d's hand into the role of Messenger.

Through all of this, truly for the first time in my life, I feel mission-aligned. I feel like I'm doing what G-d wants. Logically, I have no way of knowing if it's real; that I am indeed a Messenger. Frankly, I don't know if anything is "real" or "true" just because it's in my head and my thoughts. However, if you look back two years and see that the ideas with which I've been blessed and the knowledge that I have saved the lives of millions of people, that's pretty good evidence that it's true. Therefore, I feel rather confident that I can write to you as the Messenger.

The healing I have performed and the lives I've contributed to saving were not from my individual ideas anymore than they were from my work as a physician. It was a Messenger thing, and I wouldn't be so emboldened as to take credit for its existence. I simply have allowed myself to be open to being led by G-d. I know that many people throughout the world have come to look to me as being a sort of leader. In that regard, I'm reluctant, as it isn't a role I've sought out because I feel as if I've been the one led along the way.

And still… no one is asking me what I want. If I had my choice right now, what would I want to be doing?

I'd be in Northern Israel in the mountains. I would be enjoying the Kabbalah and getting lost in ideas of mysticism and faith, all found within divine books.

However, G-d has made my choice to be his Messenger, so I must carry out His message. That is why I write. I write to share His message of my journey. A dear Christian friend of mine said to me that, with regard to the revered pilgrimage sites associated with his faith, you don't have to actually visit the site physically to experience the miracle. I like that. So, nobody who reads this book can visit the physical sites of my personal journey, but perhaps they can experience the miracle that it has been.

Understanding Altruism, Risk Taking, and Leadership

During the COVID-19 pandemic, we heard the call to "act altruistically," enough so that it was a mantra of sorts, repeated by those in positions of leadership. Let's reflect on this.

Altruism is an oft-evoked concept that seems, to all intents and purposes, to be used by different people in different ways. Many Christian leaders use the term in describing Christ's teaching, which is interesting because the term itself only came into the vernacular eighteen hundred years after the death of Christ and was popularized by the noted atheist, French philosopher Auguste Comte.

Altruism is fundamentally about a form of self-sacrifice. Let me define it in the context of Divine service.

Understanding Altruism, Risk Taking, and Leadership: The Hierarchy of Love & Fear

I believe that there is a hierarchy in the development of a relationship with the Divine made up of the juxtaposed states of love and fear. Moreover, there are two levels of love and two levels of fear. The order of the conscious development in service of the Divine goes like this:

1) Lower Fear
2) Small Love
3) High Love
4) High Fear

As I share this, I am not making value judgments on humankind. Rather, I am defining terms as I have come to understand them.

Lower Fear is best described by the following statement: *I am afraid to carry out a sin because I don't want to get punished by G-d.* This reveals a basic fear of punishment.

Small Love says, *I want to serve G-d when I get good stuff. I want a long life. I want good health. I want a nice wife and good kids. I want to be respected. I do not want to get punished.* In terms of consciousness development, it's natural to be in this stage of Small Love because we're born as small animals that are completely self-centered, so the concept of self-transcendence and connecting to something outside of ourselves, or bigger than us, can be somewhat challenging. It requires a mindfulness that many of us are lacking, and it requires analysis, experience, and maturation.

High Love, also known as "The Great Love," takes this form: *I want to serve G-d because I want to cause my Father in Heaven pleasure and I do not want to transgress the will of G-d because I do not want to cause my Father displeasure.* Here, the emphasis is on G-d, not one's self.

High Fear is a result of having attained the highest level of love for G-d, being certain of His existence, and knowing that the betrayal of that knowledge has damning consequences. *I serve G-d purely for serving G-d.*

THE HIERARCHY OF LOVE & FEAR

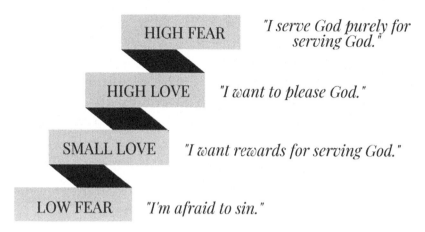

HIGH FEAR — *"I serve God purely for serving God."*

HIGH LOVE — *"I want to please God."*

SMALL LOVE — *"I want rewards for serving God."*

LOW FEAR — *"I'm afraid to sin."*

In my construct, altruism in its proper sense is found in High Love. When people ask me if I think my work has been altruistic because of the suffering that my efforts have brought upon me through public lies, threats, and humiliation, I respond that I am uncertain if such is the case. I say that because I'm not sure if I have been serving myself or serving G-d. The truth is that it's a dynamic process. The battlefield is perpetually changing, and there have probably been elements of both along the way; there is a ratio to these things. Very few people probably reach the ideal of serving G-d purely for G-d. Because we're locked in a body, and the body has its needs, it's a natural part of the human condition to need to focus on the self in order to survive.

This awareness has led me to analyze my true motives over the past couple of years. Perhaps I'm altruistically serving the needs of G-d, but another potential motive is maybe I simply want to die a hero's death. Maybe I want to go out as a martyr. This feels logical because I am subject to an incurable form of cancer. What do I have to lose? As a passage in the Kabbalah states: "You live against your will." In many ways, I'm alive against my will. I am alive against my will because I see deeply what is going on in our world. I see malevolence and I see darkness. I have suffered tremendously, both physically and emotionally. Consequently, to me personally, if there was no collateral damage to others, I don't know if I would offer the world much resistance. I wouldn't do things to be harmful to myself or others, but I wouldn't necessarily go out of my way to commit good works.

But it's not about what I want. The question is: What does G-d want from me? And what do the people – my children, my wife, my parents, my brother, my friends, my patients – want? What do they need? How does G-d call upon me to sacrifice for them? When I frame these thoughts in that manner and look at my duty to serve G-d and to sacrifice, the answer is that I'm not ready to go on vacation (my metaphor for the life beyond this one). I feel I still have work to do, and I choose to do it with the kind of inner sense of duty that sometimes feels contradictory to my own will.

The truth is, if I felt I truly had my own choice, and if there was no blowback or negative consequences on others, or indeed on my relationship with G-d, I wouldn't mind checking out, even as I share this. My work, though, isn't done; my sacrifice and altruistic work is not complete until G-d decrees it so.

Understanding Altruism, Risk Taking, and Leadership: Leadership in The Face of The Serpent

When asked about how he showed such leadership and courage following the PT-109 incident, John F. Kennedy reportedly replied simply that "somebody sunk his boat."

Kennedy didn't ask to be a leader at that moment; the moment asked him. If nothing else, in that way I am humbled by my reputation as a leader, which I gained by simply doing my job. I am a doctor who treated and saved patients, and then I enlisted others to do the same. Yet, somebody sunk my boat.

There are two types of leaders. There's the cult leader who wants the followers to blindly attach themselves to him so that he can manipulate them. Then there are true leaders. True leaders derive their pleasure from watching their followers develop the skills to become leaders in their own right—to function independently of the mentor. In this sense, they aim to see the student become the master. A true leader doesn't relish the recognition. In my case, I hereby deflect any praise of my leadership to direct your attention to my source: To G-d.

Allow me a moment to pause to reflect on the notion of martyrdom. In this book I've detailed the moment I learned that I was on an ANTIFA assassination list. Following my cancer diagnosis, I learned the art of surrender. I have experienced the freedom of detaching myself from my mortal outcome, save my desire to protect and provide for my family once I am gone. I have become aware that the decision to become a martyr isn't mine.

Over the past two years, I have resisted the most lethal forces in creation; forces that are evil in the true Biblical sense of the word. Each of the lead actors of the pandemic, including Gates, Schwab, Harari, Fauci, Dr. Ralph Baric (who will be discussed later in the book), represents the primordial embodiment of the Serpent, or evil incarnate. Together, and even individually, they represent a formidable enemy. As a result of my battle against them, I've been looking right into the eye of that Serpent and saying, "F#@k you." There are people who will not only cheer when I leave the planet, but they would likely be happy to give me a push. I know this and I am at peace with it.

The facts of this knowledge were made clear to me sometime back. They came to stark clarity when I made a post on social media, in which I said that every American home of law-abiding citizens should own a shotgun. Of course, they must have proper training and be in accordance with the laws of their states, and, of course, that shotgun would need to be stored in a way that doesn't give children access.

That said, I believe that every American home should have a shotgun, period. In defending our homes from either intruders or governmental tyranny, we prefer buckshot to bullets. A shotgun will neutralize an enemy but its shot is unlikely to go through walls, potentially causing unnecessary collateral damage. I do not condone reckless actions that can harm the innocent (unlike the CDC or NIH).

I wrote that post in alignment with the Second Amendment, careful not to cross any lines that might incite violence. My intention was, and still is, to advocate for proactive security measures. Coincidentally, my activism during the past couple of years has compelled me to develop intelligence assets in various places. One well-connected ally and friend shared with me that the FBI discussed my shotgun "recommendation" and shortly thereafter considered a dawn raid at my home. The potential raid was intended to intimidate and harass an American citizen who had done nothing wrong.

Ultimately, they decided not to raid my home, but not because I was innocent of any wrongdoing; it was because it would only bring more light and publicity to my work, thereby allowing me to be even more impactful. Thus, I was spared the potentially platform-elevating raid.

If I was a PR strategist and wanted to take out a threat, I would take him out early. Thankfully, the FBI and the government missed their chance to take me out before I had accrued some level of fame. Had they acted aggressively when I was already well-known, that act would trigger a higher level of consciousness in the minds of the very people they were trying to enslave. It would add "political martyr" to my obituary.

That's one of the reasons I believe that, if I am martyred, it will not be the decision of my murderer, but of G-d's. He may have determined in his Infinite wisdom that my assassination will help the true narrative spread by elevating me to a certain hero status. I risk altruism, but I am willing to sacrifice myself to propel G-d's Will.

I'm not an actuary, but I do wonder if G-d might one day say, "Well, in the grand scheme of all the infinite calculations, this would be a good time to make Zev a martyr for the purpose of the revelation of Divine knowledge." Until then, my day-to-day operations include gratitude for the day while trying exceptionally hard to be G-d's PR agent. Hopefully, this book will inspire you to do the same. And that, too, is why I write.

On People & Power

The pandemic has changed my views on humanity, not universally, but by segment. When I examine the people in government: The politicians and bureaucrats; the people in positions of authority overseeing healthcare; and the titans of large industry, in particular the pharmaceutical companies, I no longer have any confidence, trust, nor faith in them.

I find this desperately sad because these are the people we have been systematically taught to trust the most. They have betrayed us, and they're being exposed, caught red-handed while withering away in denial.

This is not a universal statement because, naturally, I believe there are individual stars and exemplary human beings in each realm; even among politicians. Overall, though, they have performed not just badly, but in a way that has been beyond homicidal: it has been of the purest evil.

Decent individual human beings can be found almost anywhere, but our institutions have all been corrupted by the same unG-dly influences.

Throughout the pandemic, we have all borne witness as those in power placed their filthy boots on the throats of millions of people, letting them die and suffer needlessly while simultaneously forcing many to inject a poisonous substance into their bodies. People ask me what could be the motivation behind these people: Is it about money? Is it about power? Are they just harming others en masse for sport? I believe it's about power and the preservation thereof.

I had a friend in Monroe, New York, who was a politician. He used to say to me that the game was all about power. He would use Michael Bloomberg as the example of somebody who acquired extraordinary amounts of wealth and used it to attain and hold on to power. Bloomberg's wealth, he would say, was never enough. It was only a means to an end. For Bloomberg, so many others, the real payday was power. It's like the line from the famous Al Pacino movie, *Scarface*: "First you get the money, then you get the power." To the elite, money is a tool, a means to an end, not the end itself.

Power in the wrong hands allows for a manifestation of the narcissistic need to be a deity who tries to manipulate, control, and destroy others. The killing or causing of others to suffer becomes a sort of sport at that point. Perhaps there is a sort of sexual element to it in that by stepping on the hands of others, they get themselves off from the thrill. I think that, deep down, these kinds of people hate themselves so they transfer it into a hatred of humanity. Hurt people hurt people. Their exercising of power is part adrenaline rush and part aphrodisiac. It has a most seductive effect on them.

This is the story of human history. The only new element we've introduced is the recent development of a man-made bio-weapon for these monsters to use as foreplay. Imagine, if you will, what Hitler or Stalin would have done with COVID-19. I certainly know what they'd have done to me had I been alive during those times and speaking out with the honesty and directness that has become my habit over the past few years.

There is a saying that is attributed often to Gandhi, but I suspect there is insufficient evidence he ever actually said it. "First they ignore you. Then they laugh at you. Then they fight you. Then you win." I have experienced each of these stages over the past two years and now, I find myself in the stage between being fought and finally winning. What I win is the joy of watching millions of people wake up to learn that their leadership has been lying to them about virtually everything during the pandemic; I've been compelled by G-d to help them with that awakening.

The Divinity of Individual Humanity

While my trust in leadership has been perhaps permanently destroyed, my faith in the sovereignty and Divine character of individuals has increased. I have chosen to see the unexpected, heroic, self-sacrificing behaviors from average people that I never anticipated. These heroes stand in direct contrast to the cowardice we've seen within the supposed leadership of humanity.

I've become a fan of a decentralized, almost blockchain-like type of societal structure. The second a system becomes centralized, it allows the few to subjugate the many. We have witnessed and been subject to the evils of that subjugation during the pandemic. Centralized systems in society also facilitate the corruption of otherwise good individuals through the intoxicating effect of power over others. Men were meant to be ruled by G-d and to serve Him, not to serve the self-interests of capricious leaders.

In a decentralized setting, it is easier for individuals to see the spark of Divine goodness than when attempting to gaze at it through a behemoth of organizations and institutions; it does not exist in those places. That also goes for religious institutions, and while there have been notable exceptions, for the most part we have not seen our religious institutions step up in support of individual rights; modeling faith and confidence in G-d during the pandemic. Instead, they have acted like sheep, following the wrong shepherd.

I have witnessed that spark of Divine goodness consistently in recent years as I've been fueled and humbled by the outpouring of love and gratitude that I have received from tens of thousands of everyday people from all over the world. While simply visiting a local restaurant, my table will typically be approached by at least one or two groups of people who introduce themselves and express gratitude for my work. Many have stories about how they or a loved one was treated with my protocol and came through COVID-19 without complications.

Knowing that my work can save millions of lives is a profoundly humbling realization, yet I remain a novice at this. At times, I find myself speaking with people and lapsing into a certain zone of consciousness, and I do not remember what I have said when I'm finished. I understand this is a common phenomenon with artists, where they will create a beautiful painting, take a step back and look at what came out of them, and fail to recall who did it. The painting might sell a week later for 10,000 dollars, but while they painted there was a transcendence; almost a nullification of their sense of self. I feel that way sometimes.

This is akin to what I feel when people approach me and tell me what I've contributed to them; it's like they are showing me the finished painting. It is at these points that I realize that I have simply been a conduit, G-d's conduit, to bring an idea, in this case a treatment, into the world. The gratitude shown by people reminds me of G-d's gift given to me.

The most touching part of this was when I got sick; the amount of concern, love, blessings, prayers that were sent toward me and my family was awe-inspiring. I have been blessed with the ability to effectively heal and help people from across the globe. While we may never know the true extent of my impact, I feel grateful in the knowledge that it's been measurable before I die. I'm an artist whose work has been adopted while I'm alive to see it; how fortunate I am.

Yet It Moves

I've long been a sad admirer of the great but tragic life of Ignaz Semmelweis, the 19th Century Hungarian doctor who discovered antiseptics. Ignaz Semmelweis, known by many as the "Savior of Mothers," was the first to identify the existence of harmful germs, or bacteria, because he observed that doctors would perform a surgery, notably childbirth, and complications due to infection would often arise. In many instances, babies would die from infection. He made the connection and thought: Maybe surgeons should wash their hands in between procedures. In modern times, we see the intelligence and logic in this. For Semmelweis, however, this innovation led to him being professionally destroyed, vilified, and dying in a psychiatric hospital. Posthumously, he was vindicated, and now he has a medical school named after him. Galileo suffered the same sort of fate as Ignaz, as did so many others. There is a legend that says that when Galileo was forced to recant his heliocentric model of the universe before the Inquisition in order to spare his life, he mumbled under his breath, "*eppur si muove*" (yet it moves). I am blessed in that I have not been forced to mumble, and that people in my lifetime know that the Zelenko Protocol "moves."

I have lived to see the value and acceptance of my work by those who choose to receive the gift that G-d has bestowed upon us. For every attack I have suffered at the hands of the government, the press, and even my own medical community, there has been one everyday citizen who has visited me with love and prayers tenfold.

Most of human history has consisted of the many living under the thumb of a tyrant. Knowing this, I fear for those supportive everyday humans who have fueled me with their gratitude and prayers. It stands to reason that, to at least some extent, it is the tendency of man to allow himself to be ruled by others. I have learned from Scripture that only around twenty percent of Jews left Egypt and followed Moses. The rest remained, exhibiting a sort of Stockholm Syndrome. It is with fear that I must admit that people might not have the ability, willingness, or the combination of both to wake up and fight back against their oppressors. They will accept their defeat and mourn it behind closed doors.

Through a combination of critical thinking, prayer, and Divine revelation, I became inspired to reverse engineer the worst crime in human history. This virus was brought to man by man; what remained was a trail of breadcrumbs large enough that it should have been impossible to trip over them.

How wrong I was. To this day, many fail to see how they have been deceived or seem incapable of thinking one nanometre beyond what they were told. This means that, while I feel much hope, and while I have seen much goodness, much of humanity finds itself at a tipping point where people are either going to collectively wake up and rise up, or they are going to return to a state of sheep-like compliance. The pandemic may have been our last best chance to create a critical mass of energy within people and have it be the catalyst for change.

Nothing, of course, does more to hold people back at a base level than fear. People in power know that if they can generate a sense of fear in others that those living in that state will become pliable; easy to manipulate and control.

On Fear

"You are entitled to know that two entities occupy your body. One of these entities is motivated by and responds to the impulse of fear. The other is motivated by and responds to the impulse of faith. Will you be guided by faith or will you allow fear to overtake you?"

Napoleon Hill, Outwitting the Devil

Fear has been the subject of philosophers, then political scientists, and then psychiatrists for more than two thousand years. There are numerous theories debating its usefulness, its damages, and the exploitation of those who suffer from it. Perhaps the first person who made fear a centerpiece of his work was the English political scientist Thomas Hobbes, who, in his 17th Century work *Leviathan*, suggested in part that humans were so fearful by their nature that only the rule of a strong monarch could provide them with the sense of security they craved. He proposed that humanity was destined to be ruled.

A view of the past two years, and society's response to the pandemic makes it hard to argue that Hobbes wasn't right. The fear that was created so quickly and profoundly on such a mass scale allowed those in authority to control people, even "free" people like Americans, virtually overnight. It wasn't just death people feared; it was the general sense of uncertainty that sent them cowering to their basements with windows sealed and masks on, sometimes even when only in the presence of their own company. Uncertainty may not be as intense a cause for fear as is the threat of death, but uncertainty serves fear's purpose. Combine uncertainty with a fear of death and you have a population that will do just about anything you tell them to do; it's the blind trust that someone else knows what is best for them.

On a personal level, acknowledging my long-running battle with cancer has led to my relationship with uncertainty changing. In my past, uncertainty in my life often led to fear. Now, when I come into a situation of uncertainty, I hit it head-on with a smile. Life is a beautiful mystery. The unknown fills it with adventure and provides countless opportunities for broadening consciousness. Uncertainty is a source of mystery that takes me to the deepest dimension of reality.

I would wish for everyone to have that same gift and embrace uncertainty; to embrace uncertainty and see its existence as a way to access the unknowable aspects of the soul. Uncertainty should serve as a positive call to action and a chance for self-discovery. We should run toward it and embrace its unknown mystery with joy, because the unknowable is the origin of a person's pure, simple faith in G-d. Faith begins where knowledge ends. That mystery of life brings immeasurable opportunities for the expansion of self-transcendent consciousness, which in turn leads to an increasing unity with the essence of G-d and the revelation of His presence, even in this very moment as you read (or listen to) these words.

Unfortunately, this is not the way most people view uncertainty. Instead of seeing it as an opportunity for self-discovery and furthering their connection to G-d, they see it as a mysterious force that causes them fear. Over the past two years, many people have lived in an almost perpetual state of fear. Fear has become their baseline, and you don't need a doctor to tell you how extremely destructive it is to exist within a constant fight or flight mode. An epinephrine-induced sympathetic nervous system fueled with adrenaline, which is meant to be only used in certain instances and for a short period of time, has become the state of rest for many. This is the sort of thing written about by the psychologist Dr. Mark McDonald in his book, *United States of Fear*. People are becoming psychologically destroyed by their fear–exactly what the leadership has craved. Through fear, brought about by unhealthy relationships with uncertainty, people can be controlled.

Three Habits Of Faith

We are right back to Hobbes.

In the opening credits to the book *Outwitting the Devil* by Napoleon Hill, we learn that although this manuscript was written on a manual typewriter in 1938, locked up and hidden by Hill's family for over seventy years because they were "frightened by the response it would invoke," the CEO of the Napoleon Hill Foundation, Don Green, stated, "It was the objections of Hill's wife, Annie Lou… didn't want the book published because of the role of the devil."

Imagine that a manuscript was written detailing the blueprint that the Devil has ostensibly concocted to overtake the world -a strategy underpinned by fear - and that the manuscript was hidden for seventy-two years because of that fear. Hill's wife and family members admitted outright that they were all consumed with fear about what the result would come of unleashing Hill's account of his discussion with the Devil.

Now, I don't mean to sound as though I do not experience fear, because like every other human, I do. Fear is a natural and beneficial response to danger. I am also not here to chide or wag my finger at you for reacting to fear. Again, this is natural, it is what the fear response is for, and it is difficult to overcome. I have, however, chosen to relegate fear to the background, to the extent that it no longer has a domineering grasp on me. As you learned about me in this book's first chapter, in 2020 I was informed about my presence on an ANTIFA assassination list. It is worth remembering that I have two small girls living with me at home, so naturally, I have made a concerted effort to protect myself and my family, such as by procuring a security detail and flying on a private plane when I travel. This is for protection, but it is not driven from a place of fear. Fear would render me incapable of leaving my home. Instead, I freely walk my path without allowing fear to consume me. I am allergic to fear, and I'm allergic to the tyrannical people who are trying to hold it over me.

Conquering fear requires a mix of both faith and reason. If you allow fear to displace reason, fear governs you. If you have enough faith to move fear back to a primal instinct as opposed to a constant companion, you overcome fear.

A series of bad decisions over decades, maybe going back to the Enlightenment, have ushered in the moral degradation of society. As part of this moral degradation, the Divine presence has been removed from many people's consciousness. Without Divine presence, people attempt to survive through reason alone. Paradoxically, people have become less and less capable of reasoning because critical thinking skills have gradually diminished. As a result, when they face fear, they face it alone, without G-d, relying only on their impaired human ability to reason.

People may viscerally feel that they have faith in G-d, but I have seen acts of cowardice by those in spiritual leadership and acts of faith and bravery from those in which you would not expect it. It is for that reason that I have become cynical; words that people say have become irrelevant to me.

My own ability to conquer fear originates from two sources: G-d, and the examples of others who show courage and sincerity and who take action. Happily, the ability to conquer fear can be learned; it can be imitated. Although we're sickened with rampant abuses of power around us, we are wise to imitate the courageous, the sincere, and the brave.

When I started to see the work of Dr. David Martin, a seemingly fearless man who exposed the real villains at the very outset of the pandemic, I became inspired. I'm still in the process of discovering who the bad guys are. He knows exactly who they are, and he has been fearlessly taking them on. In Dr. Martin, I found someone I could look up to and try to emulate, someone who compelled me to raise my game. Through the example of Dr. Martin, I am engaged in a constant process of development, one in which I haven't even begun to mature. I am still learning courage and how to conquer fear, right alongside you.

Faith, reason, and just a bit of mimicry are the ingredients we need to remove fear as a state of permanence and relegate it to its proper role of a protection mechanism against physical harm. It's there to protect us in that moment when we are faced with a sinister character in a dark alley or those knocks on your door from someone at the CDC telling you they are there to do a "wellness check" on your family. It's not meant to be your baseline.

Is Fear the Baseline or the Background?

Faith, reason, and mimicry can be either accessed or denied through the exercise of free will. People are capable of either conquering fear or giving into their fear and allowing it to overcome them. Those who are aware of the struggle of light and darkness around them are wise to practice biofeedback. Use self-awareness to gauge whether or not fear is the baseline or the background. For instance, I can sense when fear is beginning to take hold. I have become conscious of it, and I have countermeasures ready to deploy against it. The problem is, if I don't recognize it in time and it secures a foothold, then it becomes much more difficult to stop it. I believe that everything is determined in heaven (except for the belief in heaven itself) and so free will actually means to open yourself up to receiving G-d's message and acting upon it. Free will is the willingness to accept G-d's will, but only if you are open to receiving it.

As you calibrate this self-awareness and biofeedback and become more in tune with your intuition and more grounded in your reasoning, you learn how to choose your battles. You'll know when to hold 'em, fold 'em, walk away, or run. This intuitive, grounded decision-making skill is what I call discernment. Discernment allows you to move thirty thousand feet above your present moment fear, adopting a helicopter, disembodied view, and identify whether or not it's merely a test. I simply would not still be here if I hadn't learned to temper my own instincts. Return fear to the minor character it's designed to be - a primal warning system - and relish the peace that comes from a life of faith, reason, and, of course, continual improvement by the mimicry of conscious humans around you.

I have detailed my faith in previous books that I invite you to find, study, and share. However, because G-d plays a central role in every aspect of my life, I do wish to share some thoughts on G-d that I feel are especially relevant to the remainder of this book and the "COVID storm" through which I've sailed.

Chapter Five

On G-d

Considering my health, I don't take awakening each day from slumber for granted. I arise and state, "Well, I'm still here. He isn't done with me yet." I am in G-d's service and shall remain such until He decides otherwise.

Those who know me will almost constantly hear me speak of tranquility, serenity, and surrender. Prior to the last couple years, these characteristics were elusive. Counterintuitively, my trials have ushered me into the fullness of serenity and surrender. I was born for this; an inner voice and sense tell me that everything in my life up to this point has been preparation for this moment in history.

The Talmud says, "There is no greater joy than that experienced through the resolution of doubt." As to the purpose of my life, I have no doubt. That assuredness and confidence gives me serenity. When that which is difficult is overshadowed by the sense that you're doing the will of G-d, you are in alignment with purpose.

The Deep Clean

G-d is doing a deep clean on the Earth, and so, we are all presented with a choice: Drown in the floodwaters or get in the ark. This is a binary choice, allowing those of us who are awake to clearly distinguish good from bad as though we are in the Garden of Eden, before a state of sin existed. You see, Adam and Eve knew exactly what it meant to take and eat fruit from the tree. The bite from that apple launched us into a post-Original-Sin state. In the post-Sin state, good and bad are enmeshed. In this state of confusion, things are less clear-cut. Today, it takes a lot of digging to extract and discover the diamonds; we are swimming in a sea of evil.

With discernment, we can more easily identify the good. To assist you in discerning good versus evil, particularly with regards to the government or in pandemic-related messages, there's a simple test. Whoever promotes fear, whoever tries to isolate or scare people, and whoever creates barriers between one person and another, is simply an instrument of evil. Fear leads people down a path of destruction, making it a tool for darkness.

Knowing this truth, how then can we identify good people and leaders? One sure determination is that they encourage the reintegration of people and their friends, family, or loved ones. Good people and leaders help build strategies for people to deal with fear by creating conscious awareness of the greater global scheme that we're experiencing. Those are the people we mimic because they will help us become brave enough to withstand the schemes of the evil ones.

Good people are typically people who are G-d-centered, even if they are not formally religious. In my experience, there are many atheists who are more G-d-centered than some who are formally religious. People who spread hope, whether they intend to or not, are spreading the message of G-d's existence and love. G-d is the source of all love, and having Him constantly and dynamically involved in our lives is the antidote to fear, which fills a vacant psychological and physical space where G-d's consciousness is absent.

Consciousness & Free Will

Over these past two years, I have become hopeful for humanity on a macro level. The consciousness of G-d is gradually rising. If two years ago our baseline was a level one, I would say we're now at a solid three, with the goal of transitioning our collective consciousness to an average level of four.

Consciousness is awareness of G-d. Higher levels of consciousness provoke in us questions about G-d that have been asked for millennia. Among those is a variation of, "if there is a G-d, why did He give us the pandemic?"

This is a worthy question. My answer to it is this:

What makes you think that you were born to experience only good? What have you done with your life to deserve exclusively good things? Despite decades of self-centered choices, do you also experience good in your life? Have you nevertheless made choices that have contributed to the destruction of the world?

Let's return back to the concept of free will. The ability to make choices is a gift from G-d. He created the possibilities for both good and bad and has made them equally appealing. What we do not do well is connect the cause and effect of our own choices. This is fundamentally self-awareness.

Now, imagine I give you a beautiful crystal as a gift. This crystal is priceless, refined, and delicate, but you fail to guard it well and it falls, shattering. Then, you cut your foot on it while walking, and start to bleed. Did G-d make you cut your foot?

You may think you weren't personally responsible for creating COVID-19, so why should G-d allow you to contract it? Going back to the macro level, are any of us truly innocent? Just because we did not put on a lab coat and play with Petrie dishes, that does not mean we haven't been negligent in not doing what we could have done to help prevent a circumstance where people in lab coats could play with viruses in Petrie dishes! We have made choices, and we have made choices even by sometimes looking the other way and refusing to choose. That is a choice in and of itself.

There is a simple film from some decades back that had as characters two friends who grew up together, a Catholic and a Jew, both of whom liked the same girl when they were young. The Catholic went on to become a priest, and when the girl resurfaces he must deal with feelings of internal conflict. In one particular scene, he is talking to a more senior priest and is lamenting his life. After running off a list of various complaints, the character says, "My life wasn't supposed to be like this."

The older, wiser clergyman says to him, "It wasn't supposed to be anything."

Exactly.

Our lives given to us by G-d are to be only that which we choose to make of them. They are not preordained. We must allow ourselves to be open to hearing G-d's voice and accepting G-d's instructions if we are to live what philosophers call "the good life."

I believe there is an answer discovered in the simple, singular account of Abraham and his son Isaac. This lesson was brought home to me through a conversation I had with a dear friend, Robert Bernstein, a rabbi in Monroe, New York.

Early in the story, G-d told Abraham that his son, Isaac, would be special. Abraham and his wife Sarah were miraculously blessed with a son at the age of a hundred and ninety. G-d promised Abraham that through Isaac, all the nations of G-d's people would issue forth. Then, only a few chapters later, G-d tells Abraham to sacrifice Isaac. That's a logical inconsistency. What is even more puzzling is that Abraham woke up earlier than usual in the morning with alacrity. He was highly motivated – psyched up – to do it.

Now, Abraham wasn't stupid, which begs the question of how he processed this dichotomy with such enthusiasm. To further compound the issue, Isaac gladly goes along with him. Nothing makes sense.

Until it does.

Up to this point, Abraham had served G-d through his faculty of reason. He had deduced or derived that there is a G-d using logic, and everything up to this point was a rational relationship with G-d. Now, we can make an argument that Abraham's mind was the most brilliant mind in the history of the human race, but, in comparison to the Infinite, his mind was insignificant. Abraham knew that there is a higher level of consciousness or connectivity with the Divine which transcends reason, but he had never been really challenged with that–that is, until G-d told him to sacrifice his son; the son he waited so long for, the one who was supposedly destined to carry on his name and help populate G-d's chosen people.

Abraham must have a calculated the situation through a lens along these lines:

> *OK. G-d is perfect. He keeps his word. He does everything right. He's asked me to do something which is logically impossible to reconcile with the previous statement. The problem is mine, not G-d's, because I cannot use reason to truly understand the source of reason.*

Abraham knew that his initial lack of understanding was his lack of perspective. Accordingly, this meant he intended to sacrifice his son, so much so that an angel had to call out his name twice to stop him. Only a human being who is aware of the dimension of time has the wisdom to make sacrifices in the present for the benefit of the future. Abraham's story is an even higher level of consciousness. He was willing to sacrifice his future in order to benefit his present, and in turn to get nearer to his G-d.

Abraham began to discover G-d at the age of three. Up to that point in his life, his relationship with G-d was based on reason and logic. Through intellectual analysis of the physical world, you reason that there must exist a divine consciousness that created and continues to create all in existence; an "unmoved mover," in Aristotle's terms. However, Abraham also understood that there were severe limitations with the use of reason in trying to connect to G-d. The intellect does not have the ability to grasp its own source. This was true even for Abraham, who may have possessed the greatest intellect in human history.

I repeat, reason cannot be used to grasp the source of reason.

When G-d asked Abraham to sacrifice Isaac, Abraham was driven by a spiritual exuberance and by the thought that he could finally connect to G-d in a transcendent way. Abraham set his rationality aside in order to fulfill G-d's command, and, therefore, he did not receive G-d's command to sacrifice Isaac as something contrary to G-d's righteousness. G-d's command to sacrifice Isaac was Abraham's test and final trial. His success in this trial was only possible because he had succeeded in his first, which was to leave the comforts of what was familiar to him and to follow G-d. Scripture says that G-d told him to go from his land, from the place of his birth and his father's house to the "Land of Promise." Over time, G-d commanded Abraham to build four different altars, the last of which was to be an altar of provision, meaning that G-d was telling Abraham to connect with the essence of his soul. This happened through his acceptance of the need to sacrifice his son, Isaac.

I have learned much from this telling and interpretation of Abraham's story. Through these past few years, I have felt as though I have been instructed to do things that seem contrary to what I have been told before. G-d giving me cancer seemed contradictory to G-d giving me the strength and perseverance to complete medical school. Years were invested in my learning how to save lives and now He seemed to want to take my mine. My future has been taken away, but my present has had greater meaning and I have drawn ever closer to G-d. The more He reveals, the less I realize I know, and the more I realize that I don't need to know. He knows.

Socrates said that the only true wisdom is in knowing that you know nothing. I came across a variation of that in my readings, which stated that the purpose of knowledge was to know that you know nothing. This means that you actually have to know everything, but once you have put the puzzle together and you do know everything, the puzzle tells you that you know nothing. Not to try to know is unacceptable. In other words, the faith trophy lies where reason ends. A person is obliged to push his faculty of reason to the ultimate extreme, to its boundary, and then realize that there is a point beyond which it is inadequate. You have to do your due diligence. I don't believe you have a heart; I know you have a heart. I have held hearts in my hand. There are things that we can come to know, and we are obliged to try to come to know them, but beyond that, we must believe.

I believe I don't exist. I don't understand it, but I believe there is nothing but G-d, and a logical derivation from that is that everything is zero in relation to Him. I know I seem to be a healer, but that is not a logical conclusion. I take the principle that has been taught to me that there is nothing but G-d and try to reconcile it with the fact that I see a world, I feel myself, but I have learned an ability to self-transcend and lose myself in something bigger than just me.

This can sound too abstract to some, and perhaps crazy to others, but to me it is fundamental. To understand my journey through the pandemic, the one through which I am about to take you, you need to understand that I did not go on this journey alone, nor in a real sense did I go on it at all. It was, and is, G-d's journey, and I trusted Him enough to allow myself to be led so that I might discover Him in the present moment regardless of what it meant to my future moments.

I learned the lessons from Abraham. He was smarter than me, but I have been the best student I could possibly be.

Other Musings & A Segue

I have to tell you, I'm tired. Having experienced such a high dose of emotional voltage and charge, nothing in my life is normal. Everything has been highly charged for an extraordinarily long time. I understand the sentiment where people feel that they want to express their affection and gratitude, and I welcome it. I'm aware that it could seem like I needed this or looked for this to happen. I didn't; never have I sought attention or acclamation. I try to be gracious and make people feel comfortable, not bad, for interrupting me if I'm sitting with my family at a dinner table. I do my best, but it depends on my frame of mind.

I am regularly reminded of a conversation I had while in residency. I had a professor, a Doctor of Psychology, who said to me, "If your three-year-old daughter makes you a cookie, and you tell her that cookie is not good, she'll be one hundred and nineteen at her nursing home and still feel the pain that her daddy rejected her." I never want to be the person who leaves a mark of hurt or rejection upon another human being. Yet, the struggle has been real. To do what I have done in the poor health that I have been in has seemed almost impossible at times; almost too much. I remind myself that I'm not doing anything–G-d is doing it and until He is done with me, I cannot be done with anything.

I have been outspoken, sometimes seemingly recklessly so, yet I live only with a sense of duty and without any fear. I live that way not because I am special, but because I have been open to receiving Divine revelation. You need to have an open mind to receive the gifts that are available for you, even if those gifts aren't easily recognizable as being such at the moment they are presented. You have to be able to believe.

Before we enter the COVID Storm, allow me to share a favorite story of mine that comes from the Baha'i faith. So poignant is this simple story that I often pull it out and read it aloud to guests. It captures the simple essence of the need to believe.

In a mother's womb were two babies. One asked the other: "Do you believe in life after delivery?" The other replied, "Why, of course. There has to be something after delivery. Maybe we are here to prepare ourselves for what we will be later."

"Nonsense," said the first. "There is no life after delivery. What kind of life would that be?"

The second said, "I don't know, but there will be more light than here. Maybe we will walk with our legs and eat from our mouths. Maybe we will have other senses that we can't understand now."

The first replied, "That is absurd. Walking is impossible. And eating with our mouths? Ridiculous! The umbilical cord supplies nutrition and everything we need. But the umbilical cord is so short. Life after delivery is to be logically excluded."

"Well, I think there is something, and maybe it's different than it is here. Maybe we won't need this physical cord anymore." Insisted the second.

"Nonsense. And moreover, if there is life, then why has no one ever come back from there? Delivery is the end of life, and in the after-delivery, there is nothing but darkness and silence and oblivion. It takes us nowhere."

"Well, I don't know," said the second, "but certainly we will meet Mother and she will take care of us."

"Mother?" Replied the first, "You actually believe in Mother? That's laughable. If Mother exists then where is She now?"

The second said, "She is all around us. We are surrounded by her. We are of Her. It is in Her that we live. Without Her, this world would not and could not exist."

Said the first: "Well I don't see Her, so it is only logical that She doesn't exist," to which the second replied, "Sometimes, when you're in silence and you focus and listen, you can perceive Her presence, and you can hear Her loving voice calling down from above."

Now, let's walk through the greatest deliberately man-made pandemic in all of history.

Part Two
The COVID Storm

Chapter One

In the Beginning, Man Created a Virus

As December 2019, merged into January 2020, news reports were slowly emerging from China that a mysterious illness was rapidly spreading and developing. Nobody really knew its nature and there was growing global concern but the chaos that would define what would follow had not yet begun. The world had made tentative steps in preparing for a pandemic, but this pandemic was still in the abstract.

Then, on January 20, the first case of COVID-19 was reported in Seattle. A few weeks later, a British cruise ship, *Diamond Princess*, had an outbreak reported while docked in Yokohama, Japan. Of over three thousand passengers on board, seven hundred tested positive and nineteen passed away.

COVID-19 had now grabbed the attention of the United States.

As we began to hear about patient cases, I figured that, sooner or later, this mysterious illness would hit my community. I was hoping that by then there would be some wisdom, some guidelines and direction from the governing bodies of medicine to help us treat these patients. I wasn't particularly worried; this wasn't a new phenomenon. Then, in the final week of February, cases were reported in Jewish communities in the Brooklyn neighborhoods of Williamsburg, Borough Park, and Crown Heights.

This concerned me because, even though my practice was in Monroe, New York (only an hour and a half to two hours from Brooklyn), many of the residents of Monroe traveled to Brooklyn and vice versa because their families in the Jewish community would come in for weddings, other celebrations, and for the Sabbath. As a result of this intermingling, I started to hear about people that I knew peripherally or knew by one or two degrees of separation being admitted to the hospitals with flu-like symptoms. By the first week of March, there were people I actually knew well in my community reporting the same flu-like symptoms.

As I began seeing these patients, I noted that they were presenting with symptoms that closely mimicked those of the flu. They were unique, though, in that many of these patients were also losing their taste and smell, which is not a common symptom of the flu. Due to the similarity, I would give them a standard flu test as part of a simple diagnostic process, and they would all come back negative. That made it pretty obvious to me that we weren't dealing with the influenza virus and that this was something new, something unexplored (in the US anyway). I wasn't even aware of the name COVID-19 yet, despite the fact that the World Health Organization (WHO) had named it as such back on February 11, 2020. Whatever the name was, I knew my patients were getting sick from it. It wouldn't be until the early part of April that we would start receiving PCR test kits that we were told would detect the disease.

By that time, many of the patients I had seen in the early part of March had already begun being admitted to hospital a week or two later with severe breathing problems. It was clear that whatever this syndrome was, it was aggressive for certain people within the population. Most young people were recovering, but many older people were getting much sicker, often ending up in the hospital and then, in many cases, dying.

This disease seemed to take a while to progress, and it also seemed to be changing in its nature as it progressed from a flu-like disease to a respiratory disease. It was at this stage that the people who were predisposed to severe illness were crashing. The clinical course I was seeing was one that I wasn't familiar with from anything in my past medical career. Oxygen levels would go from being normal on a Monday to crashing into the 70s by Friday, often leading to hospital admissions.

At the time, I ran the local volunteer EMS system. Since New York City was only ninety minutes away without traffic, we tended to take our patients to the city's specialty hospitals rather than those in the local community. A lot of the patients ended up in Mount Sinai Hospital, Lenox Hill Hospital, NYU, and Columbia. Sometimes we had to divert in New Jersey because patients were crashing and they couldn't make it to the city. In that case, Hackensack Hospital was the choice. Some patients took themselves to the hospital and in that case they would end up predominantly at the hospitals in the local community; places like Orange Regional Medical Center in Middletown, and Good Sam Hospital in Suffern.

By the time we started performing PCR testing in early April we found that it took about six days to get the test results back from the lab. In that time frame, the disease left on its own had often progressed to the point where there was nothing that could be done for a patient, especially if they had already had symptoms for several days before coming in for testing. Not only was the timing bad, but the case incidence was incredible. Out of the first sixteen tests I performed, nine came back positive. Given the size of Monroe, with a population of about forty thousand, you can start to extrapolate and get a grasp on just how big this problem had the potential of becoming just at my own local level.

In almost the blink of an eye, the nation was locked down and people began panicking and hoarding supplies. Our national health leaders provided absolutely no guidance as to how to medically combat this aggressive, deadly disease. It seemed as though we were simply destined to have millions of people die without being able to offer them any hope for recovery, save for G-d answering prayers.

This was how everything seemed, but thankfully, it was not the case. There was hope, and it came to me in the middle of the night from a combination of technology and G-d answering at least one prayer: My prayer.

Inspiration Strikes

It was in the middle of the night on March 12, a night where sleep wouldn't come. I was lying in prayer and meditation, looking for some way to do something to help the patients I was seeing who were getting sick and dying from this new virulent form of disease. I decided to use this sleepless time to check my email. It was there that I found a message containing a link to a YouTube video that would forever change my life and would, more importantly, save the lives of millions across the world.

The video was put together by MedCram, an online organization that provides medical courses and information. It was narrated by Dr. Richard Seheult and was a short seventeen-minute-long presentation. I will discuss the video in more detail and my treatment protocol derived therefrom in a subsequent chapter, for our purposes here I will just briefly summarize.

Dr. Seheult pointed to research that suggested that zinc, a common over-the-counter supplement, could effectively kill coronavirus inside the cell level before it has a chance to reproduce and spread throughout the body. He also noted that zinc was not able to get into the cell easily on its own, but needed to attach to something, an ionophore, to allow it to successfully break through. One of those ionophores was hydroxychloroquine, also known as HCQ.

HCQ is one of the most widely used prescription medications in the world, and has been around for decades. It has a proven track record of safe use with little to no known side-effects, and as a result was in abundant supply.

To be clear, the video was not suggesting that HCQ could kill coronavirus. Zinc was the killer. To use a metaphor I have used often over the past two years, HCQ was the gun and zinc was the bullet.

I immediately began to perform additional research, and decided to formulate a treatment method to try with patients. I mean, what possible harm could it do? What was being discussed in that video involved a safe and proven prescription drug and a supplement you can buy over the counter, typically two-for-one, in any grocery store in the country. Given how fast this disease was spreading and how severe it was demonstrating to be, the risks of inaction far outweighed those of action.

Over the next couple of days, the HCQ storm started to grow. On March 13, investor James Todaro and lawyer Gregory Rigano tweeted a link to a paper they had put on a file-sharing service. They pointed out that they had been tracking chloroquine that had gone through early trials in China and France and seemed to show promise as a COVID-19 treatment. Elon Musk tweeted about the story and it was also picked up by Breitbart, Fox News, and others. The established medical community was quick to discount the notion - too quick as it turned out - but the story was in play. At the time, I had no involvement whatsoever in any of what was taking place in the public forum. I was a private citizen trying to do some good for the people I treated.

On March 15, 2020, I used HCQ on a patient for the first time, combining it with zinc and azithromycin. The patient was an elderly man in his mid-eighties who had numerous health issues, including diabetes and heart disease. He was very high risk, had been unwell for a week, and his oxygen level was in the low 90s. He was the first to be treated with what would become known internationally as the Zelenko Protocol.

I'm sure you're wondering... he got better.

The document drop by Rigano and Todaro was responsible for bringing HCQ into the national spotlight. It eventually led to President Trump stating at a March nineteenth White House COVID-19 briefing that, "It's (HCQ) been around for a long time, so we know if things don't go as planned it's not going to kill anybody." In what seemed odd at the time, the very next day at the same daily briefing, Dr. Anthony Fauci was quick (again, too quick), to step up to the microphone and tell the world that there was no evidence that HCQ would work and that clinical-controlled trials would be needed. His exact statement that day when asked about the readily available, very safe drug, was as follows:

"No. The answer is no. The evidence that you're talking about is anecdotal evidence. As the commissioner of the FDA and the President mentioned yesterday, we're trying to strike a balance between making something with a potential of an effect to the American people available at the same time that we do it under the auspices of a protocol that would give us information to determine if it's truly safe and truly effective. But, the information that you're referring to specifically is anecdotal. It was not done in a controlled clinical trial, so you really can't make any definitive statement about it."

At this point, I was already busily immersed in doing my own trial with my own patients and it was working. People were getting better, and they were getting better quickly. There were so many that it became difficult to know how to prioritize treatments. I called the local hospitals where I had fairly good connections because of my volunteer EMS work and spoke with their intensive care unit doctors and nurses, and I asked which patients were dying. They told me most of the patients were older with chronic medical problems. I asked about the younger, healthier patients. They said they weren't really seeing them in ICUs.

Now, I had the ability to risk stratify patients (more details to come later). This meant that I was able to make a determination of how to treat patients earlier, even without confirmation they had COVID-19.

Patients I treated were getting better, and they were getting better rapidly, often in just six to twelve hours. This all came with an important disclaimer that they must come to me within the first week of the onset of their symptoms. To be parochial, in my Orthodox Jewish world, I'm the one who first was educating everyone to start coming to the doctor and get treatment within day one or two of the presentation of symptoms. Prior to that, people would sit at home for two weeks before seeking help. I was starting to clearly demonstrate that if someone came in the right time frame, I had a way of preventing them from going to the hospital. No patient who came in the right time frame, even the high-risk patients, went to the hospital. It was a promising protocol, to be certain.

The right time frame part was critical. There were people being sent to the hospital because they were coming to me too late. I also saw a lot of people from the surrounding areas from New York and New Jersey coming to me looking for hope, but they came two to three weeks after their initial onset and, in most cases, there was really nothing at that point that I could do for them.

Doing Something Drastic

I was observing a clear pattern; treat early with HCQ and zinc, and patients recovered regardless of their risk profile. Treat them late, however, and the treatment was largely ineffective. After watching the press conferences on the twentieth and twenty-first of March and realizing that the bureaucracy of government and medicine were likely not going to respond to using HCQ in a timely fashion, I decided I needed to do something drastic. I was convinced enough to risk my reputation, my career, everything that I've built, to try to get this information to President Trump. My rationale was this: I'm a frontline soldier, I found that enemy map. The map has time-sensitive information about troops and weaponry, in locations. If I get that information to the five-star general who's running the war effort, we can win the war very quickly. Going through the regular chain of command wouldn't work because it would take too long and the battle might well be lost.

I felt it was time for me to share the information with the world. On March 21, 2020, I recorded a video directed toward President Trump and, two days later, I supplemented it with an open letter addressed to all doctors of the world. I was able to do this because the beauty of my situation was that I was self-employed–independent physicians over the past decade have been made rare because of larger institutions acquiring practices. The medical industry, especially primary care doctors, has been "rolled-up," as the term is used in business. I had been approached numerous times about having my practice acquired but each time I refused. It's not that I was prolific in doing so but I valued being self-employed and patient-centric over the alternative. Because of this, I had the autonomy I needed to act. All I needed was my patients' permission to treat them, and I needed nobody's permission to write a letter or record a video. I had the flexibility to be nimble, to be like the Marines: improvise, adapt, and overcome. I had been in my community practicing medicine for almost twenty years, and I was the physician to about seventy-five percent of the local population. I had their trust, and I had my own resolve.

The letter I wrote, which closely followed the tone of the video, read as follows:

Dr. Vladimir (Zev) Zelenko
Board Certified Family Practitioner
501 Rt 208, Monroe, NY 10950
845-238-0000

March 23, 2020

To all medical professionals around the world:
My name is Dr. Zev Zelenko and I practice medicine in Monroe, NY. For the last 16 years, I have cared for approximately 75% of the adult population of Kiryas Joel, which is a very close knit community of approximately 35,000 people in which the infection spread rapidly and unchecked prior to the imposition of social distancing.

As of today my team has tested approximately 200 people from this community for COVID-19, and 65% of the results have been positive. If extrapolated to the entire community, that means more than 20,000 people are infected at the present time. Of this group, I estimate that there are 1500 patients who are in the high-risk category (i.e. >60, immunocompromised, comorbidities, etc).

Given the urgency of the situation, I developed the following treatment protocol in the pre-hospital setting and have seen only positive results:

1. Any patient with shortness of breath regardless of age is treated.

2. Any patient in the high-risk category even with just mild symptoms is treated.

3. Young, healthy and low risk patients even with symptoms are not treated (unless their circumstances change and they fall into category 1 or 2).

My out-patient treatment regimen is as follows:

1. Hydroxychloroquine 200mg twice a day for 5 days

2. Azithromycin 500mg once a day for 5 days

3. Zinc sulfate 220mg once a day for 5 days

The rationale for my treatment plan is as follows. I combined the data available from China and South Korea with the recent study published from France (sites available on request). We know that hydroxychloroquine helps Zinc enter the cell. We know that Zinc slows viral replication within the cell. Regarding the use of azithromycin, I postulate it prevents secondary bacterial infections. These three drugs are well known and usually well tolerated, hence the risk to the patient is low.
Since last Thursday, my team has treated approximately 350 patients in Kiryas Joel and another 150 patients in other areas of New York with the above regimen.

Of this group and the information provided to me by affiliated medical teams, we have had ZERO deaths, ZERO hospitalizations, and ZERO intubations. In addition, I have not heard of any negative side effects other than approximately 10% of patients with temporary nausea and diarrhea.

In sum, my urgent recommendation is to initiate treatment in the outpatient setting as soon as possible in accordance with the above. Based on my direct experience, it prevents acute respiratory distress syndrome (ARDS), prevents the need for hospitalization and saves lives.

With much respect,

Dr. Zev Zelenko
cc: President Donald J. Trump; Mr. Mark Meadows, Chief of Staff

Overnight, the YouTube video went viral. Within the first twenty-four hours, there were roughly two hundred thousand views and the local media started contacting me to find out what was going on. I didn't respond to the media, but they came to my community and started asking questions to anyone who would answer. They were digging.

I didn't realize at the time that the media would eventually become the third leg of an evil axis of power during the pandemic that included them, national and international political leaders, and the bureaucratic and corporate medical establishment. I was optimistic, thinking that since the media was exploring this perhaps the effectiveness of my newly-discovered treatment protocol would become widespread.

It took only a day after the release of my video to the President, Mark Meadows, the White House Chief of Staff, to call me from the White House. At that moment, I had every reason to believe that we were about to see a Washington-directed program to get this new treatment protocol, discovered in real-time by treating real patients successfully, into the offices of every doctor and emergency room in the country. It seemed that quite possibly I had triggered something that could make the new COVID-19 the shortest-running pandemic in human history.

On March 23, at his daily press briefing, President Trump gave me further reason to hope when he authorized the distribution of HCQ to the

State of New York from our national stockpile reserves. This was exciting news because now, the work I was doing that had garnered such positive patient outcomes would be able to be easily replicated by every doctor in the state.

Little did I know, and no way I could have foreseen, what the purely evil governor of New York, Andrew Cuomo, would do only four short days later.

Support, Care, and Duty

At the start of the pandemic, my medical practice was rare and unusual. I was once called a family member to four thousand families.

I practiced medicine in a very paternalistic way, and I didn't have much tolerance for patient "non-compliance" over the years. I was known for being very direct, and patients who were not comfortable with my style, or being held aggressively accountable for their following of my medicine and lifestyle prescriptions, chose not to be my patients. I suppose that is why I was the doctor for seventy-five percent of the community and not for everyone. The simple fact is that my personality is not for everyone. It's assertive and it's confident. It comes with love, but sometimes, that love is a tough love.

As an example, I was very surgically oriented. In my practice, if someone would come in with an abscess - quite commonly what's called an MRSA abscess - the typical physician approach, especially in a corporate controlled practice, would be for the physician to diagnose, then make a small incision, drain the puss, put the patient on antibiotics, and then make a follow up appointment for a week later (another chance for insurance billing). During that week, the patient would suffer excruciating pain, and possibly even end up in the hospital (another, bigger, insurance billing opportunity).

What I did was, say, "Well, you have an MRSA abscess. This is a serious infection, but I'm going to take care of it right now. I'm going to numb it up as much as I can, but it's still going to hurt like hell. I promise you within five minutes you will be on the way to recovery, and you'll be better." Then I would take a scalpel, cut the hell out of this thing, and remove it completely. It took about five minutes, and during those five minutes the patient hated me. However, once through it, by the time they left they were kissing me.

I concluded that sometimes being inappropriately timid because you don't want to hurt someone resulted in a higher chance of negative clinical consequences. That means there are times where it is appropriate to intervene in an aggressive manner, doing your best, of course, to mitigate the suffering. Sometimes it's unavoidable, but for a few minutes of pain, you could resolve the issue comprehensively and have the patient on the road to recovery. No follow-ups. No surgeons.

That was the kind of approach I adopted to my general overall practice of medicine. It became almost like a medical philosophy for me. It's not for everyone, but I earned an unusual amount of trust from my patients and that trust allowed me to practice successfully in that manner.

No matter my style, I could not have had the success I enjoyed in years of private practice without a remarkable supporting staff of dedicated professionals. Prior to the pandemic, my team of nurses and physician assistants would see about fifty patients per day, give or take. When the pandemic hit, that number soared to over two hundred and fifty. As a result, they were pushed to and beyond their limits. That was why the risk stratification I developed for treating patients was so important. It wasn't that I didn't want to help the young and healthy, it was simply that we couldn't get to everyone.

The incredible people who worked alongside me were unbelievably courageous in the performing of their duties, but they were also human. They were scared, which in turn means they got sick. By the third week of March, half my office staff was out sick. They were younger people and they all got better, but the physical and emotional strain was incredible. We were fortunate that with our Monroe team temporarily decimated, we had a secondary office in Muncie, which is in Rockland County. I had a physician assistant working there and he truly stepped up when the staff in Monroe went down.For that though, he too paid a price.

He became very sick and it led to him being on a respirator for three weeks, even though he was young. The amount of viral load exposure he accumulated was metaphorically as if he was one of the first responders in Chernobyl. He is a pediatric physician assistant, so he was seeing kids that were sick and while they all got better, after seeing a hundred patients per day face-to-face with COVID-19, he almost died. It took him six months to recover his stamina and get back to his pre-COVID-19 lung function. He's a real hero.

Fortunately, his situation was the exception. I let the members of my staff who would work on scheduling and insurance authorizations work from home. Only those involved with direct patient care would come into the office. Our otherwise quiet practice, set in a medical office building, saw so many patients that they were literally lining the hallways, sitting sick on the floor.

The building we used had radiology and testing labs within it, which were vital for performing complete patient diagnostics. Unfortunately, they were closed, which meant that I lost access to some of the important tools that would normally be available in order to fully understand a patient's condition. This also applied to conditions unrelated to COVID-19; it wasn't the only medical emergency taking place. One of the things that has received attention amongst the fray of COVID-19 was the number of people that died *with* COVID-19 but not *from* COVID-19. These were people with other conditions that simply couldn't get access to doctors or diagnostics. Patients suffering from cancers like mine (well, fortunately not too many cancers are like mine) and other life-threatening ailments were not able to get access to care or were too scared to come to a doctor's office to try and get care. These are the people whose deaths are not recorded as being part of the one-million or so Americans who died as a direct result of COVID-19. They are, however, just as dead as everyone else. Undertakers don't do autopsies.

My staff marched on as best they could, despite the unknowns and the peril they put themselves in. As for me, I was drinking a lot of coffee. I was working twenty-plus hours a day, even with my cancer and missing a lung. I was not in the best of health by any means and remember thinking that I knew I wasn't a Navy Seal or a soldier, but what I was called to do was everything I'd been trained to do. I had a duty, a moral duty born from my oath as a physician, and more importantly, my oath taken before G-d to push myself as far as I possibly could. I thought, *I must hold the line here.*

I also had my rational mind intact, so I calculated that I had a forty to fifty percent chance of dying from this disease.

My wife was frightened just like every other American. She had a husband who was leaving the house every day and walking into a line of fire that not only could kill him, but meant that when I returned home it was akin to having a terrorist's bomb strapped around me that could detonate at any moment. When I did come home, I wasn't of much use to her or the children. I would say hello, take a shower, sleep for a few hours, and then do it all over again. I had left her on her own to take care of the home and the children.

One of my dear friends approached me and said that I really shouldn't be on the frontlines because of my health. I think he tried that just as a matter of course because he knew I wasn't going to relent. He knew that his admonitions would fall on death ears, but he did make a compelling argument that I should step back out of the frontlines a bit and spend more of my time performing research and instructing the world about how to treat the disease. His argument was a variation of the adage about giving a man a fish and you feed him for a day, teach him how to fish and you feed him for a lifetime. He reasoned that I could save more patients by spreading word about my treatment than I could simply by seeing the patients that were presented directly to me. That did make some sense, but this was very complicated for me, and I was dealing with some complex internal struggles.

There is a reason why a five-star general doesn't typically take point on a ground unit. Their usefulness to the entire operation is their ability to direct others and to make sure they are around when difficult and complex situations need to be addressed. I had been taking point on patient care right from the outset, but at the same time I was the doctor who had discovered how to treat this very deadly and new disease. Where was my time best spent? What risks were prudent and what risks were reckless? Was I taking those risks because they were necessary, or was I seeking an adrenaline rush? There was a lot to sort out about my reasons why.

I have always had a strong love and respect for the military, but I never had the body for it. I admired their discipline and courage, and in some ways, especially during those early days of the pandemic, I was excited that I had been given a chance to actualize that courage and prove to myself that I could be a real man. Recognizing that, I had to step back and ask myself: Am I serving G-d or my own ego? Ultimately, I took my friend's remarks to heart and began to alter my behavior and how I allocated my time.

The one thing I did hold to was honoring the Sabbath; I wouldn't work from sundown Friday to sundown Saturday. I did have my phone open because, as the leader of the EMS system, they would be calling 24/7, but I did try to redirect those calls to others. To maintain some degree of sanity, I needed to disconnect, even for just one night, to be able to sleep and show some attention to my wife and children. We would enjoy meals, read stories, and simply be together in peace. Those Sabbaths spent with my wife and two daughters would energize me for the week to follow.

Those two children were from my second marriage. Like many other mothers and fathers, I didn't have access to my other children, who were living in Philadelphia, because everything was in lockdown mode. Regrettably, even if it hadn't been, my work schedule would have made it difficult to spend time with them regardless. I spoke to them as much as I could, but I regret that I didn't see them for three months. With the way I'm wired, that was excruciatingly painful for me. When I finally did see them, just before I found out my cancer had resurfaced, I found myself unable to talk for an hour. I just sat on the couch with them and looked at each one, held them, and cried. I couldn't verbalize anything and my absence from them was perhaps the highest personal cost I suffered.

As far as my patients were concerned, this was a true experiment into the realm of faith and trust; remember that I had discovered a treatment protocol for a disease that was terrorizing the country, but I didn't have any "air cover" in terms of clinical research or CDC affirmation. People are taught to trust the medical community and to trust the people they have elected into positions of leadership. They were not getting any kind of reassurance from them that this Zelenko fella was on to something. That meant that they simply had to trust a non-notable family physician from a small New York town. Even I have to admit that is asking a lot.

As to the faith part of it, while people were trying to reach me from throughout the state of New York, the United States, and even globally; it was stunning. At first, most of the people turning to me came disproportionately from within my own Orthodox Jewish community because everyone in that community is connected–it's as if there is one degree of separation from one individual to the next. Also, because I was running the volunteer EMS, and because each major Jewish community around the world has their own, I was even more connected to that demographic. The EMS units have a way of communicating with each other, so I shared my clinical experience through that platform. The word spread rapidly.

Instantaneously, on every continent, every major Jewish community had the information. It intensified when President Trump moved into the picture, and after I was featured on a Rudy Giuliani podcast. Without exaggerating, there were days where over twenty thousand people attempted to reach me via phone, WhatsApp, email, text, and through friends. It was all understandable because, at that point, people were dying in hospitals at a horrific rate. The carnage was unprecedented in my lifetime and knowing that the people trying to reach me were scared, in need, and possibly dying themselves or watching a loved one as they died put immense pressure on me. To answer that pressing demand, I needed help.

White House Attention

When Mark Meadows reached out to me, I couldn't help but be encouraged; I finally had the attention of the White House. After our conversation, there was nothing more for a couple of days until Stephen Hahn, the Commissioner of the FDA, called me on my cell phone.

He introduced himself right away by saying, "This is Dr. Stephen Hahn. I'm the Commissioner of the FDA." I mentioned that it was unusual to receive a call on my cell phone from the Commissioner of the FDA, to which he laughed and he said that Mark Meadows gave him my contact details and he wanted to know what I was doing. I told him in as precise a manner as possible, given that he was obviously extremely busy dealing with a pandemic, as was everyone. He was intrigued and wanted to be kept apprised of what was happening, and he gave me his cell number.

In that conversation, Dr. Hahn also referred me to the head of one of the departments at the NIH, asking me to speak to her to present my data. That conversation happened two days later, but it went nowhere. The reason it was stagnant to her was that the data I offered was real-world evidence, not derived through trials. It was neither in an academic setting nor pharmaceutically sponsored, so to her it was just some doctor presenting observational data of what was happening to his patients.

It became clear that, without some sort of peer-reviewed study, my newly discovered treatment was not going to gain widespread acceptance. In some cases, though, it seems that you can make an argument for an orderly process before introducing some new medical procedure, such as a DNA-altering mRNA "vaccine" for example. In this case, people were dying by the hospital load on a daily basis but that wasn't as pressing as peer review studies and Big Pharma sponsorship. I imagined what it would be like if the medical-industrial complex were in charge of defending against an airstrike on Washington DC. I surmised that if such an attack was actually underway, they would resist firing with any on-hand weaponry, preferring to resort to a lengthy study to determine exactly what weapons would work best against the airstrike.

As for me, I would be standing outside trying to at least throw a shoe at the airplanes.

My hope of government support quickly grew to an understanding that no help was coming to me from outside of my tiny community of Monroe. I was just going to have to continue to treat patients through my practice as best I could, and work on being that five-star general who was helping to inform and coordinate any enlisted soldiers, here referred to as doctors, who were on my side and willing to listen. The only good news was that, thanks to President Trump releasing the emergency supplies of HCQ, I would at least be able to successfully treat patients in my community, as would other doctors throughout New York who were willing to listen to my real-world evidence without the blue blanket of a peer-reviewed study to comfort them. Safe in that knowledge, I thanked G-d and took some comfort.

However, my comfort was short lived, and a "death follows me everywhere" person was about to change the tides.

Chapter Two

Cuomo on a Pale Horse, Followed by Death

President Trump's announcement that HCQ reserves were going to be made readily available offered me every reason to express optimism. It lessened the severity of having to wait for a peer-reviewed study in such a time of crisis to be conducted before an all-out national treatment program could be approved. I figured that since I was going to be able to treat patients, along with other doctors in my state and elsewhere, that our results would be so impressive that the process would accelerate.

Even though I received a hat tip from the government by allowing treatment, I did find myself under attack from the most unexpected of places: My own Orthodox Jewish community. My video had gone viral and one of the things I was warning about was the outbreak potential I saw within my community. My warning led to the closing of the community's school and a good deal of press coverage.

Particularly outraged was the Orange County Health Commissioner, Dr. Irina Gelman. A story in a local paper dated March 19, 2020 read in part:

Dr. Irina Gelman, the Orange County health commissioner, said in response on Thursday that it was "highly irresponsible" for Zelenko to draw that conclusion from only 14 tests of sick people. Applying that positive rate – which is actually 64 percent – to the entire village population made no sense in mathematical or statistical terms.

Gelman confirmed that a high number of people have reported illness in Kiryas Joel, and said the village's population density raises concern about the coronavirus spreading. But she said it was "very early to even begin to estimate" the extent of the cases.

Following that story, on March 24, members of Kiryas Joel sent an open letter that was picked up by the press. I share the letter here in its entirety. For some clarity, Kiryas Joel is a village coterminous with the Town of Palm Tree in Orange County, New York. The village shares one government with the Town. The vast majority of its residents are Yiddish-speaking Hasidic Jews who belong to the worldwide Satmar Hasidic sect. We are, quite literally, a village within a village. Turning on one another is truly quite rare.

KIRYAS JOEL
OFFICE OF EMERGENCY MANAGEMENT
COVID-19 Special Team

Hatzoloh EMS · Village of Kiryas Joel · Fire Department · Public Safety · Ezras Cholim Health Center
Congregation Representative · Private School Representative · Chaverim

Phone: (845) 276-4413 · Email: kjcovid19@gmail.com · Information Line: (845) 951-1133

For Immediate Release
March 24, 2020

AN OPEN LETTER FROM KIRYAS JOEL

The community of Kiryas Joel has mobilized to stop the spread of the Corona Virus by activating the Kiryas Joel Office of Emergency Management, a coalition of government offices and private NFP organizations that are leading the fight to inform the community and protect public health in the Village of Kiryas Joel/ Town of Palm Tree.

With heavy hearts, we are writing this Open Letter to Dr. Vladimir Zelenko, a physician that has a private practice with offices in Monsey and Monroe, also serving members of the Kiryas Joel community. For many years, Dr. Zelenko has been an important and respected health care provider in the neighboring town, one of many physicians that work with Kiryas Joel patients, at an office located outside of the Kiryas Joel community.

Though Dr. Zelenko is not a specialist in infectious diseases, nor an expert in epidemiology, he has taken to filming almost daily videos posted to YouTube on this crisis, referring to the Kiryas Joel Community, that have been widely disseminated outside of our community. Though none of his patients are likely seeing these YouTube videos, they have been viewed by literally tens of thousands of individuals all over the world who are influenced by their content. Mistakenly, Dr. Zelenko has been viewed as the Chief Physician of Kiryas Joel, a designation that is both inaccurate and currently damaging to the community's reputation.

We the undersigned institutions strongly believe that the predictions presented by Dr. Zelenko have been proven false and are not supported by the overall medical establishment, specifically in his wild conclusions as to the spread of the virus in our community. His figures have been disproved and discredited by the Orange County Health Commissioner, Dr. Irina Gelman, who called his extrapolation from a small survey to be "highly irresponsible." Sadly, we must concur with that assessment.

For the last week, all schools, Synagogues, libraries and ritual bath houses have been closed, and more distancing is being practiced throughout the community. These measures have, thanks to the Almighty, resulted in a rate of 90% of the community being healthy, the opposite of Dr. Zelenko's outrageous prediction of a 90% infection rate. In fact, all data indicates that the infection rate in Kiryas Joel is mirroring the rest of Orange County, and therefore should not be a cause for panic, or the singling out of one community.

Most disturbingly, Dr. Zelenko's videos have caused widespread fear that has resulted in the discrimination against members of the Hasidic community throughout the region, as well as making it impossible to staff the vital services and businesses in and around Kiryas Joel that are

permitted to remain open, such as food stores and pharmacies. This exploitation of a crisis ;
a community is unacceptable because it fuels Antisemitism and only exacerbates a problem
making it only more difficult to manage.

We would be happy to work in partnership with Dr Zelenko to benefit his patients and the
thousands of other residents who see other qualified physicians in and around our commun
But first, we are calling on Dr Zelenko to immediately cease and desist from creating and
posting more YouTube videos that are putting our community in an unfair and undeserved
spotlight, or at minimum, he must stop referring to his patients as Hasidic Jews or Kiryas Jo
residents, in any public setting.

None of our statements are meant to minimize the accomplishments of Dr Zelenko or the ca
that he professionally provides to his patients. However, in this emergency situation, we mu
provide stable and responsible leadership, with sound medical and spiritual advice to all
residents, free of bias and stigma. At this time of crisis, we hope that Dr Zelenko will join us
this vital mission.

Emergency Management Office of Kiryas Joel

Village of Kiryas Joel, Member

Congregation Yetev Lev, Member

KJ Hatzoloh EMS, Member

KJ Public Safety Department, Member

KJ Fire Department, Member

Ezras Choilim Health Center, Member

Chaveirem of Kiryas Joel, Member

The impact upon me from this response was profound and hurtful
in that it came from the community I had been serving and of which I'd
been a member for seventeen years. There were no names attached to it,
just faceless organizations and departments. Their motivations for such an
attack were not stated, but it seems the likely cause is that I'd created such
a problem for local politicians by going public with the declaration that the

virus could be successfully treated that they leaned on receptive individuals to have them discredit me.

After being slandered by my own community (which became very public), I had a patient that came to the office and was prescribed the HCQ protocol by my PA. However, when he heard about what the leaders of the community had said about me, he chose not to take it because he lost confidence and trust in me.

Tragically, he died.

The letter, and the fallout thereafter, had the additional unintended (or perhaps intended, though not by me) consequence of leading to the unnecessary death of New Yorkers and citizens of Israel as well. On April 2, it was announced that Yaakov Litzman, the Health Minister of Israel, was being treated for COVID-19. In one report of his health it was said that he and his wife were being, "suitably treated and are in isolation, under observation in accordance with Health Ministry guidelines." What wasn't disclosed was that I was the one treating them using my newly developed protocol. Litzman was seventy-eight years old and hardly a robust physical specimen, and he and his wife were both "high risk" just based upon age alone absent any other considerations.

Litzman was also Orthodox, and it was through this tight Jewish community communication network that he had been connected to me. We had been speaking prior to the onset of his illness as I was trying to get the Israeli government to listen to me. I wanted to save the lives of my Jewish brothers and sisters in our native land, and initially Litzman was not terribly responsive (he kept pushing me off to underlings), but when he became unwell, who did he call? Not the very capable doctors in Israel. He reached out to me.

I had sent essentially the same letter I wrote to President Trump to Bibi Netanyahu, who was at the time the Prime Minister of Israel, and I was told he received it on April 5. I had hopes of being able to help Israelis, even if I was facing a combination of hostility and indifference here in the United States. Unfortunately, when news broke of the Kiryas Joel letter, the response I got from the Israeli Ministry of Health was, "Why should we take you seriously if your community is rejecting you?"

Irina Gelman did not miss her opportunity to seize upon this letter to further attack me. In my opinion, she was driven purely by ego and because I was just a local GP coming up with a life-saving treatment, to her and her ego, that couldn't be. I had talked with Gelman directly and shared with her what I was seeing in the community. I had told her that I was seeing tremendous results with HCQ, and I asked if she could help procure HCQ since she ran the Health Department for the county. I believe she discussed it, at least she said she did, with the health commissioner for the state. Their consensus was that they had no interest in what I was doing.

But when the story broke, they were interested in slandering and marginalizing me by attacking my credibility.

Gelman used that letter as a way to show "proof" that I was out of control and she passed it up the line within the state of New York to the folks in Albany. While I can't say I'm certain, it is reasonable to surmise that the open letter found its way to the desk of then-Governor Andrew Cuomo, likely with a post-it note attached saying something like: *This Zelenko guy is causing an uproar.*

While the above is conjecture, what happened next is not.

Denying Treatment

On March 27, Governor Cuomo added to his existing emergency order a new provision that barred pharmacies from filling prescriptions for HCQ, aside from a few very limited exceptions. Knowing he did not have the authority to stop a doctor from prescribing, he used what authority he did have to choke off the supply. It doesn't do a doctor any good to write a script that the patient can't get filled.

The order from Cuomo, part of a series of orders issued that day, effectively did the following, according to the National Academy for State Health Policy:

New York: Executive Order from Gov. Andrew Cuomo restricting dispensing:
• *Bans pharmacists from dispensing hydroxychloroquine or chloroquine except:*

> o *When written as prescribed for a US Food and Drug Administration (FDA)-approved indication; or*

> o *As part of a state approved clinical trial related to COVID-19 for a patient who has tested positive for COVID-19*

• *Positive COVID-19 test results must be documented as part of the prescription.*

• *Prohibits use of hydroxychloroquine or chloroquine for experimental or prophylactic use.*

• *Any permitted prescription is limited to one 14-day prescription with no refills.*

New York was joined by Nevada, Ohio, Idaho, Kentucky, North Carolina, Texas, Louisiana, Kansas, and Missouri (note, not all blue states). I was incredulous. This made no sense to me, at least not yet. Here, I had found a way to treat patients, the federal government was slowly climbing on board, and the Governor of New York had surreptitiously and arbitrarily sought to eliminate a doctor's ability to treat people with a safe and proven drug, supplemented by an over-the-counter supplement. What gives?

What made the Governor's decision even more bizarre was what happened the next day, when the FDA granted Emergency Use Authorization (EUA) to the use of my protocol. In a letter dated March 28, and addressed to multiple recipients including the Department of Health and Human Services, Denise M. Hinton, Chief Scientist for the Food and Drug Administration, wrote this as part of the EUA:

…Having concluded that the criteria for issuance of this authorization under 564(c) of the Act are met, I am authorizing the emergency use of chloroquine phosphate and hydroxychloroquine sulfate, as described in the Scope of Authorization section of this letter (Section II) for treatment of COVID-19 when clinical trials are not

available, or participation is not feasible, subject to the terms of this authorization. Clinical trial data results, and any information derived from clinical trials, as well as clinical trial results from studies of other investigational medical products to treat COVID-19, will continue to inform this risk benefit assessment.

I have concluded, pursuant to Section 564(d)(2) of the Act, that it is reasonable to believe that the known and potential benefits of chloroquine phosphate and hydroxychloroquine sulfate, when used for the treatment of SARS-CoV-2 and used consistently with the Scope of Authorization of this letter (Section II), outweigh the known and potential risks of these products.

I have concluded, pursuant to Section 564(d)(3) of the Act, based on the totality of scientific evidence available to FDA, that it is reasonable to believe that chloroquine phosphate and hydroxychloroquine sulfate may be effective for the treatment of COVID-19, when used consistently with the Scope of Authorization of this letter (Section II), pursuant to Section 564(c)(2)(A) of the Act.

Having reviewed the scientific information available to FDA, including the information supporting the conclusions described in Section I of this letter, I have concluded that chloroquine phosphate and hydroxychloroquine sulfate (as described in the Scope of Authorization of this letter (Section II)) meets the criteria set forth in Section 564(c) of the Act concerning safety and potential effectiveness.

What in the hell was going on? Andrew Cuomo says no the day before the FDA says yes…

This was all about Andrew Cuomo.

As much as I was in disbelief over this, I should have sent Governor Cuomo flowers because he is responsible for my expansion of consciousness, my "red-pilling" in today's vernacular. He started the process on March 27, 2020, with that executive order obstructing patient care. With that pronunciation, when I called in a prescription I had pharmacists ask me for the first time in my career, "What is the diagnosis?" This was something that had never happened to me in the seventeen years I had been practicing medicine. But now, for dispensing HCQ, the pharmacist would interrogate me. He wanted to know the diagnosis, he wanted to know if the patient had a positive PCR test, and I had to provide the proof.

A governor had wedged himself in the middle of a doctor-patient relationship, which had been historically considered sacred. Cuomo knew he could not limit a doctor from prescribing if he had license to practice medicine and surgery in the state of New York, but he could limit the pharmacists from dispensing. This gave him the sophist's ability to make a nuanced, meaningless distinction. He could say, "Yeah, I never limited a doctor from prescribing." That was true, but he had obstructed patients from getting it. So, what's the difference? The net result was the same; delay of care, progression of disease, complications, lung damage, blood clots, death by respirator. I personally saw two patients die because they could not get HCQ in the State of New York.

Then, he went further by mandating that nursing homes should accept COVID-19 positive patients. I have patients who own nursing homes, and I have friends that work in nursing homes and in the Jewish community. Some of them told me that their patient-resident census went down by sixty percent. That was from death, not discharge or relocation. These were the people most vulnerable, most fragile, most frail, most in need of protection, mercy, compassion. They were effectively slaughtered.

What was even more disgusting about the nursing home situation is that in the first week of April, President Trump had sent the USS Comfort to be docked in New York with over one thousand empty beds to be used for patients suffering from COVID-19. Cuomo had other ideas, and he left the vessel all but empty, instead opting to send people to nursing homes to further spread the disease. It was as if the New York state slogan should have been changed to, *Come die in New York—and bring along a friend.*

Crimes Against Humanity

Please don't just take my word for it. In March 2022, the New York Times, the "paper of record" that mostly used its ink and digital footprint to provide cover for the corruption of public officials during the pandemic, ran a story with the headline, Health Agency Under Cuomo "Misled the Public" on Nursing Home Deaths. The story opened with:

> *The administration of former Gov. Andrew M. Cuomo failed to publicly account for the deaths of about 4,100 nursing home residents in New York during the pandemic, according to an audit released on Tuesday by the state comptroller, Thomas P. DiNapoli.*

> *The audit found that Health Department officials at times underreported the full death toll by as much as 50 percent from April 2020 to February 2021, as Mr. Cuomo faced increasing scrutiny over whether his administration had intentionally concealed the actual number of deaths.*

The forty-one page report concluded that the Health Department often acquiesced to the narrative Mr. Cuomo and his top officials wanted to promote during the pandemic, sometimes failing to meet its "ethical" and "moral" imperatives to act transparently.

It pains me a bit to cite the *New York Times* as a reference, but if the devil can cite scripture for his purpose then so can a simple Hasidic Jewish family doctor from Monroe. The *New York Times* has been no friend to me over time, and on April 2, 2022, they ran a story written by Kevin Roose and Matthew Rosenberg that was in essence a hit piece on me, in addition to their usual target of President Trump. In this article, I was the rock they were hurling from their Trump-killing sling. The piece started out harmless enough, mentioning my freshly discovered treatment method, but then the *New York Times* did what it does and quickly changed the tone:

What happened next is a modern pandemic parable that illustrates how the coronavirus is colliding with our fragile information ecosystem: A jumble of facts, falsehoods, and viral rumors patched together from Twitter threads and shards of online news, amplified by armchair experts and professional partisans and pumped through the warp-speed accelerator of social media.

Dr. Zelenko's treatment arrived at a useful moment for Mr. Trump and his media supporters, who have at times appeared more interested in discussing miracle cures than testing delays or ventilator shortages.

The article went on to mention that I had been working with the President of Brazil, Jair Bolnasaro, and also mentioned that I had been consulting with other countries like Israel, Ukraine, and Russia (Yes, Ukraine *and* Russia), but overall it was designed to cast a poor shadow on me for moving forward with treatment aggressively before there were clinical trials.

Idiots! People were dying. If not at that moment, when? I challenge that it is exactly in a moment of extreme medical crisis where lives are clearly in jeopardy that you need to try anything. I wasn't being reckless, either. I had based my treatment on research that did previously exist. I simply put two and two together and got the Zelenko Protocol.

For a monster like Governor Cuomo, however, the only math he does relates to votes, and he must have calculated that the people who would die from him denying them treatment and forcing them into nursing homes were people who would have likely voted against him.

The Governor's arrogance knew no boundaries. At a press conference on April thirteenth, he made sure that people knew that he was responsible for "flattening the curve," or whatever term he might like to use. He deserved no credit for this. The number was down because *we* brought the number down. G-d did not do that. Faith did not do that. Destiny did not do that. A lot of pain and suffering did that. That's how it works.

He said, "It's math… Our behavior has stopped the spread of the virus. G-d did not stop the spread of the virus. And what we do, how we act, will dictate how that virus spreads."

Far be it from G-d to try to claim any credit from the needs-practicing Catholic, now utterly disgraced, misogynistic former Governor of New York. Cuomo was responsible for the good things that were happening, excluding, of course, the nursing home deaths that had clearly been hidden by him and his minions.

It reminded me of what happened in the aftermath of a horrific period of time for Jewish people. After WWII, the media and the politicians in Germany who contributed to the propaganda were severely punished, in some cases even executed. I do believe that once the dust has settled and once all the truth is revealed regarding what notable bad actors did during the pandemic, the major actors in this, like Andrew Cuomo, should stand trial by military tribunal, and if they are found guilty, they should receive an appropriate punishment. I see no difference between what has happened since 2020 and what happened in Nazi Germany. None. I see the role played by government, media, and the medical-industrial complex as genocide and all those responsible for it need to be held accountable.

Especially the disgraced former Governor of New York, Andrew Cuomo.

In response to one of my media appearances, where I called for Cuomo to be arrested - taken to some type of Hague, Nuremberg, military tribunal forum and, if convicted, he should be hung for mass murder, crimes against humanity, and genocide - the Attorney General of the State of New York, Letitia James, sent a cease-and-desist letter to my office. She also included a demand letter for all the records of my practice. This coincided with a false accusation that was made against me by someone from the community that I served. I don't have any evidence of who it was, but I was told it was from Monroe. They said that I had claimed that a finger prick blood test to check for COVID-19 infection was FDA approved when in reality, it was only at an EUA. I had never claimed that either. It was a false accusation. This gave Albany something to use to come after me.

The good news was that by that time I was developing friends in higher places than New York. I made a phone call the next day to someone in a position to help and said, "Listen. Letitia James is on my ass." The person on the other end of the line (who shall remain unnamed) told me not to worry. The next day, Trump announced that he was taking HCQ and that he got a letter from an upstate New York doctor. Quite coincidentally, that shut down any further inquiry.

An Act of Sheer Malevolence

When I looked at what Cuomo did in issuing that executive order, I knew right away it was bad, I just didn't understand the motivation of why he would intentionally do something bad. In terms of it being bad, that was a simple matter of logic. It goes something like this:

Death is bad;

New disease is causing death;

Treatment for disease is preventing people from dying;

Treatment is forced to stop;

People start dying again;

My epiphany came when I realized this was not an error in judgment – a failure to understand the above logic – but it was an act of sheer malevolence. I had never come into contact with such a level of direct malevolence. I mean, I know history and I know my family was affected by genocide, but it wasn't in my generation. This kind of malevolence was a sort of abstraction to me. It was a theoretical or intellectual perception; not tangible. I think of my own people; do you think that the Jews in Europe in the 1930s and forties knew right away that they were going to be thrown into ovens in Auschwitz? I don't think so. Maybe some did, but the majority of people still held on to their delusions of, "You know, this is just a temporary thing."

That was how I felt at the moment of Cuomo's order, but I came around to reality fairly quickly in understanding who and what he was/is. What really revealed the essence of his character to me was when I would watch him on television. Just by looking at his face, and being a sensitive soul who naturally intuits who is decent and who is not, I felt like I would not want to be in a room with Cuomo. That was my internal sense, but it was nothing more than that. I wouldn't incarcerate him for my feelings, but I just didn't like seeing him. I didn't like the tone of his voice. I didn't like his arrogance, the arrogance that showed so clearly in his statement about G-d.

When I saw the "G-d" press conference, I said to my colleagues: "This guy will have a fall from his heights to such low depths because he doesn't credit G-d. He is actually denying of G-d." I was certain that a man of such arrogance could not remain in power.

In that assessment, I ended up being right. What I didn't anticipate was that it would be his grotesque and abusive treatment of women that would lead to his downfall. While that is a clear sign of hubris and arrogance, and while nothing he did to abuse women should be discounted, it pales in comparison to the loss of human life for which he was responsible through his actions. The deaths that are tied to Governor Cuomo are not the inadvertent consequences of a bad decision made with incomplete information, in real-time, during a crisis. Cuomo knew exactly what he was doing and I cannot help but attempt to speculate what could have been going on inside of his head. What I do know is that G-d knows what was in Cuomo's head, and G-d will eventually get around to dealing with him.

As a bit of a postscript to the Cuomo story, I did try to make an appeal to him to see if perhaps he was just being "handled" by those around him and that he really might be interested in moving forward with a treatment if he just heard directly from me. On May 15, 2020, I tried to appeal to his better angels by sending him a letter. The entirety of it is below:

Dr. Vladimir (Zev) Zelenko M.D.
Board Certified Family Practitioner
501 Rt 208, Monroe, NY 10950
845-782-0000

May 15, 2020

To the Honorable Governor Andrew Cuomo:

I have the privilege and responsibility for providing healthcare to thousands of patients in Kiryas Joel. During the 2nd week of March, the community experienced a widespread outbreak of COVID-19 and my practice began seeing hundreds of very sick people. After witnessing so much human suffering up close over the last two months, I have become very passionate about finding an immediate solution to this pandemic.

In early March, based on studies from around the world, I developed a three-drug protocol (Hydroxychloroquine, Azithromycin, Zinc Sulfate) for the primary-care setting. Within 5 days of the onset of symptoms, I treated high-risk patients with this protocol.

After treating approximately 500 high-risk patients in this manner, I would like to report the following outcomes: one death (patient already had advanced cancer); three intubations (all patients have since returned home); four patients hospitalized for IV antibiotics for opportunistic bacterial pneumonia (all patients have since returned home).

In collaboration with two world-class medical researchers from Germany, data related to the outcomes of my patients will likely be published in 2 to 3 weeks in a highly respected medical journal. This study will show an impressive relative risk-reduction of patient hospitalization and death when the protocol is followed within the first 5 days of the onset of symptoms.

I have been contacted by many prominent people in politics and media, all with intense interest in this study. In addition, governmental officials and prominent physicians from around the world (e.g. Brazil, France, Honduras, Israel, Italy, Mexico, Peru and Ukraine) have contacted me and are waiting to receive this study. I anticipate that once published, this study will receive significant national and international attention and may change the standard of care for COVID-19.

I would be honored to work together with you to help solve this pandemic. So as a courtesy, I am informing you of this pending study and if you'd like I would be happy to send you a copy in advance of publication.

In this way, my hope is you will have the critical information you need so you may continue to best protect the great State of New York.

Please let me know if you would like an advance copy of the study.

Respectfully,

Dr. Vladimir Zelenko

The silence in response to my letter was both deafening and deadly.

Breaking Through the Chaos

While I was engaged in battle with the State of New York, neither the pandemic nor I were standing still. As previously referenced, in consultation with Dr. Nise Yamaguchi, I helped to treat the President of Brazil. I was advising the members of Ukraine's health department, and Leonardo Sanchez, the Health Minister of Honduras reached out for information on my protocol. That conversation led to a press conference in Honduras on April 22 to announce the rollout of my protocol. There were successes, but not enough of them and not anywhere near fast enough.

On April 30, the Attorney General of New York sent me a cease-and-desist letter in an effort to fully extinguish any possibility of my office using my protocol. This sort of action is again unprecedented. What I had still not pieced together at the time is that the resistance to my simple, safe, and effective treatment was coming from larger institutional players. What I had found to treat COVID-19 was so readily available and inexpensive, it just didn't leave enough money to be made from its prescription. If we were going to have a man-made global pandemic, well then by gosh there was an opportunity to make money here that just wasn't going to be passed up. There was also an opportunity to keep people controlled and locked down so that they could possibly get used to authoritarianism. Big Pharma wanted money and Big Government wanted control. All that fit nicely together when you consider that the people who run Big Government also want Big Pharma's money and vice versa. People dying for no reason? Not a problem. It was merely a bit of collateral damage for promoting greater money and power—that was viewed as good.

I was fortunate that after the executive order by Cuomo, I still had access to HCQ. In advance of its issuance, I had asked one of the pharmacies that I was dealing with to secure as much HCQ as possible. That wasn't because I knew Cuomo's order was coming, it was because my work had revealed that the real key was early treatment. I wanted to make sure I was going to be able to treat as many patients as possible as quickly as possible. HCQ wasn't a common drug to stock in bulk, so they had to get it ordered and I ended up with a stockpile of thousands of pills. I rationed them judiciously, again in accordance with the risk hierarchy I developed, and was still able to assist patients, just not every patient with a need.

Once I started to run low, they started scrambling to other states. They went to Connecticut, New Jersey, Pennsylvania. Then, through contacts I had in the nursing home industry, I was able to get more pills; approximately ten thousand of them. This was also something I set in motion prior to the executive order because I had a sort of premonition that something wasn't right. As I shared in an earlier chapter, I am open to hearing G-d's voice and am always actively seeking it. I believe He was warning me and I heeded that. Because of this advance planning, I continued to save lives in direct defiance of the State of New York that seemed to be actively trying to end lives.

This back and forth with my treatment protocol had my head spinning like Linda Blair's in *The Exorcist*. On one hand, the FDA said my treatment could be used, while on the other hand, the governor of New York prohibited its use. Governments in Ukraine and Honduras supported it, while multiple US states were banning it. Jews from around the world reached out to me for advice and treatment while Jews in my own local community chose to be slanderous and libel me. Sean Hannity had me on his show and praised me, only to have *New York Times* and *Vanity Fair* publish hit pieces on me.

The nation was in such a panic that information was not being processed rationally and thoroughly. It was reminiscent when there is some sort of a mass shooting or terror event, and all of the initial reporting is conflicting and mostly inaccurate. In the case of a single event, it often takes hours or days for the story to come out accurately. The problem with the coronavirus pandemic was that the story was ongoing and developing which meant that everybody was continuously getting the "reporting" wrong.

I needed a way to break through the chaos, misinformation, and propaganda. I knew that my treatment was working. What I needed was a way to create credibility and get both regular people and the people in positions of power to take notice.

The most pressing requirement was a study, and it had to be done quickly. The bias and cowardice of bureaucracy needed to have one so that they could offload the risk of making a decision on something that was new and unproven, perhaps going sideways. No person, or a person's ego, likes to be known for making a decision that leads to deaths. By approving my treatment protocol, it meant that people might die from its use. For a bureaucrat, if they let people die by inaction then the death doesn't get attached to their name. They don't really care if people live or die, they just don't want to be blamed for the result.

Fortunately, I was about to be given the opportunity to have one conducted. Unfortunately, it was going to go sideways.

Chapter Three

I Should Have Studied Harder

As we moved into the early part of the summer of 2020, I was facing challenges in treating patients because of my inability to have HCQ prescriptions filled. As I mentioned, I had seen fit to create a stockpile of the drug and I did have some other sources through which to obtain it, but for the most part my stores were running dry and my tiered level of treatment based upon risk profile became ever more important to follow.

By this time, the restrictions had spread far beyond New York. Neighboring states like Connecticut, New Jersey, and Pennsylvania had all restricted access to HCQ, as did other states around the country. We were seeing the advent of telemedicine, which allowed me to see patients from around the country. I would see these patients, but the rules governing the ability to prescribe were still being developed and I was operating in a gray area in terms of what I could and could not do for them. I tried to help them as best I could within the still-forming legal constraints governing the practice of medicine.

The majority of the patients I would treat were coming to me from my own Jewish community. This was a little disappointing but not surprising. Jewish people are drawn together not just by our faith, but also by our long-shared history of persecution over centuries and throughout the world. It creates a sort of inherent trust that is not universal – clearly – but is prevalent. While I was being crucified in the mainstream media, those in my own community had come to distrust established institutions based on historical experience. They were the ones most likely to defer to a Hasidic doctor as opposed to the *New York Times*.

The requests I was receiving were overwhelming in number and I found myself unable to keep up. I started triaging my own calls and texts: If I heard from someone about a patient in the hospital, I did not return the call. I knew at that point what I had discovered was not going to be of any help. I would take about a hundred to a hundred and fifty calls per day; as many as I could before my vocal cords would actually wear out. I stopped seeing patients face-to-face–in part because of the time it required and in part because of the death threats I was receiving.

I hid in my private office and placed a mattress and a mini-fridge in the room. In that setting, I would simply deal with patients remotely. Writing this book is the first time I have stepped back and thought about what I was dealing with in those days. No sleep, no peace, an inherent fear for my life and for the safety of my family. Nobody ever really asked me how I was doing. I was face-to-face with the Primordial Serpent and I felt like I was standing there all alone.

That Serpent worked in some exceptionally sinister ways. One such way was to place me into conflict with my former wife and the mother of my six older children. She filed a petition in Pennsylvania to be granted sole custody of my children. This was traumatic for me, and I came to understand that it was that sort of innate, ever-present evil that had sort of taken possession of her to use as a tool against me. Given my love for my children, if the Serpent wanted to distract Zelenko from carrying out G-d's mission, there was no better way to do it than to go after the most loved and treasured thing on earth: His kids. The Serpent knew he couldn't scare me with death, and he knew he couldn't scare me with threats of legal action, but he did know that my children are my Achilles heel.

At first, I started to take steps to fight the legal battle with her, but then I ultimately surrendered to the belief that G-d loves my children more than I do. He will protect them. What I did not want to do was drag my kids through a messy two-year or more battle in the court system. I relented, letting go and letting G-d take the reins.

This played out over time, but eventually I made the very difficult decision to cut a deal. It was hard to process that it had come down to the necessity to do that and there were conditions. My kids could not go out of state and I could not be the driver in a car with them. Our visits also needed to be supervised, and so on. Since I realized this was the work of the Serpent and not my ex-wife, it was easier to intellectually come up with a tactical response that mitigated all around damage, and to forgive her.

Doctors Have the Lowest IQ

Regarding the feedback and responses I was getting from my peers, it was indeed a mixed bag. There was Dr. Robert Suskind, the founder of the California University of Science & Medicine, who called me one day, out of the blue, sharing tremendous support. This call inspired me because I had no academic backing at that time, and by most measures, I was on my own. When he gave his support - a person of that caliber, with a world-class level of academic respect – I felt assured that those were words of encouragement I desperately needed.

It's easy to look back now in hindsight, two years later with all of the research and academic papers that have been published vindicating me to feel as though it was all worth it. It is easy to trick myself into thinking I always knew it would be. In reality, I didn't know any of those things would happen with any level of certainty. This was just the beginning, and even though I saw miracles with my own eyes, it was only *my* eyes. Trying to get others to see was difficult and discouraging. I owe much to that call from Dr. Suskind.

As for other doctors, I have come to believe that doctors have the lowest IQ. The last two years have confirmed that for me. I believe ninety percent of the people that are called doctors shouldn't be, and I think that the way they have been trained to be nothing more than Pavlovian dogs responding to stimuli and algorithms has weakened our medical institutions. Doctors can no longer be critical and use deductive thought, reasoning, or analysis skills. It often felt like I was talking to a profession of individuals filled with cognitive dissonance, where the same doctor who had threatened to report me to the State Medical Board for prescribing HCQ to COVID-19 patients would simultaneously be writing a prescription for HCQ to a woman with rheumatoid arthritis who was pregnant and not seeing any contradiction. If the definition of insanity is repeating the same behavior and expecting different results, then the meaning of pandemic insanity is not to alter any behavior and expect to receive good results. That is what I saw in the medical community then, and it continues to the present day.

I started to think about Moses in the desert. Moses had a couple of million people hanging out, and they were getting a bit grumpy. A convert to Judaism confronted Moses, who had been operating as the chief justice, the teacher, the motivational therapist, basically everything to all of these people. He said to him, "What you are doing isn't good. You can't judge these people alone. You need a system."

I was no Moses, and I was taking this on all alone. I agreed that I also needed a system, so I devoted my time to reaching out to the medical community to share my news and recruit doctors willing to help. I transitioned to try to take my limited time and resources and teach any provider - from any place around the world - who showed a desire to listen. I found people worldwide, from all continents, probably more than a hundred countries, and I started to connect. Word began to spread.

I recently received some confirmation about how well that approach worked. This happened when I went to a pain management doctor in South Florida to get a shot to ease some back pain. Through conversation, I discovered that this doctor knew absolutely everything about me. He knew

I had sarcoma before I told him, and he even knew my Jewish name. He told me that he was praying for me and that he had been following my work for two years.

He then said, "I want you to know, even though I'm a pain management doctor, a lot of my patients got Covid and have been very sick. I used your protocol to save the lives of hundreds of people." This is just one example; this type of interaction grew more common. I would go somewhere for one thing, and a different experience would emerge.

One of my biggest breakthroughs was to influence the practice pattern of "Speak with an MD" telemedicine, National Telemedicine Doctors, and America's Frontline Doctors. I basically set their treatment protocols, and they've treated hundreds of thousands, if not more, patients with my protocol. I know G-d knows and that is all that should really matter, but I'm humbled and amazed to what degree of influence my ideas have penetrated.

For example, someone reached out to me from Pakistan and said he was in a small, ancient village on the border of Afghanistan. He told me that he wanted to thank me. Now, keep in mind these are probably people of the Islamic faith and from a region of the world where I don't think they have much interaction with Jews or indeed positive feelings toward Jews. Regardless, he reached out to me and said he wanted to thank me and that my protocols saved his entire village.

These anecdotal experiences are almost endless. I spoke in Waco, Texas, at the courthouse steps, where many people came from far and wide, many driving three or four hours to meet me, even though I was there for an event for a congressional candidate. They said things to me like, "I want to shake your hand and thank you. Thank you for your protocol. It saved my life; it saved my mother's life."

These experiences are ubiquitous for me wherever I go. I still don't know how to process that. G-d has blessed me to have an extremely challenging life and develop the survival mechanisms and coping skills, and skills in general, that prepared me for an unprecedented moment in history. I was placed in the epicenter of this moment in history and given the opportunity to affect the planet while being damaged financially, threatened to be prosecuted, both state and federally investigated, having my family taken away from me, and getting recurrent cancer and heart failure.

Hell Breaks Loose

Why me, Lord? In my musings, I have often wondered about this. I have found the answer on the steps in Waco, the lunch table interruptions, and the phone calls from Pakistan. That's why.

There were other doctors who came out in support of me. One of them was Dr. Rosa, an internal medicine doctor at Hackensack University Medical Center, who was one of the first doctors to take me seriously. Her primary care practice was in Passaic, New Jersey, which also served a Jewish community. From there, she treated hundreds of patients successfully. Then there was Dr. William Grace, who's an oncologist from Lenox Hill Hospital and had been a guest on Fox News. I don't believe he treated patients, but he gave me plenty of support and encouragement and saw the truth of what I was suggesting. He eventually became my oncologist, but these events happened prior to that. I gave up even trying with doctors in the New York hospital systems. They were too rigid and arrogant and bought into the Serpent's narrative way too quickly. There was no relief in my loss of respect for most of the medical profession, as it solidified how many people were responding to a situation, not trying to get it under control. What I did find was that mid-level providers, like nurse practitioners and physician assistants, were much more interested and willing to consider my treatment approach.

Eventually, one particular doctor, Dr. Joe Levine, an electrophysiologist at St. Francis Hospital in Long Island, reached out to me and was extremely encouraging, offering to help me conduct a clinical trial at St. Francis. At that time, I was close with Dr. Jerome Corsi. Along with my dear friend Ann Vandersteel, he was one of the first to give me a platform where I could hold interviews. I had no real media experience and no experience as a public speaker or representative of any kind. He became a bit of a mentor to me in that regard. Setting aside the problems that were about to follow, I must say that he is a brilliant man and came up with a brilliant idea. Since we were having trouble getting access across the nation to HCQ stations, he created a kind of collaboration with a telemedicine company called SpeakWithanMD. com, an organization with doctors in every state.

Dr. Corsi asked me to give a lecture to their group of doctors. I did so as a volunteer - an unpaid advisor - and I wasn't in any way deriving financial gain from the presentation. The goal was to generate interest in my protocol and get these doctors across the country to rise and demand access to HCQ. During that talk, I mentioned that I had helped organize a clinical trial at St. Francis Hospital that was FDA-approved. Keep in mind I was very green when it came to the media world, and I was not anybody with experience in dealing with the FDA. I knew the FDA website mentioned the St. Francis program, so I assumed that meant it was "approved."

Then, all hell broke loose. Dr. Corsi made a recording of that lecture/ podcast and intended to email it to me. Most of us who use email know the perils of "autocomplete" in email addresses. Instead of the email going to me, Corsi sent it to Aaron Zelinsky. Zelinsky was in Mueller's impeachment team and had investigated Jerome Corsi for two years. There were no indictments, but he did torture him. He truly wanted to destroy Corsi, and when he heard this talk I had given, sent to him by an endorsing Corsi, he thought he had his chance.

Zelinsky, by that time, was no longer on Muller's team. He was now on the Department of Justice's COVID-19 Fraud Prevention Task Force. So, as Zelinsky listened to my lecture, he heard me say that the trial was FDA-approved and then looked for confirmation of this on the website called clinicaltrials.gov. My trial at St. Francis was not listed on that site.

It was a harsh retrospective lesson to learn. Apparently, there is a lag between approval for the trial and its actual posting on the site. I had technically made an error when I said it was FDA-approved, and I did make an error, but it was simply because I had never worked in the clinical trial world. I did not fully understand what it meant to be FDA-approved. All I knew was I spoke to the commissioner of the FDA, who helped me source the drug for the trial.

That, to me, indicated that it was pretty "approved." The trial did have IRB approval, which was the "Internal Review Board." I thought it meant that the FDA had approved it, but that simply related to the board of St. Francis having signed off on the study.

To be crystal clear, I had come to the wrong conclusion when I spoke those words. I had presumed that since I was dealing with the commissioner of the FDA and it had IRB approval (which actually turned out to be IRB approval of the St. Francis Hospital board), I, in error, misspoke. I said that it was FDA approved before the fact that it was.

The next thing I knew (after my children, I might add) was that all this was leaked to *The Washington Post*. The headline that appeared on April 30, 2020, screamed:

Justice Department Scrutinizes White House-Connected Doctor Linked to Disputed Coronavirus Treatment.

Upon its publication, my kids called me, freaking out.

"Tati, are you okay? Are you in jail? Are you arrested?" I had no idea what they were talking about.

The story was lengthy. It opened as follows:

Federal prosecutors are examining the communications of a New York family doctor whose work has been discussed on Fox News and who has been in touch with the White House to tout an anti-malarial as a treatment for the novel coronavirus, according to people contacted as part of the inquiry.

Imagine how I felt reading in one of the nation's primary newspapers, the very one that broke the Watergate story, now had a feature breaking news that the US Department of Justice was investigating me. I was mortified.

My sources inside the government told me that they had opened an investigation on me for fraud. That said, three hours after *The Washington Post* article broke about me, quite mysteriously, my St. Francis trial appeared on clinicaltrials.gov. That ended the investigation in the crib.

No one from the Department of Justice ever contacted me. I was told (by a source I will not name) that President Trump himself told VP Mike Pence to fix the problem. Of course, this cannot be confirmed, but it is how my trial ended three hours later on the website.

The Washington Post never seemed to get around to issuing an update on my clinical trial. It is strange how the passage of time, the coarsening of sensibilities, and the revelations of truth can change a person. Today, if someone came and told me: "You know, DOJ is opening an investigation into you," I'd say, "Okay, so what?" But at that time, it was earth-shattering for me.

Meanwhile, my study was underway. I knew what it would show because I had been observing it for two months in real-time with real patients. The study was a formality, but it was necessary. Once again, I was optimistic.

Then, on May 22, 2020, *The Lancet* published a phony set of data that indicated HCQ could likely increase the chance of death if used to treat COVID-19. Two weeks later, they retracted the report as it was clear that the data used for the study was false. I will share more on that moment in an upcoming chapter, but *The Lancet* piece did its damage. Although they never officially stated it as being the reason, I learned through back channels that *The Lancet's* false study report was used as the justification for the FDA killing my clinical trial approval on June 15. Again, I can't prove that, but to think otherwise is to apply former Senator Clinton's phrase about General Petraeus, which suggested that to believe it would "require a suspension of disbelief."

Applying Science

Dr. Harvey Risch is Professor Emeritus of Epidemiology in the Department of Epidemiology and Public Health at the Yale School of Public Health and Yale School of Medicine. Unlike myself at the time, he was highly respected and very well pedigreed. On May 27, 2020, he published a paper in support of moving forward with my treatment protocol. While he did not mention me by name, we had been in contact.

The paper made the point that while clinical, double-blind studies were a good way to go in general, the rate at which people were contracting COVID-19 and dying therefrom was so alarming and accelerated that more assertive steps needed to be taken—a variation on the Churchill line of "desperate times call for desperate measures."

At the time, Dr. Risch's paper was the most compelling, clear, and credible statement that had yet been produced, supporting what I was putting forward as a treatment path. Here is an extended excerpt from his paper:

The great majority of infected people are at low risk for progression or will manifest the infection asymptomatically. For the rest, outpatient treatment that prevents disease progression and hospitalization is required…. Thus, the key to returning society toward normal functioning and to preventing huge loss of life, especially among older individuals, people with comorbidity, and African Americans and Hispanics/Latinos, is a safe, effective, and proactive outpatient treatment that prevents hospitalization in the first place.

All medical treatments have costs and benefits. In an ideal world, randomized double-blinded controlled clinical trials establish evidence for the relative degree of benefit, and if they are large enough, for estimates of the frequencies of adverse events. These trials take time to conduct: to get formal approval, to get funding, to enroll enough eligible patients, to wait for the outcomes to occur, and to analyze the data. In the context of the coronavirus disease 2019 (COVID-19) pandemic, we are presently averaging about 10,000 deaths per week in the United States, under moderately strong isolation policies that have put more than 36 million people out of work. Results of currently ongoing or planned randomized trials for use of a number of outpatient medications are many weeks or months off…We are rapidly reaching a breaking point in the ability to maintain the status quo; states have begun the process of lifting their restrictions, and we thus need to evaluate what evidence we do have for promising outpatient treatments.

Numerous reviews of HCQ efficacy and adverse events have been and continue to be published. To my knowledge, all of these reviews have omitted the 2 critical aspects of reasoning about these drugs: use of HCQ combined with AZ or with DOX and use in the outpatient setting…I will show that HCQ + AZ and HCQ + DOX are generally safe for short-term use in the early treatment of most symptomatic high-risk outpatients, where not contraindicated, and that they are effective in preventing hospitalization for the overwhelming majority of such patients. If these combined medications become the standard of care, they are likely to save an enormous number of lives that would otherwise be lost to this endemic disease.

In this context, we cannot afford the luxury of perfect knowledge and must evaluate, now and on an ongoing basis, the evidence for the benefit and risk of these medications. Available evidence of efficacy of HCQ + AZ has been repeatedly described in the media as "anecdotal," but it most certainly is not.

A Jew and Two German Doctors Walk into a Bar…

This was a significant event in my mind toward getting the medical establishment to recognize that it made sense to treat people, to treat those people early, and to do so using my protocol. Dr. Risch's well-respected place in the community certainly should have led to more doctors demanding answers from the government as to why this treatment option wasn't being made available to their patients. Between my study being underway and this paper referring to my research but saying, in essence, "let's not wait," I thought we were on the path toward eradicating the virus that shook the world.

I was dead wrong. I underestimated the putrid cowardice of my profession. Dr. Risch's work caused less than a blip on the medical establishment's radar screen and was never amplified by the cowardly mainstream media.

On April seventeenth, 2020, I was contacted by Dr. Roland Derwand of Alexion Pharma and Dr. Martin Scholz of Heinrich-Heine University in Düsseldorf, Germany. They had been made aware of my work through open letters and videos I had been sharing with the world. They were highly respected in the field and were interested in learning about my data and seeking a way in which we could collaborate.

That conversation led to them publishing a hypothesis paper on May sixth, 2020, supporting my process. The two German doctors were responsible for creating the term "Zelenko Protocol." We became friends, and I still enjoy the irony of a couple of German doctors wanting to experiment and working together with an Orthodox Jew. There is some historical precedent for this not ending well.

Irony aside, a hypothesis paper is one where the author demonstrates enough specific individual pieces of evidence that lead to inductive reasoning to construct a hypothesis. In this case, they were suggesting that my case evidence, along with other factors, was enough to warrant studies to test the following hypothesis:

Based on real world dialogue the combination of HCQ with oral zinc, often in a triple combination with the antibiotic azithromycin, is obviously already used by some clinical practitioners. In accordance with his own statement and available press reports the medical practitioner Dr. Vladimir Zelenko from Monroe, New York, USA has already treated hundreds of patients with coronavirus-like symptoms with the described triple combination claiming favorable clinical outcome. Based on personal communication the following experimental treatment regimen has been used so far: HCQ 200 mg twice daily, zinc sulfate 220 mg once-daily, and azithromycin 500 mg once-daily, each for 5 days. Detailed analysis of patient outcome is currently ongoing and might support guidance for clinical practice and the design of needed randomized clinical trials.

The doctors and I agreed to work together to publish research using our actual patient treatment data. I thought this would be a faster process and eventually a supporting document to the clinical trial taking place with St. Francis. Again, I had hope.

Drs. Derwand, Scholz, and I began our collaboration. There was a preprint of our work on June 30, 2020, just after the FDA canceled the St. Francis study, with the actual research released on October 26, 2020.

What we did was perform a "retrospective study." A retrospective study is, by definition, a study comparing two groups of people: Those with the disease or condition under study (cases) and a similar group of people who do not have the disease or condition (controls). Researchers study each group's relevant medical and lifestyle histories to learn what factors may be associated with the disease or condition.

To this day, our work can be found on the National Institute of Health's website. You might think, *why wouldn't it be?* In compiling the supporting evidence and documents for this book, I can tell you that an incredible amount of information supporting my work has been essentially "scrubbed" from the internet. Those in power, those serving the Primordial Serpent, do not want people to easily discover that Dr. Vladimir Zelenko had found an easy and affordable way to treat this disease very early on and that it was suppressed by the leaders that they trusted. So, yes, it is relatively surprising that our study is still posted on an official US government website.

When the preprint became available, which is a complete study but is not yet a peer-reviewed study to make it official, the online publication BioSpace.com wrote a short but unequivocal and fair report of the study:

NEW YORK, July 15, 2020 /PRNewswire/ --
Dr. Vladimir Zelenko, a New York based primary care physician, announced that a retrospective analysis based on his patient data is available to read online at www.thezelenkoprotocol.com. The study, which has been submitted for peer review, found that early intervention and treatment of risk stratified COVID-19 patients in the outpatient setting resulted in five times less hospitalizations and deaths. The

medications used in the treatment approach were zinc, low dose hydroxychloroquine, and azithromycin.

Prior studies of COVID-19 treatments have been largely based on severely ill patients in the hospital. This study examines outcomes of patients treated after their first visit to the doctor's office. Using simple risk stratification criteria, Dr. Zelenko identified which patients required prescriptions for the triple drug therapy, and prescribed these medications for five days.

To produce the study, Zelenko collaborated with Dr. Roland Derwand, a German medical doctor and life science industry expert, and Professor Martin Scholz, an independent consultant and adjunct professor for experimental medicine at Heinrich Heine University, Düsseldorf, Germany. Derwand and Scholz performed the data analysis while Zelenko handled all in-person treatments.

The main results show that of 141 patients who were treated with the triple therapy, only 2.8% (4/141) were hospitalized compared to 15.4% of an untreated control group (58/377) (odds ratio 0.16, 95% CI 0.06-0.5; p<0.001). Only 0.71% (1/141) patients died in the treatment group, versus 3.5% (13/377) in the untreated group (odds ratio 0.2, 95% CI 0.03-1.5; p=0.16).

"These three medications are affordable, available in pill form, and work in synergy against COVID-19," said Zelenko. "Hydroxychloroquine's main function within this treatment approach is to allow zinc to enter the cell. Zinc is the virus killer, and azithromycin prevents secondary bacterial infection in the lungs and reduces the risk of pulmonary complications."

"The world seems to have forgotten common medical knowledge: that we want to treat any patient with an infectious disease as soon as possible," said Derwand. "What differentiates this study is that patients were prescribed these medications early, in the outpatient setting. Dr. Zelenko treated his risk-stratified patients immediately and didn't wait for the disease to intensify."

"The well-tolerated 5-day triple therapy resulted in a significantly lower hospitalization rate and less fatalities with no reported cardiac side effects compared with relevant public reference data of untreated patients," said Scholz. "The magnitude of the results can substantially elevate the relevance of early use, low dose

hydroxychloroquine, especially in combination with zinc. This data can be used to inform ongoing pandemic response policies as well as future clinical trials."

"It's unfortunate much of the news coverage surrounding hydroxychloroquine has been negative," Zelenko added. "This study suggests that when taken early and together with zinc and azithromycin, this cost-effective drug can be part of the solution to the pandemic."

We had hoped we were about to change the world. What we didn't yet realize was that the world was already being changed, in a deliberate manner, and that our research stood directly in the way of letting the people behind it, those in service to the Primordial Serpent, accomplish their mission. They were not going to surrender easily.

On The Committee

I have previously noted that in early-mid July, I had a cancer recurrence. There was a way in which I had almost forgotten about it, simply owing to the frenetic pace of the prior four months. I also should have been dead long before the recurrence, especially based on the nature of my cancer and the physicians' prognoses. Yet, here I was, in July of 2020, and I had been a bit busy.

Cancer and the resulting surgery and recoveries set me back for months. Once I was home, I did what I could in terms of consulting on patients and continuing my research into the pandemic and its causes. Think of connecting dots, finding a logical order to bits of information and scattered data, and you'll understand what I was diligently doing.

In November 2020, Senator Ron Johnson from Wisconsin decided to hold a hearing of the Homeland Security Committee for which he served as Chair. I was part of a ten-person group on a conference call that helped him to prepare for the hearing. Dr. Peter McCullough, Dr. George Fareed, and Dr. Harvey Risch all credited my work. Dr. Fareed would call me his "hero" on the Senate floor.

I prepared a letter for submission to Senator Johnson and the Committee for the official permanent record ahead of that hearing. Below is a copy of the main points of substance of that document. I include it because it is a concise version of a complete argument. This letter is my appeal, my plea, to try and get the people at the highest level of government to recognize that there is a way to end the madness that has overtaken the country and stop the needless loss of life. I still had not realized that those lives were being sacrificed as part of a larger plan. This was always about control and never about medicine.

Nonetheless, here is the case I made driven by a mixture of sincerity, frustration, knowledge, and naiveté:

U.S. Senate Committee on Homeland Security
Full Committee Hearing, Early Outpatient Treatment: An Essential Part of a
COVID-19 Solution,
Statement for the Official Record, by:
Vladimir Zelenko MD
Board Certified Family Physician
November 19, 2020

Summary

Research and development of medicine is now a matter of national security. Prior to COVID-19, medicine was generally left to the pharmaceutical industry and a few agencies ("Big Pharma"). Big Pharma relies on an economic incentive model that prioritizes fiduciary duty to shareholders over public benefit, resulting in expensive, proprietary, patented drugs that take significantly more time to develop. This incentive model is leading to a mortality count that may be greater than the civil war - historically the most deadly war for the USA.

The cure to COVID-19 is a combination therapy of generic drugs and supplements that must be administered within the first four (4) days of symptoms. It was the fastest a cure for any disease has ever been developed (months), using open source Real World Evidence data exchange at global scale, of non-patented drugs for public benefit – this is the opposite of the Big Pharma incentive model.

The development of new medicines in this way is an elegant solution which provides extreme value to society, dramatically reduces load to the healthcare system and allows for overall greater production in the economy. This can be done for many other diseases and conditions if the proper resources were allocated – so that a COVID-19 like situation never happens again. There must be an organization that functions as an intelligence agency for medicine whose exclusive duty is to the people, not shareholders – building on this solution. Significant funds must be allocated to implement this - a gap which can be filled by an organization funded by Homeland Security similar to how the TSA was created in response to 9/11. COVID-19 must be swiftly ended and a situation like this must never happen again.

Background

The 21st Century Cures Act (the "Cures Act") is a law that was passed in 2016. Section 3022 of the Cures Act is titled Real World Evidence. The Cures Act defines Real World Evidence as: "data regarding the usage, or the potential benefits or risks, of a drug derived from sources other than randomized clinical trials ... including ongoing safety surveillance, observational studies, registries, claims, and patient-centered outcomes research activities..."

The Cures Act goes on to state Real World Evidence may support the approval of new indications for generic drugs. There is very significant Real World Evidence that supports the approval of using generic drugs to effectively treat COVID-19 in the outpatient setting.

While formal clinical trials can provide significant insight into a drug's safety and efficacy in a patient population, it may also provide misleading data - as was the case with the opioid clinical trials which resulted in a fatal epidemic. Reliance on these clinical trials has led to over 200,000 deaths from opioids in the USA - which only started to decrease recently as of 2016 - 2017, because of use of Real World Evidence. To clarify, the clinical trials for some opioids did not show how addictive the drugs actually were. These clinical trials were used to push opioids prescriptions, which has significantly increased the demand for heroin in the USA. Below is a chart of opioid based deaths over time.

Figure 3. **National Drug Overdose Deaths Involving Any Opioid,** Number Among All Ages, by Gender, 1999-2017

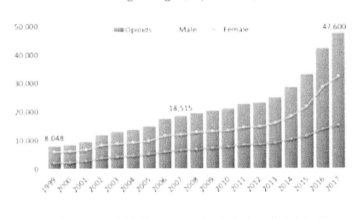

It was only the use of Real World Evidence by physicians in the clinic that showed their true effect - how dangerous opioids can be. Why? Because patients in the clinic is an actual real world setting, with real clinicians and patients whereas clinical trial data is generally paid for by a pharmaceutical company who has an economic incentive to optimize data presentation for FDA approval. For example, details from "failed" clinical trials are often not published.

This has been the case for COVID-19 big pharma drugs. For remdesivir - an alleged COVID-19 drug that was given emergency use authorization, there is clinical trial data which shows no statistically significant benefit in mortality, yet it has received emergency use authorization by the FDA. The World Health Organization has even stated that remdesivir should not be used to treat COVID 19 due to lack of efficacy in mortality. A significant amount of data has not been published for remdesivir. This is generally the case with Big Pharma clinical trial drugs, a significant portion of the data is not published because of economic incentives.

Reliance on clinical trials as the only evidence to support the use of medicines in the market has led to significant problems such as COVID-19 and the opioid epidemics.

Incentives - No one can serve two masters

The financial interests in drug development are significant. Specifically, pharmaceutical companies and biotech's are generally publicly traded and therefore owe a fiduciary duty to their shareholders. This means that the standard Big Pharma corporation has a special duty to act in the best interest of the parties that hold their stock. Notably, these Big Pharma companies do NOT owe a fiduciary duty to patients nor the general public. Big Pharma owes the same duty to their shareholders that any publicly traded company owes to their shareholders - make as much legal profit as possible to make the stock price go up. If a CEO does not do this, he/she will be replaced. Big Pharma's total market capitalization is over $2 trillion USD, which is larger than 90% of all country's GDP and is approximately 10% of the USA's GDP.

In the USA, because of the fiduciary duty, Big Pharma spends significant funds on lobbying. The pharmaceutical industry as a whole spends more on lobbying U.S. government agencies and officials than any other industry by over $100 million USD, per year.

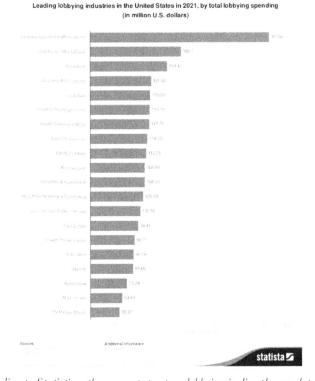

Leading lobbying industries in the United States in 2021, by total lobbying spending (in million U.S. dollars)

According to Statistica, the amount spent on lobbying is directly correlated to deaths by opioids. A recent 2020 JAMA Internal Medicine article, "analyzed publicly available data on campaign contributions and lobbying in the US from 1999 to 2018 and found that the pharmaceutical industry spent $4.7 billion, an average of $233 million per year, on lobbying the US federal government; $414 million on contributions to presidential and congressional electoral candidates, national party committees, and outside spending groups; and $877 million on contributions to state candidates and committees. Contributions were targeted at senior legislators in Congress involved in drafting health care laws and state committees that opposed or supported key referenda on drug pricing and regulation."

The government agencies that execute the policy, regulations and/or pricing that flows from this lobbying are Food and Drugs Administration ("FDA"), the Centers for Disease Control ("CDC"), the National Institutes of Health ("NIH"). All three (3) of these agencies have significant financial interests aligned with Big Pharma - as outlined below.

FDA

The FDA budget for 2019 was approximately $6 billion. Approximately 50% comes from taxpayers while the other 50% is paid for by industry user fees. User fees are paid by industry, e.g. Big Pharma for drug approvals such as a PDUFA fee. A PDUFA fee is $2 - $10 million USD paid for by a drug sponsor to the FDA to allow a drug on the market, after the drug has been approved. The FDA does not receive PDUFA fees when new indications or uses for generic drugs are discovered or invented.

Additionally, it is quite customary for FDA employees to go work for industry. This is the case of former high ranking FDA officials working for Big Pharma companies after they finish at the FDA. Throughout the COVID-19 epidemic, these former FDA officials regularly go in the media and "update" the country as to the state of the COVID-19 epidemic. To date, they have generally not advocated for the use of Hydroxychloroquine or Ivermectin drug combinations (e.g. Hydroxychloroquine or Ivermectin, Zinc, Doxycycline or Azithromycin).

The FDA has warned against the use of Hydroxychloroquine in both the hospital and outpatient setting. It is unlikely the FDA has received fees for generic drugs to treat COVID-19 in the outpatient setting. It is very likely the FDA has received fees for patented Big Pharma drugs and "vaccines".

It is known that the combination therapy of Hydroxychloroquine, Zinc and antibiotic (azithromycin or doxycycline) is a cure to COVID-19 if administered within the first 4 days of symptoms. This has been proven with real world evidence. There is no clinical trial that refutes this. The data is overwhelming. The FDA has not removed their restrictions on hydroxychloroquine nor supported the use of this drug combination.

CDC

Established by Congress as an independent, nonprofit organization, the CDC Foundation is the sole entity authorized by Congress to mobilize philanthropic partners and private-sector resources to support CDC's critical health protection mission. Although the CDC Foundation was chartered by Congress, it is not a government agency nor is it a division of CDC. It is a private, nonprofit organization classified as a 501(c)(3) public charity. Donors to the CDC Foundations include the top Big Pharma companies. The CDC Foundation then funds the CDC's work and becomes a partner.

NIH

The NIH budget is approximately $40 billion per year, paid by taxpayers. This is the biggest bio R&D operation in the world. The NIH is financially involved with almost every Big Pharma company. A significant portion of Big Pharma drugs originate at the NIH, generating approximately $100 million a year in royalties paid to the NIH and NIH employees. According to End Points, "from 1988 to 2004, NIH entered into almost 2,500 license agreements and generated more than $500 million in royalty revenues. More recently, royalties have amounted to more than $100 million per year."

The NIH is paid for by taxpayers but is incentivized with Big Pharma's fiduciary duty to shareholders. As such this can have a significant effect on research and markets as support for one drug may increase or decrease sales of a competing drug therefore affecting economic flow (royalties, relationships, etc.). Such a model favors research and support to patented drugs over generics and supplements. The NIH budget allocated towards drug repurposing (generics) is approximately .015% of the budget.

A significant amount of NIH research data is generally not publicly available for collaborative data mining. Notably, from 2013 - 2019, the NIH spent over $250 billion USD in research and US life expectancy actually decreased. How can this be?

During the COVID-19 pandemic, approximately $10 billion was committed by the federal government to big pharma companies for patented drugs and "vaccines". Less than 1% of this was allocated to researching generic drug combinations - even after the cure was announced in March 2020. The cure to COVID-19 is a combination of safe generic drugs and supplements administered in the outpatient setting. NIH started a clinical trial for a combination outpatient therapy of hydroxychloroquine and azithromycin - but terminated the clinical trial after only two (2) months due to *"lack of enrollment." It is known that such trials can take significantly longer than just two (2) months.*

The NIH funded the development of Remdesivir in a $37.5 million grant to the University of Alabama at Birmingham - with the grant's principal investigator being a board member of Gilead Sciences. Remdesivir is Gilead's drug. On April 29 2020, Anthony Fauci MD, the leader of the National Institute for Allergy and Infectious Disease at the NIH, declared Remdesivir as the "standard of care" for COVID-19 treatment. On April 30, 2020 Gilead's stock reached its annual high of $84 per share. On November 20, 2020, the World Health Organization recommended "against the use of Remdesivir ... regardless of disease severity, as there is currently no evidence that Remdesivir improves survival and other outcomes in these patients." As of November 30, 2020, Gilead's stock is trading at approximately $60 per share. A drop of 40%, and a loss of over $20 billion in market capitalization.

Markets

Stock markets have moved considerably on positive COVID-19 research news, e.g. advance of treatment, "vaccines", etc. In February and March 2020, the stock market had decreased the most in the shortest period of time, ever, likely due to COVID-19 fear. This is despite significant injections of capital by government and institutions. It was only on March 19, 2020 when President Trump announced the combination therapy of Hydroxychloroquine and Azithromycin that the trend started to reverse. President Trump even stated that this combination therapy is expected to provide most benefit early in treatment, e.g. outpatient, before hospital. On this news, Gilead's stock went down and the entire market went up. The exact bottom of Tesla stock was the day before, on March 18.

As stated by the hearing witnesses, there is not consensus amongst medical professionals regarding effective outpatient treatment. This lack of consensus is due to an incentive model that has led to faulty message propagation, controlled by shareholder value as opposed to public benefit. If the generic drug combination therapy was promoted as the cure, it would take profit away from the patented Big Pharma drugs and likely eliminate the mass panic and state of emergency, which would reduce funding to

Big Pharma. The economic incentives are misaligned at the expense of tax paying American citizens.

The cure to COVID-19 did not come from large pharmaceutical companies nor the government - it came from private citizens engaged in open source R&D at global scale. According to Harvey Risch, MD, PhD of Yale University, to date the generic combination therapy is better than anything that the pharmaceutical industry or government has put out, including Remdesivir and monoclonal antibodies. It is clear that generic drug and supplement research can provide significant benefit.

The Zelenko Protocol

I have treated over 3,000 COVID-19 and suspected COVID-19 patients in a unique orthodox Jewish setting in New York. Additionally, I have consulted physicians who have treated over 10,000 patients in total. 100% of my patients that are high risk have fully recovered if they received the triple combination therapy of Hydroxychloroquine + Zinc + Antibiotic (Azithromycin or Doxycycline) within the first 4 days of symptoms, and take it for at least 5 days. This triple combination therapy administered immediately in the outpatient setting has gained international acclaim and has become known as the Zelenko Protocol. High risk patients that have been cured include the elderly including Holocaust survivors that are over 90 years old, cancer patients, diabetics, etc. This group should have a fatality rate between 5% - 20%. The fatality rate of these patients that follow the Zelenko Protocol in the first four (4) days of symptoms is 0.00%.

To my knowledge, I am the first person to publicly integrate a high dose of Zinc into the combination therapy as of March 2020. Zinc has proven to be extremely efficacious when used in combination with a zinc ionophore such as Hydroxychloroquine or Quercetin. These combinations have proven to be very safe in the outpatient setting. The Zelenko Protocol calls for risk stratifying patients into high risk and low risk groups and treating empirically the high risk group within the first 4 days of symptoms.

I have published an initial study of my findings with two prominent German researchers, Dr. Roland Derwand of Alexion Pharma and Dr. Martin Scholz of Heinrich-Heine University Düsseldorf Germany, which can be found here:

REMOVED INTENTIONALLY. Further publications are currently in process.

In addition, patients that have been successfully treated with the Zelenko Protocol have gone on to develop antibodies to COVID-19. We have provided a cure and immunity quickly and inexpensively.

The Zelenko Protocol was developed based on the work of Didier Raoult MD PhD at the main COVID-19 hospital in Marseille, France - the IHU. Dr. Raoult is known as one of the top infectious disease doctors in the world and the most widely cited microbiologist in Europe.

Incredibly, the French government decided to place a ban on the use of Hydroxychloroquine to treat COVID-19. Dr. Raoult ignored the ban and continued to treat his patients with the combination therapy, while the rest of France abided by the ban. As of July 2020, the case fatality rate of Dr. Raoult's patients (3000 +) were less than 1% whereas the rest of France had a case fatality rate of more than 15%. Dr. Raoult has been a strong proponent of early treatment.

Any professional who states this combination therapy does not work must explain the below difference in COVID-19 fatality in France as of July 2020. (Source: Worldometer, IHU website)

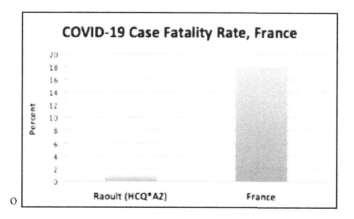

Dr. Raoult and his team have been rapidly publishing throughout the pandemic, for which this recent publication conveys their results from 3,737 COVID-19 patients which is consistent with my results: INTENTIONALLY REMOVED

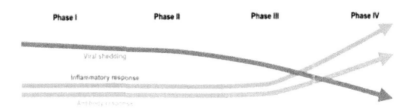

The reason why it is so important to engage in early treatment is because COVID-19 is effectively two different diseases. The first being a replicating virus and the second being respiratory inflammation including pneumonia in the lungs. If the virus replication is stopped early, the respiratory inflammation can be limited in which patients can be back to normal quickly. If the virus is not effectively treated early on, it can be difficult to treat the respiratory inflammation especially in high risk patients - as their lungs may become severely infected. This visual was created by Dr. Raoult and his team to illustrate the stages of COVID-19.

The Zelenko Protocol is a cure to the viral shedding phase, not a cure to respiratory inflammation. Once the virus has replicated too much, the inflammation cascade may not be reversed - hence time is of the essence. This is why outpatient therapy is so important.

Additionally, I put my high risk patients on a prevention protocol which includes use of Zinc and a zinc ionophore (Hydroxychloroquine or Quercetin). To date, none of my patients using prevention have been hospitalized or died…

Despite all of this evidence, the FDA and state pharmacy boards have imposed legal liability on physicians who prescribe these generic drug combinations. Some states have severely restricted the use of hydroxychloroquine - effectively governors telling physicians how to practice medicine. Incredibly, while the FDA and states have imposed legal liability for prescribing generic drugs off-label, Big Pharma companies have been indemnified by the federal government, effectively eliminating their legal liability, for patented treatments and/ or "vaccines".

Due to the media driven hysteria around these generic drugs which resulted in restrictions, we also use ivermectin in place of hydroxychloroquine which has also provided outstanding results in the combination therapy. Ivermectin is also a generic drug, safe and inexpensive.

Conclusion

Significant funds must be allocated immediately to search and develop generic medicines under Real World Evidence standard without the influence of the pharmaceutical industry. Research and development of medicine is now a matter of national security. There must be an organization that functions as an intelligence agency for medicine whose exclusive duty is to the people, not shareholders – building on this solution. Significant funds must be allocated to implement this - a gap which can be filled by an organization funded by Homeland Security similar to how the TSA was created in response to 9/11. COVID-19 must be swiftly ended and a situation like this must never happen again.

Without this, the people are reliant on an incentive model that is leading to a mortality count that may be greater than the civil war - historically the most deadly war for the USA. Enemies of the USA are standing by observing how a virus has destabilized the wealthiest nation on the planet.

There is a cure for COVID-19 as well as effective prevention options. The Zelenko Protocol could have saved over 200,000 lives. Implement it immediately for early outpatient use.

All of this, of course, went nowhere. That was no fault of Senator Johnson, who offered a consistent voice of skepticism and outrage throughout the pandemic and its ensuing crisis. He is sadly one among too few. Not enough of our political leaders were willing to stand and ask questions in the way that Senator Johnson was. They remain a part of the problem and are dead-set against a solution, which has led to massive numbers of people needlessly dying.

Letters to the Top

As 2020 began to pass into the year that would become the year of Joe Biden's totalitarian reign and "vaccine" "injuries" that looked an awful lot like "vaccine" deaths, I remained active in my efforts. I received a steady increase of support, both from those in my profession and from citizens who had a chance to come into contact with somebody treated with my protocol who got better; quickly better, usually within about fourteen hours.

I was nominated for the Presidential Medal of Freedom for my work by Susan Prager, wife of conservative thought leader Dennis Prager. She was kind enough to forward me the email she submitted to the White House. The nomination was supported by Senator Johnson, Rudy Giuliani, and Peter Navarro:

> *President Trump should award the Presidential Medal of Freedom to Dr. Vladimir Zelenko for his prescient early efforts to develop an effective therapy to treat COVID-19 just as the virus was hitting the United States. He succeeded in saving hundreds, if not thousands, of lives in the Orthodox Jewish community in New York, and his course of treatment (hydroxychloroquine, zinc, and azithromycin for symptomatic patients) has saved countless lives across the nation and perhaps around the world in spite of the fact that it has been demonized by a Trump-hating medical establishment and media (simply because the president happened to mention it as a potential life-saver in the early weeks of the pandemic). Dr. Zelenko, who underwent relentless attacks and was even pushed out of medical service to his community, deserves the recognition of this honor. Please consider as a nominee this brave physician who has worked very hard and done so much to free us from both the virus and the fear it has engendered. Thank you.*

Reading this was extraordinarily humbling, as would be the effort undertaken in 2021 by supportive members of the public in attempting to get myself and other doctors nominated for a Nobel Prize for Medicine.

However, while those accolades validated a certain part of me, they didn't lessen my resolve to continue for what I knew was the right thing to do–or at least try to do. I continued to "pester" President Trump, eventually sending him two more letters, one in November, 2020 and one in December. They were as follows:

Vladimir Zelenko MD,
Board Certified Family Physician, New York
1540 Route 202
Pomona, NY 10970
President Donald Trump
45th President of the United States
Oval Office
1600 Pennsylvania Avenue NW,
Washington, DC 20502
November 23, 2020

Re: National Security and Medical Research - Operation Z

Dear President Trump:
As a war-time President, you have fathered an unstoppable medical reform movement by cutting the FDA's red tape, lowering drug prices, and successfully developing a COVID-19 "vaccine" at warp speed. Furthermore, you signed Senator Ron Johnson's Right to Try legislation into law, and significantly improved the country's opioid epidemic.

Perhaps prophetically, you promoted the use of Hydroxychloroquine, Azithromycin, and Zinc in the early stages of the COVID-19 infection. A recent large international study of COVID-19 hospitalized patients with pre-existing lung disease showed a 50% reduction in mortality when treated with (hydroxy)chloroquine. These results are consistent with over 200 studies showing the drug's safety and efficacy against COVID-19. These studies are supported by our country's top physicians from prominent institutions, such as Yale, Harvard, Baylor, etc. Mr. President, you have saved millions of American lives.

As Commander in Chief of the most powerful nation in the world, you are the tip of the spear of the global war against big pharma's corruption and abuse. The powerful big pharma industry spends billions of dollars on lobbying politicians, paying millions in royalties to the NIH, and billions in "user fees" to the FDA.

In my formal testimony to the US Senate Homeland Security Committee, I suggested the formation of a new medical research institution which is outside of the purview of the HHS. The purpose of this institution is to generate real world evidence and therapeutics by frontline primary care physicians. This can be accomplished by unleashing this country's medical and intellectual potential through the open source real world data sharing amongst frontline physicians. This approach will circumvent big pharma's influence over the FDA, NIH, and CDC and provide an efficient mechanism for the development of safe, timely, and inexpensive therapeutics for this country's most common health concerns.

The need for reform became obvious during the above mentioned Senate hearing. Dr. Jay Bhattacharya MD PhD of Stanford University testified that big pharma's influence over government agencies has created a myriad of conflict of interests and the incentive for corruption.

Quoting Dr. Bhattacharya, "We need to fix this with a system that allows formal conversation to reason observational data, rapid funding for large scale ... all the time, not just during the pandemic." I humbly request that you allocate 5% of Operation Warp Speed's budget to Operation Z. The American people's gratitude as well as history will be your enduring legacy.

Parenthetically, I have been nominated for the Presidential Medal of Freedom through Dr. Peter Navarro's office. My nomination has been endorsed by Senator Ron Johnson, Mayor Rudy Giuliani, and the Association of American Physicians and Surgeons.

With Great Respect,

Vladimir Zelenko, MD

This letter followed a month later:

Dr. Vladimir (Zev) Zelenko
Board Certified Family Practitioner
Office: 845-782-0000
December 23, 2020

Dear President Trump:
I humbly offer the following observations:

1. Based on my front-line experience, it is essential to start treatment against COVID-19 immediately upon clinical diagnosis of the infection and not to wait for confirmatory testing. There is a very narrow window of opportunity to eliminate the virus before pulmonary complications begin. Delaying treatment is the essence of the problem. My treatment regime is attached and please know that as of today it has saved thousands of patients without serious complications or negative side effects. Hundreds of top doctors across the world have embraced prehospital treatment of COVID-19 in high risk patients.

2. Based on my front-line experience, the emphasis must be on preemptive treatment for high-risk patients in the outpatient setting - primary care and urgent care settings. It makes no sense to wait until a patient is admitted to a hospital and put on a ventilator.

High-risk patients are those over the age of 45, those with underlying health conditions or compromised immune systems, and anyone with symptoms and shortness of breath.
In addition, we should consider immediate prophylactic treatment of very high-risk individuals.
Very high-risk individuals are front-line health care providers, nursing home residents, police officers, etc.

3. Based on my direct observations, the risk of side effects to this treatment regime is exaggerated. The theoretical risk of heart arrhythmia (QT prolongation) is 1 in 10,000. However, the actual risk of death from COVID-19 in the high-risk population is between 5 to 10%. The risk versus benefit analysis overwhelmingly favors treatment. And in my clinical experience, I have seen no serious negative side effects.

4. This is World War III (virus vs humanity). Under these circumstances, we don't have the luxury of operating as we do in peacetime for studies and research. Millions will die and the economy will collapse while we wait.

Dear Mr. President:
I humbly request the following:

1. We need an executive order to override any state obstacles and to (a) allow all physicians to prescribe the above regime without the fear of liability or retribution; and (b) permit pharmacies to dispense this medication without the fear of liability or retribution.

2. The pharmacies need an immediate supply of sufficient medicine to dispense the above regime to at least 150 million people. Please do everything in your power to achieve this.

4. The Task Force, CDC, FDA, NIH should all issue strong recommendations to physicians to treat their patients early and aggressively based on clinical diagnosis, without the delay caused by confirmatory testing.

5. Any bureaucratic/man made obstacles that interfere with doctors' ability to treat their patients with these well known, field tested, inexpensive and life saving medications in my humble opinion is inexcusable and should be treated as a crime against humanity.

With much respect,

Dr. Vladimir (Zev) Zelenko

Both of these letters were to no avail. Both were sent after the November election and we all know that President Trump had more than a few distractions after that first Tuesday.

Grand Collaboration

My affiliations with other like-minded doctors over the year of 2020 did lead to one sort of grand collaboration in the spring of 2021. Myself, Dr. Peter McCullough, and Dr. Harvey Risch jointly published what we called a "Plan to Reopen an American State." It was constructed for presentation in the State of Texas, but its use could have been, should have been, universal.

My affiliations with other like-minded doctors over 2020 did lead to one sort of grand collaboration in the spring of 2021. Dr. Peter McCullough, Dr. Harvey Risch, and I jointly published what we called a "Plan to Reopen an American State." We constructed the presentation for use in the State of Texas, but its use could have been, and indeed should have been, universal.

Here it is:
A Plan to Reopen an American State
By,
Vladimir Zelenko, M.D.
Harvey Risch, M.D. Ph.D.
Peter McCullough, M.D.

Multiple scientific studies have demonstrated that early prehospital treatment of COVID-19 reduces hospitalizations and death by more than 84%. This means that out of 500,000 American COVID-19 deaths (as of February 22, 2021), 420,000 could have been prevented.

Prehospital treatment of high-risk patients with COVID-19 must become the standard of care. This common sense approach has been endorsed by hundreds of leading physicians across America, such as: Dr. Peter McCullough-Vice Chair of

Internal Medicine at Baylor University Medical Center, Professor of Medicine at Texas A&M College of Medicine; Dr. Harvey Risch-Professor of Epidemiology in the Department of Epidemiology and Public Health at the Yale School of Public Health and Yale School of Medicine; Dr. George Fareed-Harvard Medical School graduate, Professor of Virology at Harvard, former Commissioned Officer (USPHS) National Institute of Allergy and Infectious Diseases, NIH.

The purpose of this document is to recommend a medical strategy to immediately curtail needless fatalities and to reopen state businesses and gathering places, such as, houses of worship, sports facilities, schools, and recreational venues.

We urge Governors to issue an executive order and/or take any other legal steps as may be required to:

1. Strongly recommend that medical professionals follow the treatment protocol attached below for treating patients based on clinical suspicion or on positive test results of COVID-19 infection within the first 5 days of the onset of symptoms.

2. Require state governmental health authorities to educate their citizens on the treatment protocol attached below that has an 84% success rate in curing patients in the early stages of COVID-19 infection and saving lives. This educational drive should include publishing on websites and elsewhere clear delineations of the recommended treatment plans.

3. Allow physicians and pharmacies to prescribe and dispense the FDA-approved medications specified in the protocols, even if they are prescribed "off-label" for the treatment of COVID-19; and remove any legal or bureaucratic impediments that may inhibit Floridian patients from receiving these life-saving treatments.

4. Require state governmental health authorities to develop and implement a logistical plan to acquire and distribute to the entire state the medications specified in the protocols attached below.

5. Require state governmental health authorities to provide physicians with current and timely access to national-level and state-specific health care data so that the treatment may quickly commence in accordance with the risk-stratification specified in the protocols.

6. Strongly recommend that medical professionals encourage their moderate- and high-risk patients to follow the prophylaxis protocol attached below before they are infected.

7. Require state governmental health authorities to educate their citizens on the benefit of taking preventative measures, including following the prophylaxis protocol attached below. This educational drive should also include publishing on websites and elsewhere clear delineations of the recommended preventative plans.

8. The above strategy is designed to complement and work in synergy with other aspects of pandemic management such as spread prevention, hospital care and immunization with safe and effective "vaccines" when they become available (without coercion and with informed consent).

Here are the two summary visual exhibits that simplified our recommendations for both treating actual cases at onset, and for a prophylactic approach…

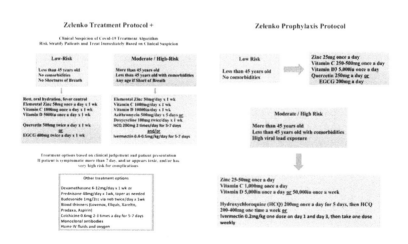

As I look back today, with all of the research that has been done and all of the patients that my treatment has saved, I do so with a profound sense of both anger and sadness. Virtually nobody needed to die. The coronavirus pandemic could have come and gone like a very bad year of seasonal flu. Instead, over a million Americans died, and they died unnecessarily and for no identifiable purpose. My heroes who gave their lives in the Second World War did so for a reason. The COVID-19 victims died for nothing.

As to the medical community that was complicit in their murder and the government leaders that orchestrated it, I can only say that these "professionals" knew better. What this chapter clearly shows is that not only did they know better, but they simultaneously presented a persona that indicated they did not. This attempt to willfully impose ignorance upon themselves cost us lives while also leading to harsh economic impacts and a loss of dignity, all of which are historically unprecedented.

They had to remain ignorant of treatment so they could get to the "vaccine": The ultimate end game. Emergency use authorizations cannot be granted for "vaccines" when there is an effective, recognized method of treatment for a disease. It disgusts me to realize that approving my treatment meant no big money for Big Pharma. We certainly couldn't have that, could we?

Chapter Four

Changes in Latitude- Changes in Attitude

Entering 2021, I found myself continuing on the journey that was taking me from "vaccine" enthusiasm, to "vaccine" indifference, to "vaccine" skepticism, and finally to my outspoken critique of what I have come to term a "kill shot." I was late to the game in terms of understanding what was going on with the rollout of the mRNA injection that was supposed to prevent coronavirus yet failed to stop anyone from getting the disease. While I will go into the subject in more detail in a later chapter, suffice it to say that my red-pilling was underway, and I would start to feel its impact at an accelerating rate.

In mid-April 2021, I contracted COVID-19 pneumonia as a result of being weakened by the chemo I was undergoing. I went into the hospital for seven days and was brought home on a stretcher with an oxygen tank at my side. When I got home, my wife was also suffering from the virus, making for a more difficult time. I took a glass of water and headed to the guest room because it was on the first floor, and I could not climb the stairs. I was as close to being utterly beaten as I have ever been. I was a man in his late 40s living on the body of a 100-year-old. I had faced persecution, been unable to see much of my children from my first marriage, and unable to be an active father with the children from my second. I felt near hopelessness.

Florida

That night, as I lay in bed stewing in the worst emotional and physical states of my life, I found myself in total despair. Then, there was this dreamlike energy in the room that I had seen in a few dreams as I was growing up, maybe two or three times. It was incredibly intense, and then it all coalesced into a singularity. It seemed to be moving around the room. I tried to follow it with my eyes in a sort of hypnagogic state, like a cat following a laser light as someone dances it along the floor. I wasn't sure what was happening, yet I yearned to focus and embrace it, whatever it was. Then it stopped and stood still. I found myself speaking with G-d.

Immediately, and I get shivers as I share this, all my pain stopped on every level. My despair vanished, making me feel the power of speaking to the essence of love and much more than a friend, lover, or father, but all of those things in one. I don't remember exactly the words He used, but I can paraphrase:

"I've been waiting for you. All you need is me."

This was the first encounter I had directly with G-d since years earlier, during my father's snow shoveling heart attack. His message to me indicated that He was not finished with me yet and that my work with Him was not complete. The question was, what exactly was I supposed to do with the message? The answer to me quickly became clear: Get up!

So, in the middle of the night, I got out of bed in the most run-down of conditions. I packed a suitcase, got a hold of my parents, and headed to Florida.

My wife and I had planned to move to Florida, but not yet. We certainly hadn't planned for it to be in the middle of the night while she had COVID-19 and I was on oxygen, having just returned home from the hospital. We had been planning to move simply because of the toxic environment that had become the State of New York. We thought that if you changed your place, you would change your luck. At least it changes dynamics.

Florida was the right choice for several reasons. One was owing to my illness; it was easier for me to breathe in warmer weather. Another was that I felt the noose tightening around my neck from my anti-Cuomo rhetoric. It was time to "get out of Dodge."

My parents came along with me in their own car. I had one of my daughters with me, and we took three days to make the trip. I actually enjoyed it. I got to know what kind of music my daughter likes, and in relation to where I was coming from, I found the car ride was part of the transformation from a highly toxic environment to a less toxic one. The home we had purchased was in South Florida. When we arrived, I was still very sick. I was unable to walk more than two blocks. My parents helped me set everything up because, physically, my body was broken.

There were no regrets about the move; however, there was an adjustment period as I strived to settle into my new home and surroundings. In time, my wife joined me, and we started reconstructing a new sort of normal. I've already shared the good fortune I had in finding the right team of physicians to treat my very unique form of cancer. That team of physicians has, with G-d's help, kept me alive and highly functioning up to this point, a point which defies the odds of the diagnosis and prognosis I was given back in early 2018.

Once I recovered some strength and acclimated, I started to resume my activism as it related to the pandemic, placing a strong emphasis on warning people about the "vaccine" and its severe side effects. I was especially vocal about not allowing its use on their children. There is no affirmative reason for vaccinating children against a disease that doesn't hurt them, then or now. Furthermore, evidence is building that the "vaccine" was not needed in children but was, in fact, harmful to them. More on that later.

I took on every opportunity to do interviews I could find. I would make frequent appearances on programs that had a large audience of "vaccine" skeptics—shows like those hosted by my friends Ann Vandersteel and Mel

K. I would go on to speak at large conferences like those of Clay Clark and his Reawaken America Tour and I would talk at smaller grassroots events like the South Dakota-based "Mama Bears," organized by Stephanie Lien D'Urso. No venue or broadcast was too large or too small. I said yes to virtually every request. If someone wanted to hear my message, that meant G-d wanted me to share it.

As for my co-author on this book, we enjoyed many conversations during 2021 about theology, philosophy, and political science, but never really about the virus and the ensuing pandemic. I would share with him how stimulating I found those discussions and developed a deep intellectual kinship. That is the reason, I suspect, that I chose him to work with me on this project.

Finally, there is my dear friend and my Chief of Staff, Moshe Knobel. He has been at my side nearly 24/7 for so long that I cannot seem to remember my life without him. As I write, I also know he will be at my side right up to the very end, whenever that end is to come. He manages my schedule, my healthcare, and he takes me to wherever I need to be. In short, outside of my wife and children, he has become my "everything else, save for G-d," and I am entirely sure that G-d sent him to me.

Along the way, I continued to treat patients remotely with the help of my assembled team. America's Frontline Doctors (AFLDS) had picked up much of my work and were bringing relief to thousands. I found myself being approached by high-profile people who were not able to get treated by their own physicians. Glenn Beck is one whose name I can share because he brought me onto his show and shared with his audience that I had treated him for the disease. I recall my phone call with him that took place over eighteen months into the pandemic. It was illuminating to me because of how informative it was to him. Here was a highly intelligent man who was a critical thinker. Yet, when we spoke, there was still so much unfamiliar to him about the disease even though it had been shared through public back channels by myself and others dating back to March 2020.

That show represented the consequences that come with the true power of suppression. Even the best informed and the most skeptical had the truth hidden from them. What chance did the general public have to understand? These were just regular people trying to navigate their daily lives amidst an economy that had been deliberately destroyed by their leadership.

A Busy Twelve Months

It was in 2021 that I launched my Z-Stack company and found wonderful people to join me on that journey. I was not a businessman by background, so I needed the help of those that knew what they were doing. I was blessed to be joined by the likes of Dave Lopez, Chris Barron, Foster Coulson, and others—too many to mention.

As a team, they helped me launch an all-in-one supplement that has been incredibly well-received by the marketplace. It combines the elements quercetin (the 20-caliber natural substitute for the 50-caliber HCQ), zinc, vitamin C, and vitamin D. There are anecdotal reports from regular users that it has been effective in helping them not only recover from the virus but has also helped them stave off the onset of the common cold. This is not something the FDA would ever allow to be placed on a label. Still, it makes perfect sense insofar as the common cold is nothing more than a coronavirus and, as you will learn in a later chapter, if you can get zinc inside the cell early during the development of any coronavirus, it can inhibit, or outright stop it, from reproducing.

As I have shared, the latter part of 2021 and early 2022 has had me busy in my battle with cancer. Regardless, it did not stop me from making public appearances, although it forced me to cancel a few along the way, always with deep regret. This regret isn't because I missed an opportunity for the limelight; I missed an opportunity to do G-d's work. I have, however, done the best I could.

In 2022 I decided to launch the Zelenko Freedom Foundation so that my ideas that have stemmed from G-d's guidance and direction might be able to live on after my time in this realm has finished. I have been fortunate to be able to select its leadership - my friends Ann Vandersteel and Kevin Jenkins - and I know that I can truly rest in peace knowing that they will carry the message dutifully, passionately, and professionally. They are the most trusted of G-d's servants.

This book project started in the first week of January 2022 at my home in Florida. It has become a big part of what has kept me going as my cancer has progressed. I have shared that it is cathartic, and it has also been fun. As we worked on it, I enjoyed immensely taking my co-author's sometimes safe and carefully-crafted wording and "punching it up" a bit with more robust language. As he has shared content with me, I have taken my turn at "rewriting" and sharing giddily over the phone how "you said this, but listen to how I changed it." I believe I could hear his head shaking through cyberspace.

So much of the past twelve months exists to me less as a chronology and more as a stream of consciousness, awakening, and revelation. I have become a bit of a philosopher and something of a sociologist for this moment in time. I want to share my reflections on a few different points of interest related to the pandemic, and as opposed to doing so in a timeline format, I will take them on by topic.

World Economic Forum

In 2010, Bill Gates - the financial strength behind the World Economic Forum - gave a TED Talk. The topic was climate change and what needed to be done to reduce CO_2 emissions. He spoke for about twenty minutes and then handled ten minutes of questions from an event host. The host drilled down on some of the things Gates had mentioned during his lecture. Curiously, there was one question he didn't ask: Why Gates thought that "vaccines" would reduce the world's population?

Early in his presentation, Gates made a list of the factors negatively impacting our ability to reduce CO_2 emissions. The size of the population was the first one on the list. He said that the world population stood at 6.8 billion people and was on its way to nine billion. He suggested we needed to curb that growth.

He transitioned to saying that with better healthcare, reproductive services, and vaccinations, we could hope to reduce the number. Vaccinations? Shouldn't successful vaccinations allow for more people to be able to live? Now, perhaps Gates meant that if people are healthier, they won't want to have as many children because of reduced fear of them dying off. This sure seems like a stretch, but I am no Bill Gates, thankfully. Regardless, he was never asked to clarify.

Over the past two years, people have become a bit more familiar with the World Economic Forum and the term "Great Reset." This is owing to the efforts of the real investigative reporters, the people who get information out through Telegram, Rumble, and other uncensored platforms. The Great Reset is a proper noun and not an abstract concept. It is a plan that has been put together by powerful international elites through the World Economic Forum (WEF), a very public version of a secret society.

The WEF is an organization committed to what appears to be – and is often called – a true communist agenda. To me, it is the primary head of the Primordial Serpent. The WEF is dedicated to creating their dystopian version of utopia, one where they get to decide what is in humanity's best interest.

There are two fundamental problems with the WEF's agenda. First, it rejects the notion of G-d, especially the Christian G-d, because of its hostile view of Western Civilization, which has been built on Judeo-Christian values and teachings. The second problem is that because they reject G-d, they do not acknowledge man's sinful nature. Since the time of Plato, all visions of an idyllic utopia have relied upon men naturally not wanting to harm or exploit others for their own gain.

Sadly, our history suggests that the presence of Satan and his attendant evil acts live in this world and can easily come to reside in any of us. The members of WEF would suggest that the only reason that Cain slew Abel was because Cain owned the lamb he offered as a sacrifice to G-d. Private property and the envy it created became the cause of the bloodletting. People who believe in G-d see a more sinister force at work. It is a force that must be fought against in each of us through prayer and with a willingness to serve Him.

Through the Great Reset (it will be used only as a proper noun going forward to acknowledge it as a proper enemy), the WEF seeks to remove the liberties that have been granted to individuals, first by G-d and then through those who were courageous enough to try to codify them into our Constitution. America's Founding Fathers found a way to institutionalize G-d's grace and mercy when they created our nation.

A nation with such a structure and history is problematic for the globalist Marxists of the WEF. They seek a world where the individual becomes indistinguishable from the whole. We seek a nation where each individual is a whole unto themselves because each one of us is created in the image of G-d.

This makes the United States special, and it makes the United States the biggest problem for the WEF. Bill Gates and his colleagues either created the pandemic to help solve that problem, or they took advantage of the manmade virus created by others as a way to solve it. Either way, they are front and center at the heart of our problems today.

The Primordial Serpent is the ultimate bad guy and manifests throughout history in different forms. Throughout the millennia, a group of people has always been hidden behind the scenes, influencing history and using their power and money to manipulate geopolitical events. These forces, if you sum them up, are the Primordial Serpent of every generation. They are kingmakers. People like Klaus Schwab, George Soros, Bill Gates, Jeff Bezos, the Clintons, and Mark Zuckerberg are permitted to function and amass great wealth and power.

Make no mistake; they are not the masters. It is a satanic force that rules them and works through them

The World Economic Forum, founded in 1971, is the most prominent and influential force of evil. And they have been responsible for raising a generation of leaders. Through their school, Young Global Leaders, they have strategically placed their graduates - their acolytes - in positions of tremendous power. Their graduates include the likes of Gates, Angela Merkel, Justin Trudeau, Jacqueline Ardern, Emmanuel Macron, and so many others. These big names in big positions exercising unified global power are facilitating the world's transition toward global slavery.

What is essential to understand is that the WEF and its members represent critical leaders within the earthly power structure of evil, but they are not in charge of it. If they were, you could try to eliminate the individuals or the organization as a whole, and evil would be defeated. However, it isn't that simple because evil exists regardless of time and place. We defeated the Nazis, but we did not eliminate evil. The Soviet Union collapsed, but evil didn't collapse into ruin next to it.

The Serpent has many ways of manifesting itself, yet ultimately, in every generation, it comes down to a good versus evil dynamic: The collision of two ideologies. One is the worship of G-d and subservience to Him, while the other is the worship of the human endeavor and the humans that lead it. That means subservience to them, and that means slavery.

If you go to the WEF website, you can look at their agenda for what the world needs to be by 2030. It has also become synonymous with the United Nations 2030 agenda. Here is what you will find today:

1. All products will become services.
2. There is a global price on carbon.
3. US dominance is over; we have a handful of global superpowers.
4. Farewell hospital, hello home-spital.
5. We are eating much less meat.
6. Today's Syrian refugees, 2030s CEOs.
7. The values that built the West will be tested to the breaking point.
8. By the 2030s, we will be able to move humans toward the Red Planet.

If that doesn't scare you, take a look at what the list was before they were scrutinized for maybe being just a little too honest about what they are up to. Here is the same list before it was scrubbed and cleaned and then backdated to 2016:

1. You will own nothing and be happy
2. The US will not be the world's superpower
3. You won't die waiting for an organ donor
4. You'll eat less meat
5. A billion people will be displaced by climate change
6. You could be preparing to go to Mars
7. Western values will be tested to their breaking point
8. Fossil fuels will be eliminated

I have favorites here. As I alluded to above, the United States is a special problem for the WEF, so saying that America will lose its dominance and a few global powers will govern is key to expanding the WEF's power.

Another favorite of mine is that "you will own nothing and be happy." They also want to limit the consumption of meat and make fossil fuels obsolete through mass taxation. What I see here is the micromanagement of human life by a few global powers. That's their 2030 agenda, and, my friend, 2030 is just around the corner.

This is obviously a one-world-government structure but in a tyrannical fashion. What the pandemic has done, what the man-made bioweapon of the coronavirus has facilitated, is the creation of an artificial motivation and justification to roll out the actual weapon: The "vaccines." The "vaccines" are a platform for the simultaneous agendas of eugenics and genocide. These are both long-term and immediate means by which you can shorten the lifespan of people.

Maybe that is where Bill Gates was going with his 2010 TED Talk.

There is the opportunity for population control, but there is also the surveillance component, where the "vaccine" can contain technology on the nanoscale. I will touch on that in an upcoming chapter, but for now, imagine that technology existing inside you will measure biometrics and transmit that data with your location to a third party. That means your biometric data can be tied to a digital or cryptocurrency in a world with one world currency (undoubtedly something the folks at the WEF would love to see) controlled by a few global sociopaths. In 2016 Klaus Schwab said that by 2026, which is (not) coincidentally the same year Medicare is predicted to become insolvent in America, leaving financial chaos, seven billion people will be tagged with a digital identifier. The patent technology already exists for this to be placed into a "vaccine." That's the mechanism of enslavement.

China has recently banned the use of outside cryptocurrencies and requires that only digital Yuan issued by the Central Bank can be utilized. President Biden has authorized the exploration of establishing an official US digital currency. Imagine these types of instruments being controlled by the government. How easy would it be for WEF types to control you if they control your ability to eat bread? To buy gas? These are rhetorical questions.

Cryptocurrency is a very convenient mechanism to control and manipulate human behavior because if they don't like you, they turn off your ability to buy what you need to live. They don't need a gulag. They don't need to put a gun against your head. All they need to do is restrict your ability to transact and travel. That is the enslavement mechanism through financial control, which will be linked to biometric data.

There is also the transhumanist dimension. According to Klaus Schwab and Bill Gates, these "vaccines" are platforms for changing who you are. Those are their words, not mine. They don't believe in G-d; they don't believe in an afterlife. As such, after death, in their understanding, there's nothing. So, they're working actively on developing platforms, both organic and inorganic, where they would be able to, in their belief system, transfer human consciousness to a new type of entity that will ensure immortality for these sociopaths. In their pagan world, where there is no afterlife, and there is only now, their search for immortality involves somehow preserving consciousness. People are at work now, trying to create a cyborg-like entity that will serve as the vessel for the transfer of the human consciousness of the elite class.

I believe that there are three organizations that are used by the very bad people, the elite people, to launder money and manipulate geopolitical events. There are: The Bill and Melinda Gates Foundation, the Clinton Foundation, and George Soros' Open Society Foundations. I further believe that they work in unison with the WEF.

To me, they're all the same, but each one has different spheres of influence. George Soros' Open Society Foundations has, in actuality, funded chaos everywhere. The creation of anarchy facilitates the move toward a global government and enslavement. It isn't complicated. The Clintons have used their Foundation to facilitate interaction between world leaders and governments. The Gates' (shame about their marriage) provide unlimited money and technological support. This is a Twenty-First Century "Axis of Evil" used to support the initiatives of the WEF and enable the Great Reset. It is an attempt to complete the work on Earth via... come on; you know this one... the Primordial Serpent.

I had barely heard of the WEF before the start of the pandemic. If I had heard mention of it, I might have thought it was some sort of caged mixed martial arts league. Over the past two years, I have studied it and the people inside it. I conclude that there is no more evil or sinister organization on Earth. Yet, it is critical to remember that the WEF and its minions are not the source of the evil, just the conduits.

This brings me to President Joe Biden.

Biden

I think the Biden presidency is a continuation of thirty-five years of treason. The Constitution of this country is being undermined, and all the security and barriers protecting our civil liberties are being eroded at their core. We are living through and bearing witness to the decline of our great empire. I don't use the term "empire" in the Ancient Roman sense; I use it in the sense that the United States was the closest we have seen in all of human history to embracing the notion of G-d's empire. This empire has been in a state of steady decay since the end of Reagan's Presidency. He was the last President we had who appeared to genuinely love this country for all of the right reasons.

My professional assessment of Joe Biden from observation as a physician (never having met him) is that he has dementia and is not mentally fit for office. He should definitely be in a nursing home, or at least assisted living, and receiving loving care from his family instead of the elder abuse he is suffering by propping him up as a puppet president. A puppet for whom, you ask? Maybe the WEF? Maybe Obama? Perhaps both, or maybe something we can't see. Certainly, he is in office ultimately owing to and serving the Primordial Serpent. We can't be sure of the go-betweens.

Biden's deteriorating mental state could be seen clearly during the election process. You could tell his cognitive state was poor, and you could also tell when he was being pumped up with stimulants to be functional. It was fun when he would go off script and say something outrageous, a comedy, albeit a dark one. Unfortunately, this is very dark humor, gallows humor almost when you consider that this man is the guy who travels with the "football" and who has the ability to start a nuclear war. That isn't funny at all. This is like having a Mel Brooks character-type running the country, only this time it's "Blazing Western Civilization" instead of "Blazing Saddles."

I do not believe, however, the biggest threat we face from the Biden Presidency is that of global thermonuclear war. Not even the degenerate pagans, the globalists, would want him to actually blow everything up. Think what all that radiation would do to adversely impact the climate! The people behind Joe Biden want controlled destruction, not uncontrolled destruction.

That is why you see the Biden administration promoting policies that weaken our military. Instead of being concerned about teaching our soldiers how to kill people and break things, they are obsessed with teaching them Critical Race Theory and the importance of acknowledging someone's gender identification. They are also forcing them to inject the deadly serum "kill shot" "vaccine" into themselves instead of encouraging them to fire more conventional lead-filled kill shots into the enemy. It's a comply or pay a life-altering price type of policy, which is the epitome of anti-American exceptionalism.

I can easily imagine how a scene would play out in some future war between the US and China. In it, an American Marine, physically weakened from his most recent enhanced booster, is set upon by a Chinese soldier. As he (or "they") begin(s) to draw a weapon, he/they stop because it's realized that the attacking enemy is of Asian descent and any attempt to defend himself/"themselves" fails to take into account past American transgressions against people of their race. As the American soldier is slain, his/their last words are, "Please, my dear Asian victim whom I've oppressed, share with me your pronouns before I pass so that I might come to know you fully."

As a lover of sarcasm, I am sadly not able to be sarcastic when I describe what Joe Biden, or those controlling him, are deliberately doing to systematically dismantle America. In addition to weakening our military, they are weakening our economy, they are increasing our dependence on foreign oil, they are ballooning our national debt, and they are forcing kill shot "vaccines" on federal workers and, worse, on children.

Biden has gone so far as to offer additional federal funds to schools that get kids vaccinated or that impose mask mandates. This might explain why a private Jewish school with which I'm familiar started offering families a thousand dollars per vaccinated child. Upon learning of that incentive, I wrote an open letter advising the parents that it's better to prostitute their daughters for two reasons: One, it's more lucrative, and two, it's safer. The school dropped the program the next day.

I mentioned the thirty-five-year time frame and drew it back to Reagan, but, in fact, the Biden presidency is really the late-stage result of a very long game plan launched by the Soviet Union decades before Reagan even took office. I understood this by watching a video on YouTube from 1984 called *The Four Stages of Ideological Subversion,* which featured an interview with KGB defector Colonel Yuri Bezmenov. In that interview, Bezmenov identified the four stages of the ideological subversion of a Western nation; something he said is referred to as "active measures" within the KGB.

The Four Stages of Ideological Subversion

The first stage is demoralization. Demoralization takes up to fifty years to complete, although Bezmenov said the United States was moving along the curve much faster than even comrade Stalin could have hoped. It takes this long to educate a generation of students in the ideology of the enemy and then turn them loose into the world to live it and teach it to the next generation. Then it becomes embedded in the national consciousness.

The second stage is destabilization, which he said takes two to five years and involves the upsetting of established systems and institutions while creating general unrest (it has been a long time since any of us have felt a sense of rest and assurance, regardless of who we vote for or the impact the virus has had on us.)

The third stage is chaos, which is what we got with the pandemic and the very timely and helpful George Floyd incident in Minneapolis. The images from January 6 contributed to the crisis sentiment because, to the typical ignorant citizen, the pictures from the capital that day looked far worse than the actual reality.

The fourth stage is Orwellian in its name: "normalization." Bezmenov acknowledges as much by using the example of the Soviet tanks rolling into Czechoslovakia in 1968 to ruthlessly crush the anti-totalitarian uprising and then saying that order had been restored and all was now being "normalized." Normalized here suggests a state of rest where people live under a form of permanent slavery.

Joe Biden's presidency is attempting to normalize what feels like a soft form of totalitarianism. Still, it will grow harsher over time (Author's Note: Zev did not live to see the 24-hour period in which the government and the FBI funded 87,000 new IRS agents and raided former President Trump's home. Had he been here to witness, he would most certainly have been outspoken in his warnings about the significance of, and connection between, both of those events.)

According to Bezmenov, once things get "normalized," there is no way to predict how long that state will survive. How long it will survive here in the United States will come to depend primarily on whether the people choose to follow the way of G-d or the way of men; men like Klaus Schwab, Bill Gates, and Joe Biden.

There is a sort of humorous note (more dark humor) that relates to Biden and the virus that took its first hold in China, specifically, and it is something that I predicted would happen. As he was inaugurated, the PCR threshold (PCR testing was initially suggested to be the gold standard in COVID-19 diagnosis and has since been thoroughly discredited) that yielded a "positive" COVID-19 result was altered so that fewer tests would deliver positive results. Magically, just as Joe Biden stumbled his way into office, he had already reduced the number of positive cases. Such powers he had!

But Joe Biden doesn't really have any power, not with the puppet masters pulling his strings. They are servants, servants of the… well, I don't have to repeat it, do I?

This brings me to a still making-the-news hot topic: January 6. I don't even need to give a year, do I? The date is now infamous, even though it is only a few years old.

I mentioned January 6 earlier as a reference point for the "chaos" stage that Col. Bezmenov described. Some people might not know or may have forgotten that I was a speaker on January 6.

I was invited to speak at the rally by a group of nurses, and I was also asked to do some interviews with media outlets. I had decided to attend because I supported the general premise of protesting the election, but I also saw it as a way to further share my message about treating the coronavirus and its ever-increasing list of new variants. I was not yet fully "awake" regarding the "vaccine," but I was slowly coming around. I also was finally going to get to meet Rudy Giuliani in person after having spent so much time speaking to him and corresponding with him over the past ten months. He had even indicated that he would introduce me to the President while I was in town.

I spoke in the morning and completed some interviews. It was interesting in the reporting afterward; there was a focus on how I said I supported the efforts of the Proud Boys, a self-proclaimed "drinking club" that has been associated with everything from patriotism, to racism, to security, to antisemitism. What I actually said in a tweet was:

"I support anyone who is willing to help people and maintain liberty and spread truth, so if the Proud Boys are doing that, then I would support them."

I don't support violence; I don't support tactics that may lead to bigotry and so on, but I do support freedom-loving patriots willing to stand up for the liberties of this country.

It remains quite humorous that through all of this chaos, an Orthodox Jew has gotten tied in with a group said to not like Jews. Another sign of an almost indescribable time.

I spoke in the morning and was right in front of the Capitol Building, where all the chaos happened. However, it was freezing cold, and in my health, I couldn't stand on my feet anymore, physically. I was hungry. I decided to leave, and I went back to my hotel. A few hours later, right where I had been standing, the chaos started.

What I saw that day while I was on site was organized and peaceful. I did see something strange: A lot of people were wearing MAGA hats, but some were wearing them backward. Later I learned that was one of the signals between the anarchists that came to cause trouble to let each other know who was who. It was their uniform, I guess. Backward hats aside, it felt powerful to be in a mass of people who were of like mind and respected personal liberties and freedom. I felt inspired in many ways to see a sort of theological army. With all the negativity leading up to that day, I felt a positive energy. Nobody around me was belligerent at all. I spoke at a "Bikers for Trump" sponsored stage and thought, "This is pretty cool."

Who would have thought that a small-town doctor would ever be doing such a thing?

I had a small security group with me. At the suggestion of my partner Dave Lopez, I had two former Navy Seals watching out for me. I don't think I would have run into the Capitol building, certainly not in my health or condition, but they did steer me away from the site. I remember barely making the walk back to my hotel. It was from there I learned of the events that would follow in the afternoon.

That night, I did get to meet Rudy. I had been wondering how that had happened since he had announced that he had come down with COVID-19. He had been taking my prophylactic regimen, and I was almost worried that maybe his case meant I had been somehow wrong about what I had been prescribing. During the evening, after more than just a few relaxing scotches, he confessed to me that he had stopped with the protocol sometime before his outbreak. His prescription had run out, and he had simply not gotten around to refilling it. This came as a bit of a selfish relief. I knew that when the Trump White House came down with the illness, Rudy was about the only one who didn't get sick. Turns out, he was still on the protocol at the time.

What has happened in the aftermath of January 6 is simply an extension of the same sort of totalitarian, Soviet-style tactics we saw launched at the beginning of the pandemic. We have had show trials, staged congressional hearings, and political prisoners arrested and held with their Constitutional rights ignored and violated. It has been a grotesque overreach by the government in an effort to clamp down on dissent and silence anyone who dares to question the status quo.

It could have been almost predictable as I watched that day from my DC hotel room. Viewing the images brings to mind the famous line of the newspaper mogul William Randolph Hearst who once said to a reporter covering the potential outbreak of war in Cuba that it just wasn't happening. Hearst reportedly said, "You send me pictures, I'll give you a war." Those people who entered the Capitol that day provided the pictures that have been used by an oppressive government ever since to create a sense of chaos among the general population. I refer you back to Col. Bezmenov and his 1984 video for the significance of that moment.

These behind-the-scenes oppressors seemed to find their perfect scapegoat in President Donald J. Trump. They laughed and welcomed him universally until they saw he seriously had the chance to win. He likes winning, you know.

I was pretty pro-Trump. I really liked his obnoxious personality and felt it was disruptive and abrasive, but mostly effective for getting things done in a non-traditional way. That really appealed to me.

Trump

I really took an interest in Trump when he was a candidate, and he went to Israel and the Western Wall. He wore a yarmulke, and I saw him praying at the Wall. I felt a certain sincerity. I thought it was real, as if he was connected to something much bigger than just him. His daughter Ivanka had converted to Judaism and married Jared Kushner, whom I don't know, but I know people who know him and his father, and they have said good things. I sensed that Trump was very supportive of his daughter's spiritual journey. After eight years of Obama's overt hatred and outright animosity toward Jewish issues and his support of the enemies of the Jewish people, it was refreshing to have a personality showing signs of appreciation, even respect, towards the Jewish people. It really irked me when liberal Jews would vote for Obama. They were undermining their own interests and those of all Jewish people.

I think that when Trump was Trump, meaning when Trump acted on instinct or intuition to read the pulse of the American people, he was kind of superior to all his advisers combined. When I saw him relying more and more on political advice, he lost some of his charm, in my eyes. Not entirely, but it was significant in the fact that my excitement for him began to lessen or be quelled.

I don't believe people begin imperfect and then transition to perfect. We are all imperfect before G-d. Trump has his imperfections. That's why I liked him because I, too, have my own imperfections, and I could relate to him. He doesn't put on many pretenses. He likes pretty women, he likes money, and he likes to have a good time. I knew that about him. Obviously, he is a sort of a megalomaniac narcissist, but many successful leaders hold those elements.

I got concerned when I saw him start to move away from HCQ and focus on Operation Warp Speed. I remember thinking, *I'm not the President of the United States, and I don't understand all the pressures and the political calculations that are being made, but we need him re-elected in order to continue this progress.* As a result, I found myself sometimes defending his shift from prehospital treatment to a "vaccine" mentality. I decided he was being pragmatic, even though that's not what I would have done. He needed to get re-elected, and I believe he felt that he was trying to do the right thing and save people.

Trump did a lot of things other Presidents spoke about doing but never did. For example, he moved the US embassy in Israel to Jerusalem. I'm not debating if that was the right or wrong move, but he said he would do it, and he did. Additionally, he commuted the sentence of Rabbi Sholom Rubashkin, who had been convicted of a white-collar crime but was given a sentence so out of whack with the standard sentencing guidelines that it was unjust. President Trump showed great courage and fairness in reducing his sentence. When Cuomo and DeBlasio singled out and attacked the Jewish community by shutting down synagogues and insinuating that the Jews were the source of the rampant spread of disease, Trump held a conference call with a group of rabbis. He listened to their concerns and then designated houses of worship as essential services that couldn't be closed. In doing that, he came to the defense of not only Judaism but religious liberty and encouraged prayer. All of this resonated with me. Compared to eight years of what I saw in Obama, I found it refreshing.

When the President got sick in late 2020, I can finally share that I was consulted in his treatment. While he had announced months before that he was taking HCQ as a prophylactic, he had stopped by then. President Trump had only taken it for about a month to show the country it was safe. When he got sick, I was in contact with Dr. Sean Conley, the White House doctor. I was in communication with him and others by cellphone. I have confirmation that the President was taking HCQ while he was at Walter Reed. He also was not as sick as some stories reported. He was taken there out of an abundance of caution.

Here is what I will say carefully but clearly: To the best of my knowledge, what the President received for treatment, and what the media said he received for treatment was not the same.

I was certainly glad he got better, and I was incredibly humbled that I had been allowed the chance by G-d to play a role in treating the President of the United States. Before I was called in, there was another badge of honor I was about to be given. Twitter would permanently suspend me for wishing the President well.

Dr Zev Zelenko wishing the Trumps well:

 Dr. Zev Zelenko
@zev_dr

Replying to @realDonaldTrump and @FLOTUS

Dear President Trump and First Lady. I bless you with a complete recovery. Please review the attached link. It has the Zelenko protocol for treatment. I STRONGLY advise that you start immediate treatment and NOT wait for complications to begin.

🔰 **Dr. Zev Zelenko** @zev_dr · 11 Sep

COMPREHENSIVE TWEET WITH RELEVANT LINKS

MY STUDY RESULTS IN 16 LANGUAGES
thezelenkoprotocol.com
TREATMENT PROTOCOL

1:18 AM · 02 Oct 20 · Twitter for iPhone

Not only did I get to play a role in treating the President of the United States, but I was also able to one-up him. I was banned from Twitter more than two months before they would do the same thing to him.

Social media has proven itself to be something we have somehow decided we cannot live without, but how can we really live if we don't get access to information that some authority deems we shouldn't know?

Social Media

I've had a somewhat "special" relationship with social media over the past two years. I know a rabbi who once said he has two piles of letters. One is the "I love you, Rabbi" letters, and one is the "I hate you, Rabbi" letters. Whenever he feels haughty or forgets his place, maybe feels a little too good about himself, he reads the "I hate you, Rabbi" letters. Conversely, whenever he feels down, he reads the "I love you, Rabbi" letters. That is as good a way to define my relationship with social media as I can find.

In the beginning, especially on Twitter (I think the cesspool of humanity lives on Twitter), the things being said about me were highly creative. I couldn't even think of insults like that to give to other people. I have learned how to since then! Facebook was not as bad, but it still felt pretty bad. YouTube just outright threw all my videos off. Early on in the onset of the coronavirus, I didn't have much time to do any social media. There was so much happening, and it didn't involve getting into a Twitter war or something like that; I was at war with the virus. However, once in a while, if I were desperate to get an essential piece of information heard, I would post something, usually a video.

My brother ran my social media for me, shielding me from a lot of toxicity and outright hatred. As an Orthodox, Hasidic Jew, I found it surprising that the platform Gab, run by an openly anti-Semitic, did not censor my content. That said, I would get lots of anti-Semitic replies from people using the platform wishing my family and me dead. Because of this and being as protective of my family as possible, I decided it best to post elsewhere.

While I got exposed to the darkest side of the human race, I also was exposed to the light and love that can be present in humanity and reflects G-d's love. The outpouring of love and prayer was incredible each time I would get sick, especially after I migrated to Telegram.

Social media, overall, tends to be quite unsocial. I loved how I could get an important message out to half a million people in a second, and I detested the way that message could be banned and taken down just as quickly. Regular decent people lost their social media accounts simply because they shared a piece of factual information I had posted. These people were innocent and often merely sharing a perspective (of course, I feel it was the right perspective), but that made them sources of disinformation for those who wanted to spread one narrative and no other. This has happened with various topics, not just COVID-19, and reveals how distorted and twisted the world of social media has become.

In the end, it has become a tool for the same kind of people who occupy seats in the WEF and who have occupied the White House, both in the past and present. These people are evil and do terrible things, but they are not in charge of anything. They are minions, all of them. The absolute master, the one who is truly controlling everything, is…

Come on, say it with me…

The PRIMORDIAL SERPENT!

For the past two years, I have been one of the most outspoken critics of how coronavirus as we know it has been handled by our leadership and how people in power have used it as a way to subjugate and control the world's population. I have argued for treatment, I've argued against the "vaccine," and I've made it very clear that this is a manmade bioweapon of mass destruction. These arguments have been made in speeches, interviews, and on social media, if even for only a brief moment before my posts got censored.

Now, I have my own book that nobody can censor. I can freely express what I feel and know it will be on permanent record in my own words.

Now, I get to make my case, which is precisely what I will do in the following three chapters.

Menashe Amitay and Dr. Zelenko working in Florida at Menashe's office.

Dr. Zelenko speaking at the Reawaken America Tour

Dr. Zelenko flying from stage to stage, bringing hope for a world in chaos.

Dr. Zelenko connecting with Dr. Stella Emmanuel

Dr. Zelenko and Mikki Wills

Dr. Richard Bartlett, Dr. Vladimir Zelenko, and Dr. Stella Emmanuel
Praying

Dr. Zelenko lovingly and tirelessly working to build Zelenko Labs in Florida, filming podcasts from his phone in his free moments.

Ann Vandersteel, Dr. Zelenko, and Kevin Jenkins finalizing plans for the ZFreedom Foundation in Dr. Zelenko's final days

Part Three
Making the Case

Chapter One

The Case For An Engineered Virus

When it comes to examining whether or not the COVID-19 virus was engineered, there are a number of questions and moving parts to consider; all of them are interrelated. They are:

1. Did the actual virus get developed in the Wuhan lab?
2. Was the US government involved in funding coronavirus experimentation research at the Wuhan lab and in subsequently attempting to cover up their involvement in said research?
3. How great of a role did one man, Dr. Ralph Baric, play in weaponizing this virus if that is, in fact, what happened?
4. If the coronavirus variant was produced in the Wuhan lab, was it released deliberately or because of a leak? (We are unlikely ever to know this answer because if it were a disease deliberately released by the Chinese, anyone who discloses such would be killed.)

I want to take a look at each of these questions in the pages that follow. By the time I'm done, it is my hope that we will have all reached the same conclusion. I suspect you know what I feel, but I will not disclose that to you; I'll let what I share reveal this. One thing can be sure; once the virus was released and the process started, its escape into the general population was inevitable, whether accidentally or intentionally.

The Curious Case of Dr. Baric

It troubles me greatly when someone, anyone, works very hard at something and then either doesn't receive credit for their efforts or, perhaps worse, sees the glory go to someone else. On a personal level, I have experienced a bit of that with regard to my development of an effective treatment protocol against the coronavirus. For me, however, my relationship with, and humbleness before, G-d allows me to process and work through any frustrations I might have on this earth for a lack of recognition. I know G-d is keeping track of anything that matters.

But I do not presume my faith upon others, so I feel bad for them when they get cheated out of recognition. Such is the case with Dr. Ralph Baric, whose work over the course of two decades has seemingly played a critical role in developing the greatest manmade virus in human history and then unleashing it upon the world. In my opinion, Dr. Baric has worked very hard at this. Despite his success, he has gone largely uncredited for his role in developing this genocidal weapon of mass destruction.

In this chapter, I hope to set the record straight and give Dr. Baric the credit he so richly deserves. After all, I owe him a great deal. If it weren't for his work in coronavirus weaponization and cross-species transfer, you never would have gotten to know who I was, and this book could never have been written. He has touched so many lives, perhaps even helped to end them.

What a difference he has made.

I have concluded that Dr. Baric deserves recognition for his significant role in helping develop the coronavirus and some of its variants through the use of inductive reasoning. People use the term "deduced" frequently but often incorrectly and rarely use the term's vital opposite of "induced." I'm going to explain the difference quickly, but the key fundamental distinction is that a conclusion drawn from inductive reasoning isn't actually proven but can be invalidated. So far, nobody has been able to invalidate my conclusion about Dr. Ralph Baric's importance to the development of the coronavirus.

The difference between inductive reasoning and deductive reasoning is that the former goes from the specific to the general while the latter goes from the general to the specific. Inductive reasoning is used to create a hypothesis, while deductive reasoning is used to test it. Most people talk about Sherlock Holmes and how he could deduce things brilliantly. The truth is that Holmes mostly used inductive reasoning. He would look at a variety of independent factors - details, if you will - at a crime scene and then create a hypothesis to draw a conclusion about what happened. That demonstrates inductive reasoning, whereas deductive reasoning was used to test Holmes's hypothesis.

What I have done in the case of Dr. Baric is observe a number of specific circumstances that seem to be associated with a crime against humanity, which has led to the creation of the hypothesis that he played a key role in engineering the coronavirus. I cannot prove this, but a hypothesis can be tested to be proven or rejected. It is my sincere hope that legal authorities get around to testing my hypothesis to see if Dr. Baric is, in fact, responsible for helping to bring this plague down upon humanity.

Dr. Ralph Baric is a professor of epidemiology, microbiology, and immunology at the University of North Carolina-Chapel Hill. Here is a general description of him that was published on the Chinese news publication Xinhuanet.com:

Results of scientific research and the related patent registration information have shown that Ralph Baric could be called as the first person who synthesized a coronavirus...He successfully created "an infectious clone of the urbani strain of the SARS coronavirus" by July 2003 at the "US Army's top bio-level three labs in Maryland," according to an article published by UNC-Chapel Hill in 2003.

Baric's team had synthetically reconstructed the bat variant of the SARS coronavirus (CoV) that caused the SARS epidemic in 2003, according to a report published in the Proceedings of the National Academy of Sciences (PNAS) in 2008.

> *Meanwhile, his team owns multiple patents concerning synthesized viruses, according to the related U.S. websites.*
> *Baric co-owns a patent "Methods for Producing Recombinant Coronavirus," with Patent Number 7279327, according to justia.com.*

Our Chinese enemies published that statement without any editorial comment, leading a reader to take it quite matter-of-factly. No condemnation, no acclamation. Of course, they couldn't condemn him, considering that he has partnered with the Chinese over time for his research.

A reader of this book may instantly ask, "Why is somebody synthetically replicating a deadly virus, and why are they getting patents for synthetically producing viruses?" This is a great question, which I will get to shortly.

A Plandemic

I have mentioned in earlier chapters how I only gradually became aware of the bigger picture relating to COVID-19 and how it was and wasn't being handled by world governments and the medical community. I went from thinking this was an aggressive and unique virus, quite possibly naturally occurring, to finding a treatment that was, much to my surprise, not openly received and widely shared. Then I moved on from having high hopes for an upcoming "vaccine" to finally seeing the devastating effects of that "vaccine" happen in real time with real patients. I finally became able to connect the dots and understand what happened. Playing a medical version of Sherlock Holmes, I was able to infer that this was, in fact, a "plandemic."

While I was able to see and reason for myself, I admit that much of what I learned I owe to the consultation, research, and friendship of Dr. David Martin, a man who has truly distinguished himself during the plandemic with his tenacity in digging up dirt to uncover the truth. He has been a mentor of sorts to me in terms of teaching me how calculated and evil people in power and people of science can truly be. His seminal work in this area can be found in a web-published document titled, *The Fauci/COVID-19 Dossier.*

Now, back to my personal inductive journey. I mentioned my late-night encounter with a YouTube video that led me on the path to discovering a treatment. That video was prepared by Dr. Roger Seheult, who was working on behalf of Medcram.com. In that video, Dr. Seheult explains the ability of zinc to effectively kill coronavirus as it reproduces inside the cell, using the assistance of an ionophore (something to which it can attach) to get inside the cell. Dr. Seheult specifically mentions (HCQ) when discussing this.

Dr. Seheult wasn't speculating in his video; he was referencing a study dated November 4, 2010, titled, *Zn+2 Inhibits Coronavirus and Arterivirus RNA Polymerase Activity In Vitro and Zinc Ionophores Block the Replication of These Viruses in Cell Culture*[1]. The very first line of that study reads: "Increasing the intracellular Zn^{2+} concentration with zinc-ionophores like pyrithione (PT) can efficiently impair the replication of a variety of RNA viruses, including poliovirus and influenza virus."

If that sounds familiar, it is because it became the foundation of the Zelenko Protocol. The reason I cite the study here, in a section about treatment, is because of who authored the study. While there are six doctors named, the one that stands out now is Dr. Ralph Baric. I paid no attention to that at the time; even if I had, it wouldn't have registered. I had never heard of Dr. Baric.

For those who like to follow the money, the study was supported by the Netherlands Organization for Scientific Research and funded by the Council for Chemical Research. This Washington, DC-based organization works closely with the US federal government.

For perspective, I watched that video that suggested a way to combat coronavirus that had been studied in 2010, in 2020, at the very beginning of the plandemic. How was it, then, that the authors of that study, assuming

---

1 | te Velthuis, A. J., van den Worm, S. H., Sims, A. C., Baric, R. S., Snijder, E. J., & van Hemert, M. J. (2010). Zn(2+) inhibits coronavirus and arterivirus RNA polymerase activity in vitro and zinc ionophores block the replication of these viruses in cell culture. *PLoS pathogens*, 6(11), e1001176. https://doi.org/10.1371/journal.ppat.1001176

that all or some were still alive, were not standing up at a podium insisting that they knew how to end the virus? That didn't make sense, but I didn't contemplate it much because I was too busy acting on the information and trying to save lives. It was possible that the research had just been somewhat random and forgotten about as over a decade had passed. Plausible? Again, I didn't even stop to process possibilities.

Completing the Puzzle

It would only be much later that I could put this piece into place alongside other pieces and complete the COVID-19 design puzzle. I deliberately started this story near the end to provide perspective. Now, let me take you back to the beginning.

I openly refer to the coronavirus we have come to know as a weapon of mass destruction, a biological bomb if you will. In order to make a bomb, you need two key components: You need a delivery system and you need a warhead. My research and observations have led me to conclude that Dr. Baric was involved in the engineering and design of both components.

In 1998, Dr. Baric was involved in publishing research in two different papers relating to the cross-species transmissibility of viruses. One was titled *Human biliary glycoproteins function as receptors for interspecies transfer of mouse hepatitis virus*[2]. The other was titled *Virus-receptor interactions and interspecies transfer of a mouse hepatitis virus*[3]. Some have discounted these studies and their relevance to the onset of COVID-19 because they were performed with mice. That misses the point that what they were experimenting with is related to what has become known as "gain of function."

Gain of function research is a term that the people at Apple must have invented because it is one of the best pieces of marketing in history.

2 | Hensley, L. E., & Baric, R. S. (1998). Human biliary glycoproteins function as receptors for interspecies transfer of mouse hepatitis virus. *Advances in experimental medicine and biology*, 440, 43–52. https://doi.org/10.1007/978-1-4615-5331-1_6

3 | Hensley, L. E., Holmes, K. V., Beauchemin, N., & Baric, R. S. (1998). Virus-receptor interactions and interspecies transfer of a mouse hepatitis virus. *Advances in experimental medicine and biology*, 440, 33–41. https://doi.org/10.1007/978-1-4615-5331-1_5

It is a cynical term because it sounds like a patient perhaps had a stroke, couldn't walk, and through physical therapy, they regain the function of their legs. That's what it sounds like; however, that is not what it is. Gain of function means "to take a benign animal virus and have it gain entirely new functions." In this case, these functions allow it to jump from animals into humans and become a weapon of mass destruction.

Going back to the two studies just cited, the conclusion in the abstract of the Virus-Receptor study was as follows: "This data suggested that phylogenetic homologues of virus receptors represent natural conduits for virus xenotropism and cross-species transfer."

The same last sentence in the Human biliary study reads: "These data suggest that interspecies transfer may remodel normal virus-receptor interactions that may result in altered virulence, tropism or pathogenesis in the original host."

I do not need to translate. Both of these studies appear on the NIH.gov website. Baric was working on his delivery system to be able to have a virus cross species.

In 2002, Baric and a team, through UNC-Chapel Hill, applied for a patent that was ultimately granted (US7279327B2) related to a virus' reproduction process. The patent is easily referenced, but I warn you, the language is tedious. It does clearly disclose that funding for the technology came from the NIH. In the "Summary of the Invention" section of the patent, I reprint only the opening sentence: "A first aspect of the present invention is a helper cell for producing an infectious, replication defective, nidovirus particle."

Again, no real translation is required. To this point, you can see how Dr. Baric has been at the epicenter of finding ways to copy and transfer viruses from one host or another to a recipient. This specifically relates to making the virus infectious and damaging to human lung tissue. I am not saying that they did that. I can't prove that. I remind the reader: I'm simply using inductive reasoning to look at an entire series of seemingly independent occurrences to posit a hypothesis, that hypothesis being that COVID-19 was an engineered virus.

Jumping ahead to 2014-15, in more work supported by the US government, Dr. Baric was back at it again with a team of Chinese researchers creating a "chimeric" version of coronavirus from bats... sound familiar? The US government prohibited this kind of research, but the work started prior to the ban. In November 2015, *Nature Magazine* ran an article titled, *Engineered bat virus stirs debate over risky research*[4]. The following is an excerpt from that article: "An experiment that created a hybrid version of a bat coronavirus — one related to the virus that causes SARS (severe acute respiratory syndrome) — has triggered renewed debate over whether engineering lab variants of viruses with possible pandemic potential are worth the risks."

In an article published in *Nature Medicine* on November 9 of that same year, scientists investigated a virus called SHC014, found in horseshoe bats in China. The researchers created a chimeric virus, made up of a surface protein of SHC014 and the backbone of a SARS virus that had been adapted to grow in mice and to mimic human disease. The chimera infected human airway cells, proving that the surface protein of SHC014 has the necessary structure to bind to a key receptor on the cells and infect them. It also caused disease in mice but did not kill them.

Although almost all coronaviruses isolated from bats have not been able to bind to the key human receptor, SHC014 is not the first that can do so. In 2014, researchers reported this ability for the first time in a different coronavirus isolated from the same bat population in a study titled, *Receptor usage and cell entry of bat coronavirus HKU4 provide insight into bat-to-human transmission of MERS coronavirus.*[5]

4 | Butler, D. Engineered bat virus stirs debate over risky research . *Nature* (2015). https://doi.org/10.1038/nature.2015.18787

5 | Yang, Y., Du, L., Liu, C., Wang, L., Ma, C., Tang, J., Baric, R. S., Jiang, S., & Li, F. (2014). Receptor usage and cell entry of bat coronavirus HKU4 provide insight into bat-to-human transmission of MERS coronavirus. *Proceedings of the National Academy of Sciences of the United States of America*, *111*(34), 12516–12521. https://doi.org/10.1073/pnas.1405889111

The findings reinforce suspicions that bat coronaviruses capable of directly infecting humans (rather than first needing to evolve in an intermediate animal host) may be more common than previously thought.

But other virologists question whether the information gleaned from the experiment justifies the potential risk. Although the extent of any risk is difficult to assess, Simon Wain-Hobson, a virologist at the Pasteur Institute in Paris, points out that the researchers have created a novel virus that "grows remarkably well" in human cells. "If the virus escaped, nobody could predict the trajectory," he said.

This is extraordinary. This piece, which is virtually unknown to the general public, was looking at the work of Dr. Baric in 2015 and sounding a warning about what could potentially happen as a result of his research. We know what did happen in 2020. Is there a connection? I can't prove one, but I'm still playing Sherlock Holmes and looking at the crime scene.

Here's an assessment up to this point:

Going back to the 1990s, Dr. Ralph Baric started researching coronavirus and looking at cross-species transference. He eventually progressed to the point where he obtained patented technology that could do precisely that. Along the way, he discovered a method for treating coronavirus in its early stage. While he published that research, he did not demand to be heard early in the coronavirus outbreak so he could share his knowledge with the world. Before that, halfway between his finding of a treatment and the outbreak, he conducted research to produce a chimeric version of a virus, which was performed in conjunction with Chinese researchers.

This is a very compelling set of facts that can lead to an inference that the work of Dr. Ralph Baric may have been used to create the virus in a laboratory setting in Wuhan, China.

I want to be clear that I am not suggesting that Dr. Baric did his work with the intention of releasing a virus to the general public. I don't have crime scene clues that suggest he was behind a plot to release a virus. I am suggesting that his work in affiliation with the Chinese government and Chinese scientists, especially the Wuhan lab, seems to create a good deal of evidence that his work could very well have been the source of the development of this weapon of mass destruction.

If Baric's intention was to develop a weaponized virus but not to release it, that could explain why he wasn't adamantly vocal about promoting the possible treatment he had discovered back in 2010—the one in the video that led to the Zelenko Protocol. He may have felt that speaking out about the treatment would draw too much attention to his work in developing a chimeric version of the virus.

Whatever the truth behind what Baric's involvement may or may not have been in developing the virus and releasing it into the general public, there is no doubt that there is ample reason to believe this virus was engineered. If it wasn't, a lot of work was done and a lot of money spent to perfect something like that with no intention of ever having it leave the Wuhan lab.

In an interview with *MIT Technology Review* back in July 2021, Dr. Baric went on record to disclaim any responsibility for the coronavirus. In a piece titled, *We never created a supervirus*, Ralph Baric explains gain of function research and explains how his work, alongside his prime cohort, Dr. Zhengli Shi of China's Wuhan Institute of Virology, was not done for the purpose of developing a chimeric coronavirus to gain function. In fact, he argued to the contrary: "…the SARS coronavirus parental strain could replicate quite efficiently in primary human cells. The chimera could also program infection of human cells, but not better than the parental virus. So we didn't gain any function—rather, we retained function."

This could be true, it could be a lie, and it could be sophisticated Twenty-First Century sophistry. What's curious is when MIT asked Baric about the use of his work in developing the then recently released "vaccine," this was the response: "Most recently, we published a paper showing that multiplexed, chimeric spike mRNA "vaccines" protect against all known SARS-like virus infections in mice. Global efforts to develop pan-sarbecoronavirus "vaccines" [sarbecoronavirus is the subgenus to which SARS and SARS-CoV-2 belong] will require us to make viruses like those described in the 2015 paper."

So, I would argue that anyone saying there was no justification to do the work in 2015 is simply not acknowledging the infrastructure that contributed to therapeutics and "vaccines" for COVID-19 and future coronaviruses.

To put two and two together, the research work that Baric helped oversee that took place in the Wuhan lab was, according to him, not responsible for the pandemic, but it was responsible for the "vaccine." We are going to look at the problems with that "vaccine" in a later chapter, but what it seems is that Dr. Baric is doing is trying to say that his research, which was predicted by some to be potentially dangerous in 2015, was not responsible for anything bad, it was only responsible for something good.

What else would you expect him to say?

Wuhan

Now on to the question everyone has an opinion about: Was COVID-19 developed in a Wuhan lab?

Fox News has not been entirely "on board" during the pandemic in terms of being willing to go against the government's and medical establishment's narrative about virus origins, treatments, protection protocols, or the "vaccine" kill-shot. They have been slightly better than CNN or MSNBC, but only slightly.

In February 2022, however, they committed a random act of journalism by talking to a group of scientists about how likely it was that the coronavirus originated in a lab as opposed to emerging naturally from a "wet market" and jumping from bats to humans. One of the people they consulted was Professor Richard Muller from UC Berkeley, a man I respect greatly. Curiously, they didn't include me in the discussions with experts. I'm speculating that my plain-spokenness likely had something to do with my non-selection. My sources have told me that I'm on Fox News' banned list. Their reputation as the cable news channel of "the right" doesn't mean they are always right in setting what stories will be covered and how.

Part of being a good skeptic, or being a good Sherlock Holmes, relates to the ability to ask questions which point out facts that simply don't jive with prevailing orthodoxy or narratives. The Fox piece pointed out ten such questions or problems as they relate to simply dismissing the idea that the virus originated in a lab. They are:

1. No animals have been found to be infected with SARS-CoV-2: Under the natural origin theory, the novel coronavirus, or SARS-CoV-2, would have originated in an animal and traveled to humans either directly or through an intermediate host animal.
2. No evidence of pre-epidemic infections: During past coronavirus epidemics, such as SARS in 2003 and MERS in 2013, there was evidence of extensive human infection from animals prior to the virus mutating to become transmissible between humans and sparking the pandemic.
3. The genetic fingerprint of the virus is so unique it has never been observed in a natural coronavirus: SARS-CoV-2 has a unique trigger on its surface called a furin cleavage site and a unique code in its genes for that site, called a CGG-CGG dimer. This combination has never been found naturally and therefore points to a lab-manipulated virus.
4. The virus appeared in humans already "optimized" into an extremely contagious version: Based on SARS1 and MERS experiences, when the virus becomes capable of human-to-human transmission, it takes weeks to evolve as it spreads through the population and the most contagious forms of the virus dominate. But with COVID-19, the virus was pre-adapted for human-to-human transmission from the first patient. Specifically, the part of the virus that interacts with human cells was 99.5 percent optimized.
5. The Wuhan Institute of Virology studies bat coronaviruses and has engaged in "gain of function" research: The Wuhan Institute of Virology in China studies bat coronaviruses and their potential to

infect humans. According to the State Department, it has also engaged with so-called "gain of function" experiments, so it was natural to consider whether a bat-related coronavirus outbreak in Wuhan came from the lab.

6. China has not cooperated, and investigators have not had full access to the lab. China has insisted the virus did not come from the lab. Furthermore, Shi Zhengli, who leads the Wuhan Institute of Virology research team on bat coronaviruses, has said that the genetic sequence of the new coronavirus does not match any of the viruses her team had sampled from bat caves in China (remember that Shi Zhengli is a cohort of Dr. Baric, so take the denial for what it is worth).

7. Lab leaks are not uncommon, so they should not have been dismissed so quickly at the onset of the pandemic: Researchers working on viruses in laboratories have accidentally gotten infected before and caused virus outbreaks in China and elsewhere. For example, in 2004, a lab-leak SARS outbreak in Beijing infected nine people, killing the mother of an infected graduate student who worked at China's National Institute of Virology Laboratory. The lab was conducting research on SARS coronavirus (SARS-CoV).

8. Researchers at the Wuhan Institute of Virology (WIV) were sick just before the community outbreak: The State Department revealed that the "US government has reason to believe that several researchers inside the WIV became sick in autumn 2019, before the first identified case of the outbreak, with symptoms consistent with both COVID-19 and common seasonal illnesses."

9. The Wuhan Institute of Virology has conducted "secret" research projects with the Chinese military: The US State Department revealed that the Wuhan Institute of Virology has collaborated on "secret projects" with China's military and warned that the country has a history of biological weapons work that Beijing has not "demonstrably eliminated."

10.There was an "orchestrated effort" by NIH officials and others to quickly shut down the lab-leak theory: Those who favor the lab-leak theory have been frustrated by leaders at the National Institutes of Health, including Fauci, who pushed the natural origin theory from the early days of the pandemic and repeatedly denied that the federal agency was funding gain of function research at the Wuhan Institute of Virology.

There is now irrefutable evidence, obtained through leaked emails and FOIA requests, that an effort was made to suppress the lab leak theory and that Dr. Fauci was at the center of the coverup. As early as January 2020, we have proof that EchoHealth Alliance was thanking Dr. Fauci (more on them below) for "downplaying" the likelihood of the virus originating in a lab. This came at the same time that Dr. Kristian Anderson of Scripps Lab was also emailing Fauci that he and other experts were offered proof that Fauci was being told that it was unlikely that this virus developed naturally, and subsequently believing that it was very likely that the virus did not arise naturally.

When you look at these in their totality, I believe it is impossible for a reasonable person not to conclude a high likelihood that this virus was engineered deliberately. Now you might say that none of the above information proves anything. We simply have correlations and questions. That's true, but here is a question to ask yourselves after walking through the above list of ten legitimate points raised:

If you had to bet your life or a member of your family's life on whether or not this virus was natural or manmade, how would you bet?

The US State Department study referenced above was released on January 15, 2021. That date is important because it means that it was authorized and compiled during the Trump administration. People can think what they would like about our former President, but one thing they can't consider is that he is a globalist puppet of the World Economic Forum or the World Health Organization. This January 15 report, just before he left office, might be one of the last pieces of trustable information we get out of Washington.

The report is very critical of China and its transparency regarding the outbreak. It makes clear statements that the Wuhan lab was engaged in research that manipulated coronaviruses, and the gain of function was part of the process. It is damning in presenting a case that this pandemic was not just a freak occurrence of nature. Supporting the assertions and questions raised by Professor Muller and others a year later, the report cites three areas of suspicion around China's involvement in manufacturing the virus. Here are those details, as provided by the State Department memo:

1. Illnesses inside the Wuhan Institute of Virology:

The US government has reason to believe that several researchers inside the WIV became sick in autumn of 2019, before the first identified outbreak case, with symptoms consistent with COVID-19 and common seasonal illnesses. This raises questions about the credibility of WIV senior researcher Shi Zhengli's public claim that there was "zero infection" among the WIV's staff and students of SARS-CoV-2 or SARS-related viruses.

Accidental infections in labs have caused several previous virus outbreaks in China and elsewhere, including a 2004 SARS outbreak in Beijing that infected nine people, killing one.

The Chinese Communist Party (CCP) has prevented independent journalists, investigators, and global health authorities from interviewing researchers at the WIV, including those who were ill in the fall of 2019. Any credible inquiry into the origin of the virus must include interviews with these researchers and a full accounting of their previously unreported illness.

2. Research at the WIV:

Starting in at least 2016 – and with no indication of a stop prior to the COVID-19 outbreak – WIV researchers conducted experiments involving RaTG13, the bat coronavirus identified by the WIV in January 2020 as its closest sample to SARS-CoV-2 (96.2 percent similar). The WIV became a focal point for international coronavirus research after the 2003 SARS outbreak and has since studied animals, including mice, bats, and pangolins.

The WIV has a published record of conducting "gain of function" research to engineer chimeric viruses. But, the WIV has not been transparent or consistent about its record of studying viruses most similar to the COVID-19 virus, including "RaTG13," which it sampled from a cave in Yunnan Province in 2013 after several miners died of SARS-like illness.

WHO investigators must have access to the records of the WIV's work on bat and other coronaviruses before the COVID-19 outbreak. As part of a thorough inquiry, they must have a full accounting of why the WIV altered and then removed online records of its work with RaTG13 and other viruses.

3. Secret military activity at the WIV:

Secrecy and non-disclosure are standard practices for Beijing. For many years the United States has publicly raised concerns about China's past biological weapons work, which Beijing has neither documented nor demonstrably eliminated, despite its clear obligations under the Biological Weapons Convention.

Despite the WIV presenting itself as a civilian institution, the United States has determined that the WIV has collaborated on publications and secret projects with China's military. The WIV has engaged in classified research, including laboratory animal experiments, on behalf of the Chinese military since at least 2017.

The United States and other donors who funded or collaborated on civilian research at the WIV have a right and obligation to determine whether any of our research funding was diverted to secret Chinese military projects at the WIV.

Right up until June 2022, when this book was still being written, we did not have cooperation from China to investigate the true origins of this virus. Even WHO, an organization commonly known to be in China's back pocket, is complaining about access to the necessary information required to assess the virus. Whether their protestations are theater or not, they need to be taken into account as part of the mounting evidence to sift at the COVID-19 crime scene. As CBS News reported in June 2022:

Over two years after the coronavirus was first detected in China, and after at least 6.3 million deaths have been counted worldwide from the pandemic, the World Health Organization is recommending in its strongest terms yet that a deeper probe is required into whether a lab accident may be to blame.

That stance marks a sharp reversal of the UN Health Agency's initial assessment of the pandemic's origins. It comes after many critics accused WHO of being too quick to dismiss or underplay a lab leak theory that put Chinese officials on the defensive. In a report, WHO's expert group said "key pieces of data" to explain how the pandemic began were still missing. The scientists said the group would "remain open to any and all scientific evidence that becomes available in the future to allow for comprehensive testing of all reasonable hypotheses."

It is always the case that reasonable people can differ, but that over which they differ must be reasonable. To me, it is simply unreasonable to conclude anything other than that the coronavirus and its subsequent rise to pandemic level was developed and leaked from the Wuhan Lab in China.

US Involvement?

This leaves another big question that demands an answer, albeit a hard one to find because of bureaucratic protections. Was the US involved in funding the development in the Wuhan lab and trying to cover that up?

That interview that Baric granted to MIT came about because of a heated exchange that had taken place days prior between Kentucky Senator Dr. Rand Paul and the evil Dr. Anthony Fauci. Paul and Fauci have had numerous well-publicized exchanges since the onset of coronavirus and its global impact. This one focused on the funding of the Wuhan lab's research, in part Dr. Baric's research, in experimenting with gain of function in bat coronaviruses. It was triggered by recent releases of emails that were quite damning to Fauci in terms of what he knew and when he knew it concerning the virus.

During one specific hearing on November fourth, 2021, Paul was grilling Fauci about allegations that NIH was funding gain of function research at the Wuhan lab. He cited the Wuhan Virology paper, *Discovery of a Rich Gene Pool of Bat SARS-Related Coronaviruses*[6], which detailed the research. During the exchange, Fauci refused to answer most of Paul's questions directly. Here is just a tiny part of what transpired:

Paul: You take an animal virus and you increase this transmissibility to humans, you're saying that's not gain of function?

Fauci: Yeah, that is correct, and Sen. Paul, you do not know what you are talking about, quite frankly. And I want to say that officially. You do not know what you are talking about.

Paul: This is your definition that you guys wrote. It says that scientific research that increases the transmissibility among animals is gain of function. They took animal viruses that only occur in animals and they increase their transmissibility to humans. How can you say that it is not gain of function?

Fauci: It is not.

Paul: It's a dance, and you're dancing around this because you're trying to obscure responsibility for four million people dying around the world from a pandemic.

Fauci's engagement in Orwellian-esque doublespeak with Senator Paul has been commonplace coming from this international villain from the day he stepped in front of President Trump at a 2020 press briefing to deny the effectiveness of HCQ in treating the disease, a treatment he supported before it became politicized.

---

6 | Hu B, Zeng L-P, Yang X-L, Ge X-Y, Zhang W, Li B, et al. (2017) Discovery of a rich gene pool of bat SARS-related coronaviruses provides new insights into the origin of SARS coronavirus. PLoS Pathog 13(11): e1006698. https://doi.org/10.1371/ journal. ppat.1006698

In October 2021, prior to Fauci's July exchange with Sen. Paul, the NIH effectively confirmed in a letter they sent to a US House Committee that US funds had been used to finance research in the Wuhan lab. In that letter they tried to have it both ways by saying that yes, they funded China-based research, but no, it did not lead to the COVID-19 outbreak—lots of convenient coincidences.

As reported at the time in *Science.org* in October 2021:

An ongoing controversy over what constitutes virology research that is too dangerous to conduct—and whether the US government funded studies in China that violated a policy barring funding for such risky research—has taken a new turn. While denying once again it had helped create the virus that sparked the COVID-19 pandemic, the US National Institutes of Health (NIH) revealed in a letter sent yesterday to Republicans in Congress that experiments it funded through a U.S.-based nonprofit in 2018 and 2019 at the Wuhan Institute of Virology (WIV) in China had the "unexpected result" of creating a coronavirus that was more infectious in mice.

NIH says the organization holding the parent grant, the EcoHealth Alliance, failed to immediately report this result to the agency, as required. A newly released progress report on that grant also shows that EcoHealth and WIV conducted experiments changing the virus that causes Middle East Respiratory Syndrome (MERS), which is raising additional questions.

EcoHealth Alliance is run by Dr. Peter Daszek, a sinister character whose organization has been receiving funding from the US government for a long time. Back in 2016, communications now available between Dr. Daszek and staff at the NIH indicate that EchoHealth had received, and was still receiving, NIH money under an original 2014 grant to fund a study titled *Understanding risk-bat coronavirus emergence*, to the of $666,442.[7] The US had placed a moratorium on gain of function research since the inception of the grant, but despite the expressed concerns of some NIH staffers,

7 | https://reporter.nih.gov/search/-bvPCvB7zkyvb1AjAgW5Yg/project-de-tails/8674931#description

the work was permitted to proceed, undoubtedly because it was being performed in China.

This is why the State Department memo said "at least as far back as 2016..." when it spoke of the research being conducted. We know from analyzing Dr. Baric's work that the date is actually well before.

I mentioned NIH funding of one of Dr. Baric's specially noted studies discussed earlier in this chapter. If you look through other work by Dr. Baric, you will see that the US government, especially through the NIH, has been a veritable crowdfunding source for Dr. Baric's rehearsals to be cast in the role of G-d. Everywhere you turn in this pandemic, you encounter the names of Baric, Daszek, and Fauci, along with the NIH, the US government, the Wuhan China Lab, and other various role players whose names come up repeatedly. Some people like to speak of conspiracy, but you don't need a conspiracy if everyone is working toward the same end.

Did the US government fund research in China? Yes. Did that research lead to the development of the coronavirus known as COVID-19 and its subsequent release? Almost certainly. Would anyone responsible for such an event want to cover it up? Of course, they would.

Which leads to the most damning question: Was COVID-19 deliberately released?

Some Men Just Want to Watch the World Burn

In my opinion, the coronavirus strand that crippled the world is probably the only thing manufactured in China that actually works. As to whether or not it was released on purpose, while the question cannot be answered with certainty, one thing we do know for sure: Men who are evil enough to create such a virus in the first place are evil enough to do just about anything with it once they have it. If they were concerned about humanity, they never would have engineered it, which I firmly believe they did.

This kind of research costs a lot of money. If you are going to manipulate a virus to have it gain biological function, you need to have an end in mind as to what the sociological function is you are trying to gain. Is it to blackmail humanity? Is it to release it to depopulate the planet as has been an expressed goal of people like Bill Gates, Klaus Schwab, and other members of the WEF? Could it be to create the need for a "vaccine" that can eventually be implanted with a biological-based tracking device?

Or could it be, to quote Michael Caine's Alfred in *The Dark Knight,* "Some men just want to watch the world burn."

The research needed to weaponize this virus was not legal to perform here in the United States. Neither was funding it anywhere else. Performing it here might have been too risky to try but supporting it elsewhere could be hidden behind layers and have plenty of plausible deniability. We've seen some of that in this chapter. This research started in the US when it was legal. Then, when it wasn't, an extensive money laundering operation took place to have the research continue inside the borders of the evilest nation on earth. If mass murder is your goal, China is an excellent choice to have riding shotgun.

The time gaps in the process are interesting, but they make sense insofar as if you are going to engineer a genocidal weapon, you might want to find a way to treat yourself first. Most murderers are not also suicidal. Remember how Baric's work led to Seheult's video, which eventually led to my treatment discovery? We won't ever know how many of the mad scientists behind this actually contracted the Chinese-based coronavirus variant and how they treated themselves while they were telling the world there was no treatment.

I believe they developed a treatment procedure for themselves and then lied to the world regarding its existence. Why do I say that? Because in March 2020, when doctors like myself discovered the effectiveness of HCQ with zinc, Fauci lied in front of the world. When President Trump said HCQ might be an answer and Fauci jumped in front of him at the microphone to deny it, an alarm went off within me. I thought he protested too much.

There is a commonsense reason to think the virus was accidentally released; the people who worked inside the lab got sick early. This suggests an accident of some sort, but it also doesn't rule out the idea that it was to be intentionally released. It's risky work; S*&t happens.

Here is what I know for certain, and this is where I can safely move from inductive reasoning to deductive. After watching that video from Dr. Seheult, I was able to construct a hypothesis using the information discovered for us by Dr. Ralph Baric. I set out to prove that using HCQ, along with zinc and other attendant medications, would severely reduce the risk of death and avoid serious illness for people suffering from COVID-19.

To test the hypothesis, I conducted experiments on humans, also known as *treating patients*. To date, with approximately seven and a half thousand patients served and only three deaths, I have deduced that the coronavirus that came from China, regardless of whether intentional or not, never had to become a deadly global pandemic.

How that treatment actually worked will be the subject of the next chapter. Why it was suppressed and never universally adopted will be the subject of debate for generations to come. Whatever the motivations were of the villains in this story, they all could have been easily stopped if only everyone had recognized the work of one of the main villains, Dr. Ralph Baric.

Chapter Two

The Case for Treatment

In March of 2022, a study was published that was reported in the *New York Times* under the headline, *Ivermectin failed as a COVID treatment, a large clinical trial found. The drug surged in popularity despite no strong evidence that it worked.*

The story referenced a study conducted in Brazil with thirteen hundred subjects, half of whom were treated with ivermectin and while the other half received a placebo. The study concluded there was effectively no difference in the outcomes for the two.

This study became the most recent example in a long line of studies that were performed for the sole purpose of creating a false scientific foundation to be used to tell people that they could not be treated for COVID-19 in an affordable and effective manner.

The story quoted an "expert" commenting on the study. This "expert," whom I do not know personally, is either an incompetent fool who shouldn't be practicing medicine or complicit in the genocidal mass murder of millions of people. Here is the applicable citation from the Times' story:

There's really no sign of any benefit," said Dr. David Boulware, an infectious-disease expert at the University of Minnesota, "Now that people can dive into the details and the data, hopefully that will steer the majority of doctors away from ivermectin towards other therapies," Dr. Boulware said.

The tragedy of the *Times'* headline and this doctor's statement is that the vast majority of people who put their trust in established institutions and authorities now believed that using ivermectin would not help them beat the virus. I mean, there was a study, after all, and a bunch of very brilliant doctors (ask them) all signed off on it being authentic. They couldn't possibly be mistaken, could they?

I agree; they were not mistaken; they were boldly and deliberately lying. The study referenced by the NYT was really conducted, but it was undertaken to produce a result that had nothing to do with the real-world use of ivermectin.

The study, titled, *Effect of Early Treatment with Ivermectin among Patients with COVID-19[8],* was discussed in an online presentation through the National Institute of Health back in August 2021, but had just been published in the *New England Journal of Medicine.* It was performed by a host of very wonderful sounding doctor-types, all happy to sign their names to the findings. Here is an extensive but redacted excerpt from the Abstract:

We conducted a double-blind, randomized, placebo-controlled, adaptive platform trial involving symptomatic SARS-CoV-2–positive adults recruited from 12 public health clinics in Brazil. Patients who had had symptoms of COVID-19 for up to 7 days and had at least one risk factor for disease progression were randomly assigned to receive ivermectin…once daily for 3 days or placebo.

A total of 3515 patients were randomly assigned to receive ivermectin (679 patients), placebo (679), or another intervention (2157). Overall, 100 patients (14.7%) in the

---

8 | N Engl J Med 2022;387:1279-91. DOI: 10.1056/NEJMoa2208343

ivermectin group had a primary-outcome event, as compared with 111 (16.3%) in the placebo group (relative risk, 0.90; 95% Bayesian credible interval, 0.70 to 1.16). Of the 211 primary-outcome events, 171 (81.0%) were hospital admissions…There were no significant effects of ivermectin use on secondary outcomes or adverse events.

That seems pretty straightforward. Said in words, not numbers, the study says there is no material difference between giving people ivermectin versus giving them a sugar tablet. They could have just as easily written, Doctors like Zelenko are lying idiots." But they took the high road.

The problem with this garbage study (emphasis on garbage) is that they treated people with ivermectin up to seven days *after* the presentation of symptoms—and didn't treat them with anything else besides ivermectin! There is not a credible doctor in the country who has been following my protocol and using ivermectin (or HCQ) as a treatment who recommends this approach.

My protocol calls for the use of zinc, along with ivermectin or HCQ, and other various drugs and supplements. This study was a product of special interests, not those of humanity, and all of the physicians who signed off on it seem to have done so deliberately. That is a harsh statement, but I stand by it. These doctors had one interest: To have people abandon any hope of being treated safely and effectively, veering them into a state of panic where they decided to live life in fear, being dependent upon Big Pharma and Big Medicine for help, and dying unnecessarily.

Fake, and Just Plain-Bad, Science—Bogus Studies

The deliberate creation of phony studies to produce desired outcomes has been a pattern ever since I first developed the Zelenko Protocol. In December 2020, a study using American Veterans, our service men and women who had risked their lives for our country as guinea pigs, was published out of Virginia. That study was titled, *Outcomes of Hydroxychloroquine Usage in United States Veterans Hospitalized with COVID-19*. The hospitalized patients (the

9 | Magagnoli, J., Narendran, S., Pereira, F., Cummings, T. H., Hardin, J. W., Sutton, S. S.,

adjective is key here; the patients were already in the hospital) were broken down into three groups:

Given HCQ only

Given HCQ along with azithromycin

Given nothing

You will note that none of the treated groups were given zinc. In this case, that isn't even the most significant problem (or perhaps, it is the co-biggest problem). The biggest problem is that these were all patients already in the hospital! Highlights of this study include:

Hydroxychloroquine (HC) use did not reduce the risk of ventilation or death

HC with azithromycin (AZ) did not reduce the risk of ventilation or death

HC, with or without AZ, was associated with a longer length of hospital stay

The conclusion to this study was:

Among patients hospitalized with COVID-19, this retrospective study did not identify any significant reduction in mortality or in the need for mechanical ventilation with hydroxychloroquine treatment with or without azithromycin.

& Ambati, J. (2020). Outcomes of Hydroxychloroquine Usage in United States Veterans Hospitalized with COVID-19. *Med (New York, N.Y.)*, *1*(1), 114–127.e3. https://doi.org/10.1016/j.medj.2020.06.001

A fellow physician criticized me during this pandemic for not being qualified to share my recommendations on treating the virus because I did not have enough experience treating in-hospital patients. My reply to him was reasonably direct: Of course, I don't have that experience, you imbecile! My patients don't go into the hospital! The problem with the VA study is that they were treating patients who were already in an advanced stage of the disease. My protocol involved very early, sometimes even prophylactic, treatment.

A Zelenko patient doesn't have to enter the death chambers that were, and still are, our hospitals if they contract this manmade coronavirus variant. They get treated immediately, and they get better almost immediately.

The reason for this is not complex. Most people still don't understand (but all of the doctors who are letting people die unnecessarily do understand) that COVID-19-10 is really two diseases. In the first week, it is in its viral phase, and nobody dies from it during that time. As it progresses, a pathogenic lethal immune reaction results in catastrophic lung damage and blood clots. That is why getting rid of the disease is vital in its early stage. As my colleagues who have followed me and I have proven, medical science is fully equipped to handle a viral infection. In the next stage, however, medical science has fallen woefully short.

I have given you examples of studies that have either used ivermectin or HCQ (they are essentially interchangeable, as I will get to later) without zinc to supplement or that have treated patients so late within the disease cycle that renders the Zelenko Protocol much less effective. These are examples of studies where those conducting them deliberately let people die in order to make whatever evil point they were inclined to make. These, however, are not the worst kind of bogus studies. That is hard to believe, isn't it? What could be worse than a study that lets people die? The answer is a study that deliberately kills them as part of the study.

The intellectual dishonesty shown in the VA study and others was troubling. However, I still hadn't put the pieces together about how these studies deliberately attempted to suppress treatment instead of just being lousy research. I mean, it is a reasonable conclusion to say that in the ICU setting, with patients being in the hospital on a respirator for an average of seventeen days, HCQ may be detrimental. That could, in fact, be a correct observation. But, based on that study, using HCQ on day two or three of symptoms while the patient's not in the hospital is an unreasonable conclusion. That's if you are giving people the benefit of the doubt. If you aren't, the only other conclusion you could come to is that the research is outright misleading and intentionally fraudulent, designed to reach a conclusion that serves an ulterior motive.

With that said, regarding the VA study, I found it infuriating, and I felt the authors were stupid, but I didn't assign any nefarious motives to them because I just wasn't thinking along those lines. There was not a pattern set into place yet. Then came a series of studies that were designed to kill people intentionally. That changed my thinking, as we had 1) a pattern and 2) clear motives.

Licensed to Kill

I had mentioned that my work in the United States to get HCQ approved for use by the FDA had been halted because of a study published in *The Lancet* and conducted by Surgisphere. That study was retracted thirteen days after publication due to the discovery that it had used fabricated data to support the claim that HCQ was unsafe. The damage to the approval of my protocol was already done, however, as that bogus study was still used as a premise for rejecting my proposal and withdrawing Emergency Use Authorization for HCQ.

As these various pieces of information came together, it became pretty easy to connect the dots. The fake Surgisphere study led to the death of millions. Imagine if my protocol had been approved in mid-2020. Of course, I can't prove it would have been approved without Surgisphere. The same dark satanic forces that have been at work throughout the pandemic still likely would have suppressed any simple and effective treatment in order to move forward with their kill shot euphemized as a "vaccine." Still, it would have been hard for them to have pulled off their genocidal plans, which would have been good.

The Surgisphere fake data research didn't just stop the approval process for my protocol in the US, but its results essentially stopped the use of HCQ worldwide for a brief moment, including in research being performed under the oversight of WHO, A.K.A the World Homicide Organization. WHO was in the process of overseeing a large conglomeration of trials under the heading "Solidarity Trial." The purpose was to test various treatment possibilities for COVID-19. The drugs being tested were:

- Remdesivir
- Hydroxychloroquine
- Lopinavir with Ritonavir
- Lopinavir with Ritonavir plus Interferon beta-1a

When *The Lancet's* report was issued, HCQ was temporarily removed from the study, only to be reinstated after the Surgisphere data was shown to be fraudulent. That should have been a positive step, but it was remarkably damaging because the dosages of HCQ that were being given to patients were enough to kill an elephant!

Thanks to the brilliant work of Dr. Meryl Nass and other truth seekers like her, the WHO-led study was exposed for using a dosage of HCQ. On June 14, 2020, Dr. Nass detailed what was happening with WHO research. Here are excerpts from her post:

Last week, I was alerted to the fact that India's ICMR, its official medical research agency, had written to the WHO, telling WHO that the hydroxychloroquine doses being used in the Solidarity trial were 4 times higher than the doses being used in India. Then I learned that Singapore had been hesitant to participate in the WHO trial due to the hydroxychloroquine dose.

Next, Dr. Nass mentioned a separate trial that had the fingerprints of WEF member Bill Gates behind it:

The UK "Recovery" trial was very similar to, but not part of, the international Solidarity conglomeration of clinical trials. The Recovery trial ended its HCQ arm on June 4, reporting no benefit. In-hospital mortality of the 1542 patients receiving hydroxychloroquine was 25.7%, or 396 deaths, about 10% higher than those receiving standard care, a non-significant difference.

"The UK Recovery trial Study Protocol notes it is funded in part by the Wellcome Trust and the Bill and Melinda Gates Foundation, and by UK government agencies. The Protocol provides the doses of hydroxychloroquine used, on page 22. Twitter users began to notice a dosing problem, with hashtag #RecoveryGate.

The HCQ dosing regimen used in the Recovery trial was 12 tablets during the first 24 hours (800mg initial dose, 800 mg six hours later, 400 mg 6 hrs later, 400 mg 6 hours later), then 400 mg every 12 hours for 9 more days. This is 2.4 grams during the first 24 hours, and a cumulative dose of 9.2 grams over 10 days.

"Even more disturbing than this, babies weighing 5 kg could be given a dose of 300 mg HCQ in the first 24 hours in the UK Recovery trial, which is 233 mg of the base (47 mg/kg), nearly 4 times the recommended maximum. One to two pills (200-400 mg) is "potentially fatal in a toddler". And authors from George Washington University say:

"Ingestion of 1-2 tablets of chloroquine or hydroxychloroquine is thought to predispose children under 6 years of age to serious morbidity and mortality… ingestions of greater than 10 mg/kg of chloroquine base or unknown amounts require triage to the nearest health care facility for 4-6 h of observation. There is very limited data on pediatric hydroxychloroquine overdoses and no reports of toxicity from 1-2 pills, but given its similarity to chloroquine, it also should be considered potentially toxic at small doses. Thus, similar recommendations should be followed for triage after accidental hydroxychloroquine overdose."

If you read the trials, you'll see that the patients really did die. They were being given up to six times the recommended dose of HCQ. I advocated for

400 milligrams a day, based on sixty years of safety data at that level. HCQ has been used for malaria prophylaxis, rheumatoid arthritis, and lupus, and we knew the recommended dosing range. We also know the safety profile at that dose. That's why I made the choice I made.

So, what would be the rationale to justify using 2,400 milligrams of HCQ? In my opinion, it would be to make sure that the people die. That seems like a reasonable conclusion.

All the WHO and UK trials proved was that if you give a homicidal lethal dose of a medication, the patient will die. The real damage here is that these trials made it look like HCQ is a lethal agent, which scared the hell out of every doctor and patient in the country. That was upsetting to me, and I was now starting to see a pattern. It became clear that no effort was made to discover an effective treatment for the virus. On the contrary, a deliberate effort is made to suppress any hope in people for there being an effective treatment.

Remember, the "vaccine" kill shot had not arrived at this point—it was still in development. What I hadn't connected yet in my mind was that for a "vaccine" to get emergency use authorization from the FDA, it had to be for a disease for which there was no approved treatment. The fix was in. This was all planned in advance. I was just playing catch-up in terms of understanding the plan.

Before leaving all of the deliberate efforts to discredit my protocol, discourage treatment, and remove all hope from people, I want to bring up one of the major fear-mongering tactics that has been used to scare people away from HCQ. This tactic was a lie that HCQ could lead to dangerous, life-threatening cardiac events.

I started to hear this regularly as my treatment methods became more widely known and discussed. It was as if doctors were trying to talk people out of pressing their physician to treat them by saying, "Well, you can take Zelenko's Protocol, but you will likely die from a heart attack instead. I'd take my chances with the virus if I were you."

Now, I do not have any proof about whether these conversations, or something along those lines, took place between doctor and patient. What I do know is that logic and good doctor/patient care strategies with COVID-19 had already been widely disregarded and replaced with fear: People were expected to blindly follow their doctors' insights, and whether intentional or not, these same doctors were choosing to believe flawed studies and research.

I needed to find out more information, so I began to do my own research. It's not that I am more resourceful than others; I am just willing to do the work, and in this case, it was work that I hoped would save a big portion of humanity from being wiped out by the virus.

This particular issue belongs to the subspecialty of cardiology called electrophysiology. It turns out there are only three thousand electrophysiologists in America, and they are all deemed geniuses. Over the years, I've gotten to know three of them just as colleagues to whom I would refer patients. I don't often need to do that, but sometimes if someone needs a pacemaker, has a troubling cardiac history, or shows an abnormal EKG, I need to refer them to a specialist, making these relationships necessary.

One of them was a fairly close friend, and I called him up and asked, "Listen, do you guys in your profession have a way you all communicate?" There are, after all, only about three thousand of them in the country. He said, "Yeah, we have a WhatsApp group."

I asked him if he could present the following question to that group:

Has anyone ever seen a negative outcome, complication, or death, associated with the use of hydroxychloroquine and azithromycin? Especially in the context of QT interval prolongation getting to a rhythm?

The answer was that nobody had ever seen it happen, outside of the rare occurrence found in intensive care units of hospitals. In ICUs, however, patients are really sick and taking all sorts of drugs, so it could be possible that HCQ might cause cardiomyopathy. However, it would be considered a rare and extreme circumstance. Remember, I was never advocating for its use in hospitals. As had already been pointed out to me, I don't have experience in treating the virus in a hospital setting, again, because my patients don't ever end up in the hospital!

So far, I have given you a relatively complete picture of the steps taken to falsely and deliberately discredit safe and effective treatments for the virus that would have stopped the pandemic in its tracks in about forty-five days or so. Representatives from the realms of politics, Big Pharma, and medicine were doing everything they could to kill the Zelenko Protocol in the crib.

The Zelenko Protocol Explained

It's time to take a look at the Zelenko Protocol and understand exactly what it is and why it works. I view it as common-sense, old-school medicine applied to an uncommon, manmade virus.

Allow me first to "qualify" myself for the purpose of writing what comes next. To this point, I have overseen the treatment of seven and a half thousand patients diagnosed with the virus since March 2020. Of those, two and a half thousand would be considered "high risk." Based on CDC estimates, the expected number of deaths within that population would be one hundred and eighty-seven.

I have lost only three patients.

This doesn't just make me qualified to discuss the coronavirus pandemic; it makes me perhaps the most authoritative expert on the subject in the world, certainly when it comes to treatment. Anyone who wants to claim to know more than I do about this manmade disease must first disclose how many patients they have treated successfully, then prove that they used something other than my protocol in their treatment.

In discussing my protocol, let me start with a candid, "big picture" look. To be very precise, I've never conducted a study; I'm not a researcher, nor do I want to be a researcher. I'm a clinician, a frontline doctor. In that role, I generated something called real-world evidence, something that other professionals have attempted to discredit.

It turned out that real-world evidence was the way that most of history has learned when using the scientific method; its value has been obvious. I would go as far as to say that my real-world evidence was the most crucial piece of information in the history of information. I mean, here I was, finding the solution to a global crisis, a worldwide shutdown, economies crippled, and the entire human psyche locked into either fight, flight, or PTSD mode. There was no hope. All you had to do was listen to the media to know that.

But then I, the nondescript family practitioner in upstate New York, stumbled across information revealing more than just an effective treatment method for a disease. It is a sort of universal principle relevant to every being that has a consciousness: People need to hope. They can't live in a hopeless state. Now it needs to be authentic hope, not like the bullshit hope of a "vaccine," but something real, and they perceive it that way. My treatment protocol gave them that hope.

Hope is the light that keeps people going onward, and it is essential that it resonates with humanity at times when it feels as if all hope is gone. Let me give you two analogies.

In analogy one, let's say you're drowning in the ocean, and you see a piece of driftwood. I don't have a clinical trial to tell you that driftwood may help you, but you know what? I bet you will try to hold on to it anyway. If you do survive, I think you should tell some people that if they are ever drowning in the ocean and they see a piece of driftwood, if they hold on to it, they just might stay afloat and survive. It's a fair statement, an inference.

Now let's consider parachutes for our second analogy. I don't really have a clinical trial to say this to you, but it seems like a good idea that if you jump out of a plane, you should have a parachute. We could do a study with a sample size of two hundred people, and we could give a hundred real parachutes and give the other hundred fake, or placebo, parachutes. We could then do a clinical trial by having all of them jump out of an airplane and observing the "controlled" outcomes. We would predict a conclusion that says real parachutes are better than placebos, but I think we can probably come to that conclusion without killing a hundred people unnecessarily.

Driftwood and parachutes provide hope in a crisis, scientifically studied or not. My efforts in developing a treatment regimen provided the same kind of hope. I won't drown. I won't hit the ground at 120mph. I won't die from a manmade virus.

Sadly, sometimes maliciously, other members of the medical community wish to deny hope to citizens. I'd never be able to explain why that is in a way that doesn't dehumanize them.

I think that what we have seen regarding the rejection of my treatment efforts and the efforts of others has been arrogance, or outright intentional malfeasance, to marginalize real-world evidence. I'm not saying clinical trials are unnecessary; I'm just saying that in those studies, especially when you have a World War Three situation with an unknown new problem where we have no data, it's reasonable to try some new things in the field that help to manage the crisis. Medical professionals must be like the Marines: Improvise, adapt, overcome. You have to think outside the box when you have nothing else available.

Imagine Anthony Fauci being in charge of Washington as it is being carpet-bombed (no, Zelenko haters, I'm not calling for DC to be carpet-bombed). Advisors would want us to act decisively, to shoot down the planes and eliminate the threat. Commander Fauci would say, "Listen, we need to perform research to see which bullets are the best: What caliber to use; what material we should use to make them. Let's just wait three, six, twelve months. We will find the right bullets, and we will tell you to use them. In the meantime, please wear a mask to protect you from the dust particles created by the vaporized buildings."

That's one approach. Another approach would be to use whatever you have to start containing the situation. Sure, do the research. That's fine. Find something better, and we will transition to its use. But in those moments when the planes are bombing you, it is time to act. I would throw my sneakers at them if they were all I had.

There was no clinical trial data behind the Zelenko Protocol, but so what! We were being carpet-bombed by a manmade virus. In your best whining voice, read these words out loud and pretend you are Anthony Fauci:

"But we don't have any trial data. We can't prove beyond a shadow of a doubt that your treatment is 100% effective. We just can't take that kind of chance with people's lives."

Wasn't that a little cathartic?

I ask rhetorically, how can you have data on something that never existed before:

Option One: Are you morons?

Option 2: Are you mass murderers?

I'll take option two: Mass murderers. A moron would be giving the benefit of the doubt to a treatment that appeared to be working with long-term side effects not known, and the short-term side effect is death! The people in power, like Anthony Fauci, who have blocked the use of my treatment, are simply malicious, genocidal psychopaths. They are cloistered bureaucrats who worship only their own minds and possess no empathy or sympathy for anyone outside their circle; sexual intellectuals aroused only through mentally masturbating using their own perceived brilliance.

I believe there was a setup for this. In February 2020, before the pandemic officially launched, the *New England Journal of Medicine* published a paper marginalizing real-world evidence and concluding, in essence, that medical truth could only be derived from double-blinded clinical trials, which are, of course, funded by the pharmaceutical industry and government and conducted by academia. I believe, but cannot prove, that it was a setup. The conclusion of the paper read:

> *In summary, the replacement of randomized trials with nonrandomized observational analyses is a false solution to the serious problem of ensuring that patients receive*

treatments that are both safe and effective. The Clinical Trials Transformation Initiative, which is supported by the Food and Drug Administration, has shown that it is possible to develop guidance that can help improve specific aspects of the design and conduct of randomized trials. There is now an urgent need to develop comprehensive guidelines based on the scientific principles underlying randomized, controlled trials that focus on those aspects that really matter for both generating reliable findings and ensuring patient safety, and that take advantage of technological advances to increase the scope of randomized evidence. Such guidelines would be relevant not only for the various phases of clinical development that lead to regulatory approval of new interventions (since reduction of wasteful practices could allow more new treatments to become available) but also for noncommercial randomized trials of existing treatments (since making more such trials affordable could lead to better patient care and improved public health).

This paper provided the aircover that bureaucrats and medical professionals would use to disregard and condemn my real-world, real-time, positive patient outcomes using my protocol.

Through Mark Meadows, I had the chance to contact Stephen Hahn, Commissioner of the FDA, who then put me in touch with some top people in the NIH. I presented to them what I had, real evidence, and they told me that kind of information was useless to them. They had no way to process it. This is like ignoring any natural learning process.

Say a baby is crying, and a set of new parents are freaking out. They don't know what to do. They start to learn almost accidentally that if they pick up the baby and make a nice, warm sound, sometimes it helps. Sometimes it doesn't. Then they learn to look to see if the baby's diaper is wet or dirty. They change the child, and sometimes that helps. Sometimes it doesn't. Then they try feeding the baby. Bingo! This is the Zelenko Protocol in metaphoric form. It is common sense and designed for one to act rapidly while adjusting to new information and customizing treatment as situations warrant. It also happens to be how most knowledge in all of human history has been acquired.

A Nobel Prize for Common Sense

Let's talk about common sense. It is shameful that I probably should win a Nobel Prize for this, but if you treat people early, they get better, quicker, and with fewer complications. The fact that this approach registers as genius is pretty pathetic, but common sense is considered as genius in this generation. Unfortunately, due to the lack of common sense evident on a global scale, it makes you a rare bird to be able to think analytically and use deductive reasoning.

If the people at the CDC are interested in acquiring common sense, they might try looking at their own website. On that site, the CDC says, in the context of treating the influenza virus, you must treat the influenza virus within the first forty-eight hours of symptoms. The reason for this is clearly understood: This is the time frame when antiviral drugs work. Did you know that the influenza virus is a single-stranded RNA virus? And did you know that the coronavirus originating in China is also a single-stranded RNA virus? They both use RNA-dependent RNA polymerase replication. Amazing! Wouldn't it be a reasonable hypothesis to draw some type of analogy and try early treatment? The answer is clearly "yes," that is, if you really want to help people. The answer is "no" if you want to maintain global fear.

I want to be very clear. The medical profession and all those complicit in suppressing treatment and who perpetrated this medical tyranny should stand trial like the Nazis, their doctors, and their enablers did at the end of World War Two. These have been crimes committed against humanity. I believe that we should have military tribunals or Nuremberg/Hague-style proceedings. I believe in the rule of law, and if we go through the legal process and any of them are found guilty, we should execute them. I won't mince any words. This is my opinion. They are mass murderers.

What they have done by denying the existence of effective early treatment and going so far as to prevent its use is akin to someone having cancer but it being too early to treat it because it is isolated to one spot.

You should wait until it spreads everywhere and then try to treat it. Or, if a small fire breaks out in the kitchen, you are advised not to put it out with the small extinguisher under your sink. You just call the fire department, even if the entire house becomes engulfed in flames. That is precisely what the government and our medical establishment are still saying as of this writing. Don't prevent lung complications until the lungs are mostly dead.

The second part of my protocol is to not delay treatment; act quickly. One of the early problems we were having was how long it took for the highly inaccurate PCR tests to come back from the testing facilities. This disease, once we had seen it clinically, was and is pretty easy to diagnose without a test. Let's say someone comes into your office with flu-like symptoms, and it's not flu season. You check for the flu, and it's negative. Further, suppose they have two people in their house already diagnosed with COVID-19, and they don't smell or taste anything. Do you think it's possible they actually have the coronavirus? We did have and still experience, to a certain extent, doctors saying, "I can't make that diagnosis until I do a PCR test and wait a week for the results to come back."

Talk about a problematic and highly inefficient use of valuable, life-saving time! A positive test does no good for a patient that may already be dead. Successful intervention gets more difficult post-life. This sounds logical, right? Because of this, my approach was, don't delay treatment. You have the ability, in theory, to think using clinical judgment, deductive reasoning, and the art of medicine. If the patient doesn't have it, you can always stop the medication, but to send someone home with a potentially life-threatening condition in which you could intervene, why would you wait to get a piece of paper or an email before you act? I mean, that's criminal malpractice; it's terrible. I'm not a criminal. I would not delay treatment or put others exposed to this person at higher risk if they do end up having COVID-19.

In addition, I learned how to risk-stratify patients because I needed to know who and who not to treat, especially in the beginning when I defined success as someone simply not dying. I didn't want them going to the hospital and dying on a ventilator. Now in 2022, I have much more clinical experience and can tweak my treatments for any particular patient. In the beginning, however, the question was, "Who is most at risk?"

I needed to answer that question. So, I came up with a very clever idea. I called the local hospitals and spoke to their intensive care unit doctors. I wanted to know which patients were leaving in a box. They told me it was the older patients and those with medical problems. Next, I asked about younger patients and typically healthy people. These people were not even being seen. I reasoned that this virus doesn't kill equally. It picks on the weak and the vulnerable. Knowing this made a big difference because I could now come to my office and send two-thirds of the patients home without treatment. They all did well. They suffered, but they didn't die.

As for the high-risk group, which had at that time a 7.5 percent death rate, those are the ones that I treated early. I treated them with HCQ, azithromycin, and zinc. I didn't tell them it was the best treatment because I didn't know that. It just happened to be the only treatment at that time.

Learn, Adapt, Change

Medicine is very dynamic. That brings me to the next part of the Zelenko Protocol, which is to learn, adapt, and make changes necessary based on new evidence. As new information is gathered and evaluated, we learn from experience and new therapeutics coming up that are just as effective, maybe even more effective. It is essential to be nimble, to assess actual data and incorporate different modalities, and tweak your treatment approach based on the best evidence available at that point in time. This is so because the target is to give the patient the best care possible, not to validate your own ego.

We learned, for example, that steroids were very important. We discovered that ivermectin could perform the same function as HCQ. It turned out that for some, blood thinners were helpful.

Then, monoclonal antibodies became available, and we turned to those situationally and when we could obtain access. The Zelenko Protocol was essentially a toolbox that kept acquiring new tools to be used in a situationally appropriate manner. It was never about me promoting HCQ. I don't get a penny on the script commission from the drug companies. It was about promoting patient care.

I also found that it was absolutely essential to customize and tailor the treatment to each individual patient and not use a cookie-cutter approach. A patient's history mattered. If they had a history of asthma, for example, I might start them on steroids. If someone has a blood clotting history or predisposition, I'm going to start them on blood thinners. Customize the treatment: It's not rocket science; it's medical science.

Another factor outside of identified high risk by age and medical history was simply when the patient showed up. There is a big difference if they show up on day two of symptoms compared to on day ten. As I've mentioned, by then, it's a different disease. Depending on the stage of severity of their presentation or timing, I would take different approaches.

There were other things that I had to consider, especially patient preferences. Because of all the fearmongering with HCQ, and before ivermectin, there was a period of time when people would say, "Oh, no, I'm not taking HCQ. No way!" I remember thinking that I didn't care. I just needed to get antivirals into the patient, right? So whatever worked was what I'd advocate for, hoping to convince the patient to take an antiviral and anti-inflammatory in the right time frame, especially with high-risk patients, then I had a chance to save their lives.

People labeled me as the HCQ guy, but that was because I validated Trump and HCQ was the first therapy I became aware of. That was never a fair description of what my clinical approach was, which was to use common sense, risk stratify, triage patients, and then when you do intervene, use the best treatment modalities for that patient that we know of at that time, custom-tailored to that vision.

All of these details reflect the overview of the Zelenko Protocol and some thoughts on those who attacked it as well as me, while also attempting to stop people from learning about, and receiving, effective early treatment. As I've made clear, I believe the majority of those people acted deliberately and should be tried for crimes against humanity.

How the Protocol Actually Works

I've told you the what, how, and why of my treatment protocol. Now let's do something that doesn't often get done for non-medical people. Let me tell you why the treatment actually works.

One of the problems that people have when listening to medical experts debate is that they are not allowed to understand the details of what is being discussed. Medical experts can be snobbish and often decide that explaining anything to the masses is a waste of time because those poor souls who weren't privileged enough to go to medical school simply can't keep up with their superior minds.

This means that when people hear doctors arguing about effective treatment, they are reduced to listening to one doctor saying the treatment works as the opposing doctor states it doesn't. People then end up believing whoever sounds better or looks better on TV.

This is your moment; let's change that narrative by allowing me to explain how treatment actually works. I'm not dumbing anything down. If you are intelligent enough to have decided to read this book, then you are smart enough to understand some basic medicine.

Viruses do not reproduce on their own. They are, in a sense, like parasites, where they need to enter the human cell and use the metabolic machinery of that cell in order to accomplish their reproductive needs. The virus needs to reproduce to spread. Let's say it makes a billion copies inside a cell, kills that cell, and then those billion copies are liberated to go on to infect other cells and repeat the process.

So, one objective of a virus is to get into the cell. That's true for most viruses, regardless of RNA or DNA type (in this particular case, we're dealing with single-stranded RNA viruses). The process I am describing is common to all coronavirus strains, including Alpha, Beta, Delta, Omega, and Omicron. Those different strains have different ways that the virus can get into the cell, different receptors, and a different kind of shape, like the spike protein that allows them to evade certain parts of the immune system and attach to different receptors and get into the cell. That's irrelevant to me from a treatment perspective.

What is relevant is if it's already in the cell, it needs to be stopped from replicating because if it doesn't replicate, even if it killed that cell, so what? One cell dies, but not a billion. The question then is, how do we stop the virus from reproducing? All you have to understand is the mechanism of reproduction. All the coronaviruses, influenza viruses, RSV, hantavirus, Marburg virus, and most likely Ebola are single-stranded RNA viruses with some variants, and they all use a common reproduction pathway. It's called RNA-dependent RNA polymerase. A polymerase is an enzyme that will put together nucleic acids, or genetic code. There are different types of codes. There are some that are RNA codes. An RNA polymerase will make RNA code. In order to make a code, it needs a template. If it's an RNA virus, and the RNA virus wants to make a copy of its RNA, the enzyme involved is an RNA-dependent RNA polymerase. In other words, it makes a carbon copy.

This gets a bit confusing because there are other variations in terms of transcription (discussed in the next chapter). For example, if you have a DNA code and want to make a messenger RNA, you need a DNA-dependent RNA polymerase. Or let's say you want to make a copy of DNA, not transcribe it, but a carbon copy. So you need a DNA-dependent DNA polymerase.

In this particular case, we're dealing with RNA viruses that want to make copies of their genetic material. There's an enzyme associated with that, and it has a name, RNA-dependent RNA polymerase, or RDR for short. Without it, the virus, all those viruses actually, are useless. They can't do it. If we had a way to block, inactivate, or damage RNA-dependent RNA polymerase, that would be wonderful because then we shut down a whole slew of tremendous health problems.

It turns out that zinc puts a monkey wrench in RNA-dependent RNA polymerase. There's the problem. Zinc will not go into the cell on its own due to biochemistry. What does that mean? Zinc is like salt. It's a compound. There's no such thing as elemental zinc in a bottle; it comes in a compound. However, when it dissolves in a solvent such as plasma, it becomes an ion, and zinc has a positive charge, according to the table of elements.

Here it feels like high school chemistry class, but I will only point out what matters. When zinc gets near water, it bonds with the water in such a way as to essentially envelope itself in a water molecule. Now the zinc that needs to get inside the cell to disrupt the virus's replication process has a water carrier to guide it through. However, a problem remains: The outside of a cell has a membrane made of a lipid, commonly known as cholesterol. At its most fundamental level, cholesterol is an oil.

Now the classic oil and water problem is not a figure of speech in this instance. It is a real problem. The zinc cannot get into the cell because it is wrapped in a "bubble" of water that can't pass through the oil barrier.

This is where HCQ, ivermectin, and to a lesser extent, quercetin come into play. If that bubble of zinc and water could just get inside the cell, the water around it dissolves, liberating the zinc. If that happens, it goes to the enzyme, raises havoc, and shuts down RNA-dependent RNA polymerase replication. So, we have an effective agent, but it cannot reach the target. We need a substance that can facilitate the entry of the zinc water bubble through the cell membrane and into the cell. It turns out there are substances like that. They're called zinc ionophores.

An ionophore, from Greek *ion* and *phore*, "ion carrier," is a chemical species that reversibly binds ions. Many ionophores are lipid-soluble entities that transport ions across the cell membrane. There are different types of ionophores; in this particular case, since we're interested in zinc, we need a zinc ionophore.

If you guessed the rest, you can likely CLEP out of freshman chemistry. HCQ and ivermectin are prescription-strength zinc ionophores. Quercetin, along with some other natural extracts, is a non-prescription strength ionophore for zinc.

For those who like research, in a paper that can be found on the NIH website dated May 2020[10], ivermectin's possible role is identified as being that of an ionophore:

However, ivermectin could prove to be a powerful antiviral, therefore also useful for a possible treatment of the new coronavirus associated syndrome, even from a new perspective. This could happen assuming its role as an ionophore agent, only hinted in the recent past but never fully described...Ionophores are molecules that typically have a hydrophilic pocket which constitutes a specific binding site for one or more ions (usually cations), while its external surface is hydrophobic, allowing the complex thus formed to cross the cell membranes, affecting the hydro-electrolyte balance.

HCQ and ivermectin were my "drugs of choice" for treating COVID-19 until people like the monster Andrew Cuomo made it nearly impossible to get a prescription for them filled. He was too determined to fill nursing homes with sick, contagious patients to let simple, effective treatment get in his way.

It was Cuomo's actions that led me to search for an over-the-counter version of a zinc ionophore. How did I eventually find Quercetin? I'm almost embarrassed to say I Googled "zinc ionophores."

Quercetin is not as effective as HCQ and ivermectin: It's almost like comparing a .22 caliber to an M50. That said, you don't go to war with the army you wish you had; you go with the one you've got. Politicians and Big Pharma have made quercetin the weapon I had available once the big guns were taken away. This medical version of gun control has cost millions of lives around the world.

10 | Rizzo E. (2020). Ivermectin, antiviral properties and COVID-19: a possible new mechanism of action. *Naunyn-Schmiedeberg's archives of pharmacology, 393*(7), 1153–1156. https://doi.org/10.1007/s00210-020-01902-5

To round out the baseline package, I also recommended vitamin D because, quite simply, there is a wealth of evidence that people with high levels of vitamin D in their systems tend to be less sick than those without it. Azithromycin is used because it is an effective broad-spectrum antiviral that is very good and mopping up what might escape during the zinc-killing fields experience for the coronavirus' RNA virus reproduction.

Finally, I recommend using vitamin C with the non-prescription quercetin regimen because vitamin C is needed to assist the weaker Quercetin in getting zinc across the lipid finish line.

That is how my protocol works in a language anyone can understand. That means, by the way, that every doctor in the country, including your doctor, understands it, too. Ask your doctor, "If I get the coronavirus, what are you going to do to treat me early?" If they say there is nothing they can do, ask them about HCQ and zinc. When, not if, but when, they tell you there is no evidence that they work, ask them if they are familiar with the zinc ionophore process and if they feel there is no evidence that zinc is actually effective against any coronavirus strains.

When they tell you there is no research supporting the concept, read the next section, and you can then address that with your doctor.

From Villainization to Vindication: They Can No Longer Say I Was Crazy

On March 31, 2022, Kansas State Senator Mark Steffen, a physician, sent a letter to all healthcare providers in the state that denounced them for not treating the coronavirus early in patients. When I read the letter, I let out an audible exclamation of support. While the letter did not mention me by name, I saw the letter as being a clear and unequivocal sign that the Zelenko Protocol had reached mainstream acknowledgment.

STATE OF KANSAS

STATE CAPITOL
TOPEKA, KANSAS 66612
(785) 296-6964
mark.steffen@senate.ks.gov

MARK STEFFEN, M.D.
SENATOR 34TH DISTRICT
2500 N. MAYFIELD RD.
HUTCHINSON, KS 67502

TOPEKA
SENATE CHAMBER

March 31st, 2022

Dear Healthcare Provider,

As we have struggled mightily over the last two years responding to the Covid virus, one issue of particular importance has now become indelibly clear. Passive early treatment of Covid infections is no longer acceptable or the standard of care. **The standard of care is early treatment with FDA-approved medications regardless of their labelled uses.** Delays in institution of those treatments are no longer acceptable. The Healthcare Provider has a legal duty to ensure facilitation of treatment as expeditiously as possible. Delayed treatment worsens outcomes.

All Providers caring for those infected with Covid must have mastery of protocols heretofore considered beyond the FDA or CDC. The lack of availability of monoclonal antibodies remains problematic. Paxlovid and molnupiravir have availability and drug interaction issues as well. Ivermectin, hydroxychloroquine, and fluvoxamine remain readily available and are historically well tolerated. The hundreds of studies utilizing these medications as part of a multidrug regimen used early and at correct dosages have a clear signal of significant efficacy that can no longer be dismissed.

With the recent passage of Senate substitute for HB 2280 by the Kansas Senate Public Health and Welfare Committee and subsequently the Senate as a whole, there is no reason to think that prescribing problems will arise from pharmacist or Board of Healing Arts interference. In consultation with the legal community, indications are that **"failure to treat"** will now be considered **"wanton disregard."** As such, any perceived statutory immunity will be rendered invalid.

Providing care to the ill is difficult yet rewarding when done correctly and with a patient-first approach. I wish you the very best as our treatment of Covid becomes more sophisticated.

Sincerely,

Senator Mark B. Steffen, M.D.

This proved to be a vindication of every single word that I said in the video to President Trump on March 21, 2020, and in the subsequent letter addressed to every medical provider in the world I wrote on March 23, 2020. I said exactly those words. I didn't know about other mechanisms at that time, but I did share the principles of early intervention using hydroxychloroquine and zinc. For what I said then, I suffered greatly for years. Now, in reading that letter from Senator Steffen, it helped me see that I had brought awareness to protocols that could better treat coronavirus if given a chance and significantly reduce the fatalities it caused.

I usually don't share this with people, but the time is now right to do so. The death threats, threats to my family, persecutions by the New York State AG's office and the US Department of Justice, the rejection and slander by my own religious community, the threats from medical boards to revoke my license, and the general evisceration at the hands of the media since 2020 has sometimes felt like more than I could possibly bear. Only my battle with cancer, the preparatory gift given to me by G-d, could have possibly prepared me for what I have faced. Seeing my protocols being used, even without my name attached, makes me feel as though G-d, not I, has triumphed. I am human. I do get pissed off when others take credit for my work, but I quickly remember that I answer to G-d, not to them.

My protocols have also been used in other countries, such as Brazil and Honduras (where it essentially eradicated the disease). The states of Florida and Kansas have now also approved it for use. American Frontline Doctors started using the protocol early on, and that group has successfully treated tens of thousands of patients. A network of courageous physicians (and pharmacists) has emerged around the country who are willing to do what needs to be done to get life-saving medications into the hands of patients despite pressure from the government, Big Pharma, and Big Medicine to suppress treatment.

For every doctor who was too afraid to fight back and prescribe medications, there are others who have been willing to take that professional risk. To each of them, I offer my profound gratitude and respect.

But what of the research? Remember, the *New England Journal of Medicine* says that without real research, we aren't smart enough to treat patients.

Despite all the efforts, born from either maliciousness, arrogance, or both, to discredit my protocol for treating the coronavirus strain that impacted the world, a mountain of research has been compiled that verifies its effectiveness over time. I have been vindicated, not in the eyes of all but certainly, hopefully, in the eyes of G-d and of history (assuming that history gets truthfully written). It is said that history is written by the winners. We are yet to see whether it will be the forces of good or evil that will prevail in this struggle in which we find ourselves to save humanity.

In a study published in September of 2021 with the heading *Early COVID-19 therapy with azithromycin plus nitazoxanide, ivermectin or hydroxychloroquine in outpatient settings significantly improved COVID-19 outcomes compared to known outcomes in untreated patients*[11], and posted on the NIH.gov website, the abstract to the study read:

In a prospective observational study (pre-AndroCoV Trial), the use of nitazoxanide, ivermectin and hydroxychloroquine demonstrated unexpected improvements in COVID-19 outcomes when compared to untreated patients. The apparent yet likely positive results raised ethical concerns on the employment of further full placebo controlled studies in early-stage COVID-19 (emphasis and italics added). The present analysis aimed to elucidate, through a comparative analysis with two control groups, whether full placebo-control randomized clinical trials (RCTs) on early-stage COVID-19 are still ethically acceptable. The Active Group (AG) consisted of patients enrolled in the Pre-AndroCoV-Trial (n = 585). Control Group 1 (CG1) consisted of a retrospectively obtained group of untreated patients of the same population (n = 137), and Control Group 2 (CG2) resulted from a precise prediction of clinical outcomes based on a thorough and structured review of indexed articles and official statements. Patients were matched for sex, age, comorbidities and disease severity at baseline. Compared to CG1 and CG2, AG showed reduction of 31.5-36.5% in viral shedding (p < 0.0001), 70-85% in disease duration (p < 0.0001), and 100% in respiratory complications, hospitalization, mechanical ventilation, deaths and post-COVID manifestations (p < 0.0001 for all). For every 1000 confirmed cases for COVID-19, at least 70 hospitalizations, 50 mechanical ventilations and five deaths were prevented. Benefits from the combination of early COVID-19 detection and early pharmacological approaches were consistent and overwhelming when compared to untreated groups, which, together with the well-established safety profile of the drug combinations tested in the Pre-AndroCoV Trial, precluded our study from continuing employing full placebo in early COVID-19.

11 | Cadegiani, F. A., Goren, A., Wambier, C. G., & McCoy, J. (2021). Early COVID-19 therapy with azithromycin plus nitazoxanide, ivermectin or hydroxychloroquine in outpatient settings significantly improved COVID-19 outcomes compared to known outcomes in untreated patients. *New microbes and new infections, 43*, 100915. https://doi.org/10.1016/j.nmni.2021.100915

Allow that to sink in for a moment. That effectively says that the benefits of the early intervention treatment for COVID-19 are so clear that using a control group to give a fake dosage is essentially immoral. You are allowing them to run the risk of severe illness or death needlessly because they just simply ought to be treated.

The tragedy of ignoring the treatment protocol gets compounded when you consider a retrospective study performed at New York University Hospitals[12] (you might have heard of them as a semi-reputable group) also released in September, only a year earlier in September 2020; a full year before the study I just cited! Here is the abstract from that study, one that never got attention in the mainstream media—keep in mind these were patients already in the hospital, a group for which even I was not advocating the HCQ-zinc treatment:

COVID-19 has rapidly emerged as a pandemic infection that has caused significant mortality and economic losses. Potential therapies and prophylaxis against COVID-19 are urgently needed to combat this novel infection. As a result of in vitro evidence suggesting zinc sulphate may be efficacious against COVID-19, our hospitals began using zinc sulphate as add-on therapy to hydroxychloroquine and azithromycin. Aim. To compare outcomes among hospitalized COVID-19 patients ordered to receive hydroxychloroquine and azithromycin plus zinc sulphate versus hydroxychloroquine and azithromycin alone. Methodology. This was a retrospective observational study. Data was collected from medical records for all patients with admission dates ranging from 2 March 2020 through to 11 April 2020. Initial clinical characteristics on presentation, medications given during the hospitalization, and hospital outcomes were recorded. The study included patients admitted to any of four acute care NYU Langone Health Hospitals in New York City. Patients included were admitted to the hospital with at least one positive COVID-19 test and had completed their hospitalization. Patients were excluded from the study if they were never

---

12 | Carlucci, P. M., Ahuja, T., Petrilli, C., Rajagopalan, H., Jones, S., & Rahimian, J. (2020). Zinc sulfate in combination with a zinc ionophore may improve outcomes in hospitalized COVID-19 patients. *Journal of medical microbiology*, 69(10), 1228–1234. https://doi.org/10.1099/jmm.0.001250

admitted to the hospital or if there was an order for other investigational therapies for COVID-19. Results. Patients taking zinc sulphate in addition to hydroxychloroquine and azithromycin (n=411) and patients taking hydroxychloroquine and azithromycin alone (n=521) did not differ in age, race, sex, tobacco use or relevant comorbidities. The addition of zinc sulphate did not impact the length of hospitalization, duration of ventilation or intensive care unit (ICU) duration. In univariate analyses, zinc sulphate increased the frequency of patients being discharged home, and decreased the need for ventilation, admission to the ICU and mortality or transfer to hospice for patients who were never admitted to the ICU. After adjusting for the time at which zinc sulphate was added to our protocol, an increased frequency of being discharged home (OR 1.53, 95 % CI 1.12-2.09) and reduction in mortality or transfer to hospice among patients who did not require ICU level of care remained significant (OR 0.449, 95 % CI 0.271-0.744). Conclusion. This study provides the first in vivo evidence that zinc sulphate may play a role in therapeutic management for COVID-19.

There are now hundreds of studies that support what I was able to figure out using common sense and critical thinking skills back in the spring of 2020. If treated early and with a combination of well-known, safe, and affordable medications, the coronavirus is easily reduced from a deadly disease to a twenty-four hour or so inconvenience.

Brave Doctors Means Brave Medicine

There are three categories of doctors in this country: One that is completely ignorant of the beneficial effects of early treatment for COVID-19; one that is aware of the benefits and is courageous and principled enough to treat patients and prescribe medications; and a third that is aware of the benefits but chooses to ignore them for financial and political reasons.

As to the first group, they should be banned from the practice of medicine. Any doctor who is truly ignorant of the research and clinical results for early treatment of this disease at this point is a special sort of medical imbecile. They should not be allowed to splint a finger, let alone diagnose and treat patients with serious afflictions.

The second group are heroes. We use the term "hero" quite recklessly these days. But those who have been willing to fight against the medical-industrial complex to treat people and save lives, they are real heroes. As I mentioned earlier, they deserve our thanks and our praise.

To that end, there are some I would like to acknowledge directly. First are the doctors who published with me, Roland Derwand and Martin Scholz. They reached out to me early in the pandemic and have professionally and personally supported me. Dr. Thomas Brodie in Australia has shown tremendous courage in fighting back against a government nobody knew was totalitarian in nature until the onset of COVID-19. Dr. George Fareed, Dr. Peter McCullough, and Dr. Brian Tyson; all have been willing to stand against the prevailing winds of genocide and yell stop!

And, of course, there are all the other brave physicians around the country, including America's Frontline Doctors, who have stood against tyranny.

The third group, the one into which far too many of my medical "brethren" (bad gene pool) fall, these individuals are nothing short of monsters. These are people who know full well that clinical evidence suggests that people can be effectively treated for this disease in its early stage. They know that treatment dramatically reduces the likelihood of hospitalization. They know it, but they also know that treating people is not politically conforming, and if they are part of a major medical group, it makes it less likely that those patients will end up in one of their hospitals where the real money is to be made.

I want to be clear because it might sound as though I am suggesting that the medical establishment has been deliberately letting people die over money and politics. To make sure there is no misunderstanding, that is exactly what I am saying

840,000

I mentioned earlier in this chapter that I am not a researcher by background, nor do I aspire to be one. That said, at the behest of Drs'. Scholz and Derwand, I was involved in publishing a report detailing our real-world patient experiences (the kind that doesn't matter) back in December 2020. I naively thought that if we could get this information out into the hands of the medical community, it would cause an instant sense of urgency for the early treatment of patients.

I was wrong.

Regardless, the data we assembled was powerful. Here is the abstract from our study:

The aim of this study was to describe the outcomes of patients with coronavirus disease 2019 (COVID-19) in the outpatient setting after early treatment with zinc, low-dose hydroxychloroquine and azithromycin (triple therapy) dependent on risk stratification. This was a retrospective case series study in the general practice setting. A total of 141 COVID-19 patients with laboratory-confirmed severe acute respiratory syndrome coronavirus 2 (SARS CoV-2) infection in the year 2020 were included. The main outcome measures were risk-stratified treatment decision and rates of hospitalisation and all-cause death. A median of 4 days [interquartile range (IQR) 3–6 days; available for n = 66/141 patients] after the onset of symptoms, 141 patients (median age 58 years, IQR 40–67 years; 73.0% male) received a prescription for triple therapy for 5 days. Independent public reference data from 377 confirmed COVID-19 patients in the same community were used as untreated controls. Of 141 treated patients, 4 (2.8%) were hospitalised, which was significantly fewer (P < 0.001) compared with 58 (15.4%) of 377 untreated patients [odds ratio (OR) = 0.16, 95% confidence interval (CI) 0.06–0.5]. One patient (0.7%) in the treatment group died versus 13 patients (3.4%) in the untreated group (OR = 0.2, 95% CI 0.03–1.5; P = 0.12). No cardiac side effects were observed. Risk stratification-based treatment of COVID-19 outpatients as early as possible after symptom onset using triple therapy, including the combination *of zinc with low-dose hydroxychloroquine, was associated with significantly fewer hospitalisations.*

The same mainstream media that has been so quick to pick up the bogus studies, like the one in *The Lancet* and the misleading studies I've pointed out in this chapter, completely ignored our work. The fact that it is now being recognized, albeit typically without attribution, proves that treatment works, and people have been deliberately killed by those who ignored that fact and allowed their suffering.

Before the widespread politicization of HCQs use in possibly treating this deadly virus, "America's Doctor," the criminal against humanity Anthony Fauci himself, indicated on March 24, 2020, that he would be willing to prescribe HCQ to a patient. In an interview with AM 990 in Philadelphia, *Townhall Magazine* reported this exchange between Fauci and host Chris Stigall:

"If you're a doctor listening to me right now and a patient with coronavirus feels like they want to try that," Stigall asked, "and you're their doctor, you're not Anthony Fauci the guy running the coronavirus task force, would you say 'alright, we'll give it a whirl?'" Yeah, of course, particularly if people have no other option," Fauci said. "These drugs are approved drugs for other reasons. They're anti-malaria drugs, and they're drugs against certain autoimmune diseases like lupus. Physicians throughout the country can prescribe that in an off-label way. Which means they can write it for something it was not approved for."

Seems as though Dr. Fauci wasn't always a science denier. Perhaps there was some good in him? Maybe I give him too much credit by acknowledging that possibility.

Here is what I have shown you in this chapter:

1. The science behind how HCQ, ivermectin, or any other zinc ionophore can kill COVID-19 before it can reproduce and spread.
2. What the Zelenko Protocol is; a process essentially veiled as a treatment.

3.The fact that there are conclusive scientific studies that prove the effectiveness of the Zelenko Protocol treatment.

4.The fact that other studies were undertaken to deliberately convince people that these proven effective treatments don't actually work.

In the end, here is a simple way to grasp the full impact of what I have shared. In May 2022, it was widely reported that the United States had surpassed over one million deaths from coronavirus and its variants. Now some could argue the number is much higher due to deaths resulting from collateral pandemic damage (suicides, overdoses, non-treated illnesses, etc.), or conversely, we could argue the number is actually lower (all of the reports we have heard of non-COVID-19 deaths being labeled as COVID-19 to profit the healthcare industry and scare the hell out of us). For the sake of argument, let's just take the number of one million as being accurate. Since we know that following the Zelenko Protocol and using aggressive early treatment intervention - especially in high-risk patients - reduces the hospitalization of those patients by 84 percent, we can reasonably assume that if we had treated all Americans under my protocol, instead of having one million body bags, we would have only had one hundred and sixty thousand.

I guess that an extra eight hundred and forty thousand dead Americans is a small price to pay when you are trying to establish a new utopic world order, paradoxically being managed by homicidal maniacs.

Chapter Three

The Case Against "Vaccines"

On May 15, 2020, President Trump stepped up to the podium in the White House Rose Garden and announced he was launching "Operation Warp Speed," the program that would produce a "vaccine" against the Chinese coronavirus and end the pandemic that had been reported to have claimed eighty-six thousand lives up to that point. In his remarks, the President said:

"Operation Warp Speed, that means big and it means fast. A massive scientific and industrial, logistic endeavor unlike anything our country has seen since the Manhattan Project…Its objective is to finish developing and then manufacture and distribute a proven coronavirus "vaccine" as fast as possible…We'd love to see if we can do it prior to the end of the year…I think we're going to have some very good results coming out very quickly."

There was considerable skepticism about the ability to develop an effective "vaccine" in such an aggressive timeframe. There was no real precedent for it. More than a month before the announcement (on April Fool's Day, which for some reason seems significant in hindsight), CNN did a story where they interviewed a stable of experts who voiced their reservations about developing a "vaccine" in what was then reported to be an 18-month horizon. Here are some excerpts from that story:

"Tony Fauci is saying a year to 18 months — I think that's optimistic," said Dr. Peter Hotez, a leading expert on infectious disease and "vaccine" development at Baylor College of Medicine. "Maybe if all the stars align, but probably longer."

"I don't think it's ever been done at an industrial scale in 18 months," said Dr. Amesh Adalja, a senior scholar focused on emerging infectious disease at the Center for Health Security at Johns Hopkins University. "'Vaccine' development is usually measured in years, not months."

Dr. Emily Erbelding, an infectious disease expert at NIAID -- which is part of the National Institutes of Health -- said the typical "vaccine" takes between eight and 10 years to develop... She acknowledged that the accelerated pace will involve "not looking at all the data."

Walt Orenstein, a professor of medicine at Emory and the former director of the US National Immunization Program, said the tradeoff is a difficult balancing act. "If you want every 't' crossed and 'i' dotted, how many more people will die or suffer from COVID-19?" he said. "It's not an easy decision, it is a breakneck speed for moving things." Orenstein added that while there are likely lessons available from past efforts to develop "vaccines" against SARS and MERS, it will be tough to complete the process in 18 months, though he said it's feasible.

Mark Feinberg, president, and CEO of the International AIDS "vaccine" Initiative, [said] that while he recognizes the importance of animal trials, the urgency of the current public emergency makes it worth the tradeoff. "When you hear predictions about it taking at best a year or a year and a half to have a "vaccine" available ... there's no way to come close to those timelines unless we take new approaches."

CNN also ran a line in the middle of their piece that almost seemed out of place, but which turned out to be the most foretelling line in an article devoted entirely to "vaccine" development skepticism: "In rare cases, faulty "vaccine" trials have proven harmful or even deadly in humans."

As for me, on May 15, 2020, I felt optimistic and hopeful. I felt that way for many reasons. One was that I was scared for my own life and hoped a "vaccine" might prolong it. Being immunocompromised, I went into the den of infection every day while treating patients. While I was still almost sixty days away from what would be a full recurrence of my cancer, just the fact that I was already missing one lung and we were facing a virus that attacked the lungs made me almost a poster child for "elevated risk."

Another reason I was optimistic is that I subscribed to the architecture of Dr. Joseph Mercola, who laid out a simple four-pillar approach to dealing with a pandemic:

Spread prevention

Pre-hospital treatment

In-hospital treatment

Vaccination

In Mercola's heuristic, you don't choose just one of the four pillars. It is a kind of integration of all four elements, and I had no reason to doubt the "vaccine" approach. In fact, because of my own health situation I even considered volunteering to receive an experimental dose. As it turns out, had I done so, I might not have been around to write this book.

So, to be clear and on the record, while I was the first to come up with a successful treatment for the Chinese coronavirus, I was not the first to become a public denouncer of the "vaccine." I came around, but initially I was still too trusting of the people and institutions I'd been taught all my life to respect.

Verifiably Safe and Effective…

On December 8, 2020, President Trump once again stood before a microphone, this time in the Eisenhower Executive Office Building, to announce that Operation Warp Speed had been a success. We were only six days away from administering the first "official" "vaccine" doses. President Trump had this to say at the December 8 meeting in response to those skeptics I cited above: "Before Operation Warp Speed, the typical timeframe for development and approval, as you know, could be infinite. And we were very, very happy that we were able to get things done at a level that nobody has ever seen before. The gold standard 'vaccine' has been done in less than nine months."

He also added this: "American companies were the first to produce a verifiably safe and effective "vaccine." Together, we will defeat the virus, and we will soon end the pandemic, and we will save millions and millions of lives, both in our country and all over the world. And we've already started."

As to the second statement, unfortunately, President Trump couldn't have been more wrong.

Since the rollout of these very nonconventional "vaccines," we have learned a great deal, and none of it has been good. The initial "vaccines" showed general ineffectiveness, as did their subsequent boosters (as I write, a study published in *JAMA* in May 2022 indicates that Pfizer's "vaccine" protection against Omicron fades just weeks after a second and third dose). Moreover, the higher viral load created by the "vaccines" seems to enable rather than inhibit the disease, generally speaking.

Finally, adverse reactions to the "vaccine" (including death, the ultimate adverse reaction) have been widespread throughout the world, and clear attempts have been made by government leaders, public health officials, and the mainstream media to hide that reality from the general public.

Before we take a look at the COVID-19 "vaccine" and how it was to be used as part of the worst crime committed against humanity in history, I want to share what should have been more than just a canary in a coal mine for me at the time of the "vaccine's" release. It should have been an entire room filled with dead birds on the floor.

I mentioned Dr. Mercola's four-pillar approach to pandemic response, one pillar of which is pre-hospital treatment. In the time that lapsed between the President's announcements on May fifteenth and December eighth, I had been treating patients successfully without mortality. I had seen evidence of other doctors around the country adopting my protocol and having the same kind of success. As mentioned in a previous chapter, early intervention worked, even on the highest-risk patients.

The moment the "vaccine" was announced, essentially all talk about treatment ended. It wasn't just about the success of my protocol and the success other doctors were experiencing with its use; it was as if all talk of treatment had disappeared. The President did mention on December eighth the success of monoclonal antibodies treatment and how it was going to be made readily available and for free to anyone who was sick (a promise that never was fulfilled), but that was essentially the alpha and the omega of treatment discussion.

Prior to the launch of Operation Warp Speed, I had been in regular communication with the White House. Once the announcement was made, suddenly and without explanation, my "calls" were no longer being returned. The insight I was given into the White House at the time was that there was a decision made to move away from HCQ and pre-hospital intervention and concentrate on Warp Speed because since it was an election year, the belief was that a successful vaccination program would ensure Trump's victory. Then, after his reelection, they would circle back and address the issue of pre-hospital treatment.

At the time, I thought I understood political calculations and expediency, but these words registered as bizarre to me. I had developed a treatment that not only was I seeing working with my own patients, but I had been having success in encouraging other doctors to use my protocol. America's Frontline Doctors had formed and were successfully treating patients over the internet. Individual doctors like Stella Immanuel, George Fareed, Bryan

Tyson, Rosy Joseph, and Peter McCullough were all reporting positive results. Off our shores, in places like Brazil and Honduras, treatment using the Zelenko Protocol was working

The pivot away from treatment puzzled me because I was still putting the bigger puzzle together at the time. I did not yet realize that these vaccinations were intended to serve a much greater purpose than just ending a global pandemic. Nor did I know that ending a global pandemic wasn't even one of the "vaccine's" purposes!

While I wasn't distrusting of the "vaccine" when it was first introduced, because of the time that had elapsed from May to December, I personally had evolved from someone ready to volunteer for an experimental dose to someone who no longer felt the need to even be vaccinated. After all, I had seen the success of early treatment, even for high-risk patients like myself. When my patients asked about it, I told them it was a personal choice for them to make. I attached no bias to that recommendation. I saw the disease as one that was readily treatable, so a "vaccine" decision to me was a point of indifference. That was then; this is now. I'm no longer indifferent. Allow me to make the case against taking these manmade kill shots. Let's start by trying to understand what these shots are and what they are not.

What Exactly is this Thing You're Injecting?

"Excuse me, Doctor. What exactly is this thing you're injecting?"

What we would call traditional "vaccines," the ones associated with the childhood shots we all received while we were growing up, all share one thing in common: Inject into the person an element of the pathogen from which we are trying to protect you.

Let's say we're talking about polio. There are two types of vaccines against that once almost always fatal or crippling disease: An inactivated (antigen) version and a live (attenuated version). The inactivated antigen form, which is the one that is now most frequently used, is a fragment of a dead virus. In simple terms, our immune system then recognizes it as a foreign threat and generates an immune response or an attack that creates antibodies. That fragment presents virtually no risk to the recipient getting polio because it was only a dead fragment of the polio virus.

The live vaccines are attenuated or neutered in such a way that even though a person is being given a live version of polio, it's been modified in a way that its introduction should not cause an outbreak of the disease but will instead engender a powerful immune response. With a live vaccine, I'm not just giving you a fragment; I'm giving you the whole thing. This generates even more powerful antibodies and will inactivate any real polio with which you come in contact. The potential problem with attenuated vaccines is that they might cause you to get the disease.

With both types of traditional vaccinations, we are talking about using some version of the actual virus and hopefully giving the body enough to trigger immunity. In simplistic terms, if you have just gotten over a cold and then been exposed to someone with a cold, you'll notice you don't typically come back down with one. You have enough active antibodies left from the actual virus to then fight off the virus. We call this natural immunity, a term that many medical professionals and politicians have attempted to discredit during the pandemic.

To recap from the previous chapter: Viruses cannot reproduce independently as a general rule. They need to get into the cell and then use the cell's infrastructure to make copies of genetic material, construct the protein capsule components of the virus, assemble it, and then have it leave the cell, usually by destroying the cell and then releasing millions of copies of the new virus, which then infect adjacent cells or to get into the bloodstream. This allows the virus to travel to faraway cells. Traditional vaccines stop that process.

Now let's take a look at the mRNA (Pfizer and Moderna) and DNA (Johnson & Johnson and AstraZeneca) "vaccines" that were developed during Operation Warp Speed.

The first difference between the new "vaccines" and the traditional ones is the nature of the disease they were designed to address. Prior diseases:

Polio, rubella, diphtheria, and so on, were all naturally occurring. The Chinese coronavirus, however, is a product of man, not nature. It is like the viral version of the straw man argument. You artificially create a problem for the purpose of being able to show you can address the problem.

This virus was made in a lab, let loose on the public, created mass hysteria, had proven effective treatment denied to millions (treatment that could have eliminated the threat in a month), and was further used to lock people down and turn them against one another. We created a *Lord Of The Flies* kind of environment. Then, into this artificially made public health emergency and attendant mass psychosis, we introduced a "vaccine" for which they had absolutely no need. That has always been the endgame of this entire farce.

With that in mind, it is no wonder we are in previously uncharted "vaccine" territory.

The word mRNA stands for "messenger ribonucleic acid." If that sounds a bit like deoxyribonucleic acid (DNA), it should. DNA is the unique, organic chemical that contains genetic information and instructions for protein synthesis. It is found in most cells of every organism. DNA is a key part of reproduction in which genetic heredity occurs through the passing down of DNA from parents to offspring. Today, most people have a conversational understanding of DNA owing to a combination of forensic-based crime shows and home swab test kits like that of 23andMe that let you find out where your ancestors are from and why you might have come to have blond hair and blue eyes. RNA is essentially a fragment of that unique genetic code, and mRNA is something that carries a message to our cell, teaching it how to make a code.

To approach this sort of top-down strategy, DNA is the genetic material that encodes for characteristics that define that organism. In most cases, that genetic material is encapsulated in another pocket of an individual cell that is isolated from the rest of the cell with a kind of membrane. That is the cell's nucleus. In that nucleus, among other things, are the forty-six chromosomes of a human being which are made up of DNA. To further subdivide, in each chromosome are a person's unique genes, fragments of DNA, or sections of code of DNA. Those are the ones that are responsible for generating unique traits or proteins that lead to those traits.

So, DNA makes genes, which are just fragments of DNA or sections of code. The genes are in chromosomes, and the chromosomes are in the nucleus. Inside that nucleus are enzymes that transcribe the code and send it out into the main body of the cell in fragments, something the DNA itself could not have done, and it's carrying a message. And hence that's why it's called messenger RNA. Once it arrives, the message then has to be translated.

These two processes of transcription and translations are terms of art that are beyond the scope of what I'm trying to convey. What you need to understand is that mRNA "vaccines" are partial versions of DNA fragments meant to leave the cell's nucleus, carry a message, and not reenter.

The idea behind mRNA "vaccines" is that they would teach our cells how to make "spike proteins," which is what you would see on the surface of a coronavirus. Once you manufacture a spike protein, and the manufacturing is happening on almost every cell, the body then notices that it has a foreign presence, which generates an immune response against that protein.

In straightforward terms, here is the difference between a "traditional" vaccine and the mRNA forms. In traditional vaccines, we inject a protein (a portion of the disease itself) into your body to initiate an immune response. With mRNA, we don't inject the protein; we inject a code to make the protein, and then it is designed to trigger the immune response.

Regarding these mRNA "vaccines," the lie was that the principal mRNA could not go back into the nucleus as a rule. mRNA travels on a one-way street; once it leaves the nucleus, it doesn't have permission to reenter. Forget these "vaccines," that's a basic Biology 101 principle.

In the case of these "vaccines" for COVID-19, that's not what we're seeing. We're seeing that something happens to the mRNA injection that allows its influence to enter the nucleus and modify the genetic code. That means that there has to be some type of modification that allows the entry of mRNA back into the nucleus, and then it's reverse transcribing back into DNA. It's not yet clear how that works, but the fact that it does happen has been proven.

Changing Your Very Essence

This means that when you take these mRNA "vaccines," you are altering your very human essence.

A myth that was spread when the "vaccines" were first developed was that, unlike these mRNA shots, the Johnson & Johnson shots, and to a lesser extent AstraZeneca, were closer to traditional vaccines in terms of how they operate. In truth, it is exactly the opposite! Those two "vaccines" inject actual DNA that gets into the nucleus of the cell. Then that DNA is read and transcribed into RNA. The mRNA leaves the nucleus, goes into the cell and is translated as described in the mRNA "vaccine" above.

By way of analogy, these two "vaccine" types are like having unwelcome guests enter your home. Pfizer and Moderna have barged into your living room, while Johnson & Johnson and AstraZeneca have made themselves comfortable in your bed! This is why, pretty quietly, the J&J and AZ "vaccines" have fallen by the wayside because it's become undeniable that DNA "vaccines" are associated with greater and more dangerous side effects, simply because you are going deeper into the essence of the person and messing with processes that are much more fundamental and long-lasting.

There have been lots of speculation and conspiracy theories regarding these "vaccines" and what is actually in them, and their exact intended purpose. People are hearing and believing all sorts of things. The tragedy is that people shouldn't have to "believe" anything. If you look at the J&J and AZ package inserts, you will find that they are completely empty. The reason why there's this conspiratorial cloud around this issue is that the companies themselves are not divulging what's in these "vaccines." Fear is being created because the government is mandating that we inject ourselves with something about which we have no information. How could anyone make an informed decision or give informed consent? It's something where you don't understand the risks, and you don't understand the benefits. You hope that your medical professional is telling you to do the right thing.

So that in itself is a crime. What we do know through third-party research is that these "vaccines" have mRNA technology that converts every single cell in your body into a factory that produces spike proteins. We're talking about tens, if not hundreds of trillions of spike proteins. The entire body is inundated and absorbing these spike proteins that have been proven dangerous, especially when they get lodged in the inner lining of your blood vessels creating turbulent blood flow.

That disruption of blood flow can contribute to the formation of blood clots, one of the many side effects of these dehumanizing, gene-altering "vaccines." There are other side effects. It's time to look at what they are. They are key pieces of evidence in making the case against the "vaccine."

Making the Case

Why are people dying?

On October 22, 2020, the Center for Biologics Evaluation and Research (CBER) issued its report on the upcoming Chinese coronavirus vaccination program. The CBER is the center within the FDA that regulates biological products for human use under applicable federal laws, including the Public Health Service Act and the Federal Food, Drug and Cosmetic Act. It is charged to protect and advance public health by ensuring that biological products are safe, effective, and available to those needing them. The report was titled: *"Vaccines" and Related Biological Products Advisory Committee October 22, 2020 Meeting Presentation.*

The report addressed each aspect of the "vaccine" rollout, including pre-rollout studies and post-rollout monitoring (including adverse reaction reporting). With regard to the latter, the report said this on Slide 10:

COVID-19 "Vaccine" Monitoring Data Considerations

- Rapid data access for near real time surveillance
- Large databases of tens of millions of patients for evaluating "vaccine" *rare serious adverse events*
- Data representing integrated care spectrum – outpatient, physician, inpatient, etc.
- High quality data to assess and confirm potential adverse events or safety concerns for COVID-19 "vaccines"
- Data with significant clinical detail or medical chart access.

I italicized "rare serious adverse events" because of the use of the term "rare" prior to their knowing the number of adverse events. It appears they were determined to have them be rare, meaning they might have to be willing to mess with the data once the "vaccines" were launched to get a "rare" result.

However, regarding those adverse reactions, they were well aware of what was coming. This is from Slide 17 of the CBER report. Remember, this was two months before the launch:

FDA Safety Surveillance of COVID-19 "vaccines": DRAFT Working list of possible adverse event outcomes ***Subject to change***

- ♣ Guillain-Barré syndrome
- ♣ Acute disseminated encephalomyelitis
- ♣ Transverse myelitis
- ♣Encephalitis/myelitis/encephalomyelitis/meningoencephalitis/ meningitis/ encephalopathy
- ♣ Convulsions/seizures
- ♣ Stroke
- ♣ Narcolepsy and cataplexy
- ♣ Anaphylaxis
- ♣ Acute myocardial infarction
- ♣ Myocarditis/pericarditis
- ♣ Autoimmune disease
- ♣ Deaths

♣ Pregnancy and birth outcomes

♣ Other acute demyelinating diseases

♣ Non-anaphylactic allergic reactions

♣ Thrombocytopenia

♣ Disseminated intravascular coagulation

♣ Venous thromboembolism

♣ Arthritis and arthralgia/joint pain

♣ Kawasaki disease

♣ Multisystem Inflammatory Syndrome in Children

♣ "Vaccine" enhanced disease

This section of the report, read nearly two years later, would be modified today to read "Known adverse event outcomes." This is a list of things that real doctors like me have been seeing in actual "vaccine" recipients right from the initial doses of this poisonous substance being introduced into the general population and thereafter.

There were experts at the time of rollout who were already voicing concerns about antibody-dependent enhancement and about exerting evolutionary pressure by vaccinating people during an active pandemic that would cause the virus to make more dangerous variants. That was a theme I heard in abundance from doctors Roland Derwand and Martin Scholz in Germany, Dr. Luc Montagnier from France (Montagnier had won the Nobel Prize in medicine for discovering the Human Immunodeficiency Virus [HIV] in 2008), and Dr. Geert Vanden Bossche, the world's most respected vaccine expert. When people of that caliber started raising concerns and messaging, I began to pay increasingly more attention to what was taking place.

I stated that when the "vaccine" rolled out, I was initially indifferent about recommending it to patients. That changed after two or three months when I was reading the warnings of these kinds of experts and as I started to witness adverse reactions in my patients and hearing their stories of relatives who were also experiencing reactions. In my own patients, the first things I saw were increases in strokes, myocarditis, and sudden unexplained deaths. I also observed that vaccinated people were still getting the virus, which didn't make sense.

The increased incidence of strokes came to make sense to me owing to research published in April 2021 by the Salk Institute. That research indicated that spike proteins cause injury to the endothelium, a thin membrane that lines the inside of the heart and blood vessels. Endothelial cells release substances that control vascular relaxation and contraction, as well as enzymes that regulate blood clotting, immune function, and platelet (a colorless substance in the blood) adhesion. At the same time, that research indicated that mRNA "vaccines" had "safely encoded" spike proteins. What if spike proteins were like life on Jurassic Park—what if they could just "find a way?"

Think about your blood vessels that carry oxygen, nutrients, and other things you need to live to every part of the body. That continuous flow of blood is usually laminar, which means not turbulent. Your vessels are supposed to have a smooth lining which allows for a smooth flow, which would make sense. You don't want to shake up your delicate blood cells. You want them to be able to travel in a nice, smooth laminar way to their ultimate target and not get damaged on the journey. However, within the blood vessel, there is an inner aspect that is in direct contact with blood cells called the endothelial. It is supposed to be smooth and delicate.

As blood flows through the arteries and veins, it is typically a very nontraumatic interaction. The problem with the mRNA "vaccines" is the creation of all of these spike proteins that coat the endothelial, leading to changes in the inner lining of this beautiful, delicate, smooth tissue that converts it to something like a rosebush filled with thorns. Now, as the delicate blood cells flow through it, they come into contact with these thorns and get damaged; when they get damaged, they leak their contents. The immune system then recognizes those contents as not being appropriate. An immune response is triggered that shouldn't be one which leads to blood clots.

If these clots happen in the heart, you get a heart attack. If they occur in the brain, you have a stroke. These "vaccine" "injuries" are typically debilitating or fatal.

Blood clotting is only one of many complications from mRNA "vaccines." All of the complications foretold in that October of 2020 CBER report have come to pass. The research in support of "vaccine" injuries (such a pleasant euphemism) is voluminous (app x-1). Some studies show evidence of myocarditis in children and healthy men under forty, miscarriages in pregnant women, and hepatitis. Virtually all of the maladies predicted in that 2020 report have come to pass.

And Then There are the Deaths

Forget for a moment (or don't) how the deaths indirectly related to the Chinese coronavirus are directly related to the draconian measures taken by the genocidal political leaders worldwide. These include suicides, drug overdoses, domestic violence that went one punch too far, and neglected medical care for non-pandemic conditions like cancer, where delayed treatment resulted in untimely and unnecessary death. These deaths were collateral damage to the pandemic, although I'm sure they were factored into the plan by WEF-types orchestrating the chaos.

In January 2022, while speaking at a virtual news conference held for the Indiana Chamber of Commerce, Scott Davidson, the CEO of OneAmerica Insurance, told the group that reported deaths in the 18-64 age range were up forty percent in Q3 of 2021 over pre-pandemic levels and that the trend was continuing in Q4. Davidson told the group, in part: "We are seeing, right now, the highest death rates we have seen in the history of this business – not just at OneAmerica…. The data is consistent across every player in that business. Just to give you an idea of how bad that is, a three-sigma or a one-in-200-year catastrophe would be a 10% increase over pre-pandemic. So, 40% is just unheard of…

The mainstream media ignored this, which makes sense because they were complicit in it. Since the "vaccine" rollout that was intended to end the pandemic, and as life, at least on the surface, appears to be returning to something resembling normal, people are dying at an alarming rate. Part of this is directly related to the "vaccine" that we have voluntarily taken or been forced to take to maintain our livelihood and save lives.

In October 2021, a study was released titled *COVID vaccination and age-stratified all-cause mortality risk*[13]. It was authored by Spiro Pantazatos at Columbia University. Here is a portion of his abstract without material omissions:

Accurate estimates of COVID "vaccine"-induced severe adverse event and death rates are critical for risk-benefit ratio analyses of vaccination and boosters against SARS-CoV-2 coronavirus in different age groups. However, existing surveillance studies are not designed to reliably estimate life-threatening event or "vaccine"-induced fatality rates (VFR). Here, regional variation in vaccination rates was used to predict all-cause mortality and non-COVID deaths in subsequent time periods using two independent, publicly available datasets from the US and Europe (month- and week-level resolutions, respectively).

Vaccination correlated negatively with mortality 6-20 weeks post-injection, while vaccination predicted all-cause mortality 0-5 weeks post-injection in almost all age groups and with an age-related temporal pattern consistent with the US "vaccine" rollout…Comparing our estimate with the CDC-reported VFR (0.002%) suggests VAERS deaths are underreported by a factor of 20, consistent with known VAERS under-ascertainment bias. Comparing our age-stratified VFRs with published age-stratified coronavirus infection fatality rates (IFR) suggests the risks of COVID "vaccines" and boosters outweigh the benefits in children, young adults and older adults with low occupational risk or previous coronavirus exposure.

---

13 | https://www.researchgate.net/publication/355581860_COVID_vaccination_and_age-stratified_all-cause_mortality_risk

To put this in layman's terms: The "vaccine" seems to be killing people, and the reported data isn't reflecting it. Bureaucratic error? Conspiracy? Evil? It will likely take G-d to sort all this out, but I suspect a visual representation of responsibility would NOT be an equilateral triangle.

We also have come to learn, based on the work of Dr. Robert Malone, about the delivery technology in the mRNA "vaccine." It is covered by a lipid nanoparticle layer, reported as being "the most clinically advanced non-viral gene delivery system." It allows lipid nanoparticles to deliver nucleic acids, a technological breakthrough that overcame a major barrier preventing the development and use of genetic medicines. Unfortunately, it also allows its "passenger" to cross the blood-brain barrier and penetrate the central nervous system. That's why we're seeing such an exorbitant number of neurologic diseases emerge because it literally crosses into the brain.

In 1987, Robert Malone performed an experiment in which he mixed strands of mRNA with fat droplets and observed that proteins began being produced. A graduate student at the aforementioned Salk Institute, he saw the far-reaching potential of this discovery in medicine. Malone wrote in his notes that if cells could create proteins from mRNA delivered into them, it might be possible to "treat RNA as a drug." Later that year, Malone's experiments showed that frog embryos absorbed such mRNA. It was the first time anyone had used fatty droplets to ease mRNA's passage into a living organism.

If you didn't connect the dots, Malone's experiments eventually led to the mRNA "vaccines."

In Robert Malone, there is a man with whom I've shared a stage. He is brilliant. His academic pedigree includes both Northwestern and Harvard schools of medicine. He gets some mixed reactions because his outspokenness against the "vaccines" now strikes some as hypocritical. I don't see it that way. At the time his research was being performed, I do not believe it was being done with malicious intent, but it has been used for malicious purposes, something he acknowledges. Had he known what was to come, I do not believe he would have participated.

Once the pure evil of this mRNA "vaccine" became known, I believe he's the only one that pivoted and changed his opinion and, in a true sense, condemned his own work by discouraging the use of the technology he helped develop. His murderous colleagues have since rejected him, and he should consider that a badge of honor.

In 1939, Albert Einstein wrote a letter to President Roosevelt warning him that the Germans might be pursuing an atomic weapon and that the United States should start researching the possibility of developing its own. Years later, after the war, he regretted that letter. In an interview with Newsweek, Einstein lamented, "Had I known that the Germans would not succeed in developing an atomic bomb, I would have done nothing."

I suspect that Robert Malone feels much the same way as Einstein.

Returning to deaths from the "vaccine." and using the World War Two reference as a segue, thanks to courageous whistleblowers and the work of Lt. Colonel Theresa Long, along with the efforts of Senator Ron Johnson, we have learned some terrifying things about the safety of our Servicemen and Servicewomen who have been forced to take this lethal shot. In November 2021 and again in January 2022, Senator Johnson held roundtable discussions in an attempt to get to the bottom of what seemed to be happening to our military members who had taken the mRNA "vaccine."

In addition to talking to Lt. Colonel Long and others, data compiled by the Defense Military Epidemiological Database (DMED) was reviewed. DMED is considered to have one of the most sophisticated epidemiological databases in the world, with an entire division of the military dedicated to monitoring it and hundreds of millions of dollars spent on building and maintaining it.

Consider the simply breathtaking numbers from DMED shown in the table below:

Diagnosis	Avg Injuries per year, 2016-2020	Injuries in (partial) 2021	Percent Increase in 2021
ALL Diseases and Injuries	2,045,555	21,512,583	1052%
ALL Cancers	38,678	114,645	296%
Diseases of the Nervous System	82,322	863,013	1048%
Testicular Cancer	960	3,537	369%
Diseases of the Blood & Blood-forming Organs & Certain Disorders Involving the Immune Mechanism	11,341	34,486	304%
Hypertension	2,360	53,846	2281%
Female Infertility	2,273	11,748	517%
Male Infertility	2,130	8,365	393%
Ovarian Dysfunction	934	4086	437%
Adverse Effect of Other Viral Vaccine, Initial Encounter	182	1,281	701%

The absolute magnitude of the increase, not just relative, is very difficult to rationalize as being related to anything other than a "vaccine" adverse reaction. While correlation is not proof of causation, if I watch ten people in a row step in front of a speeding train and meet a messy demise, I can certainly infer, without further testing, that stepping in front of a high-speed train is bad. Those numbers from DMED are evidence of the harm caused to a human recipient of a fast-traveling mRNA spike protein "vaccine."

Our men and women in uniform are supposed to be protecting us from foreign enemies and threats. It is impossible for them to carry out that mission if they are under attack from enemies within; enemies within their own government and enemies within their own bodies.

The Complications Go On

There are two other complications with regard to the mRNA "vaccines" that are yet to be known because enough time has not elapsed. One of the complications involves something called antibody-dependent enhancement. The other relates to a weakening of T-cells, something we are familiar with because it leads to Acquired Immune Deficiency Syndrome, more commonly known as AIDS.

This all starts with yet another lie we were told: The mRNA "vaccine" stays localized at the injection site. A leaked Pfizer biodistribution study performed in Japan looked at the injection of the "vaccine" into one site and then assessed if the "vaccine" affects other organ systems. Now, if you suppose that the actual "vaccine" stays at the injection site and goes nowhere else, you wouldn't expect changes or evidence of the presence of these "vaccines" in other organs. What they noticed is that every single organ system had evidence of spike proteins. Obviously, it didn't stay in one place and instead traveled everywhere. Further, wherever it went, it converted that cell into a factory to make spike proteins. When they measured which organs were most affected - where there was their highest concentration of spike proteins - they found it to be in the ovaries.

Remember the problem with miscarriages?

While ovaries were most affected, these spike proteins were everywhere. Now, consider our G-d-given immune system, which is there to defend us from enemies, both foreign and domestic. That immune system has two arms. One is called humoral immunity, and the other is called innate immunity. Humoral immunity is associated with plasma cells or B lymphocytes that make antibodies. Antibodies result from the humoral immune system generating soldiers that stand guard and take the enemy out if they come into contact with it.

Now, in most cases, antibodies are constructive and play the role of good guys. However, there are instances where that's not the case. You can have an immune response and antibody response that are pathogenic or disastrous. For example, autoimmune diseases where your immune system attacks your body by way of these antibodies. Regarding "vaccines," there is a phenomenon noted called antibody-dependent enhancement. This is where the antibodies that are produced by the "vaccine" end up killing you. They don't do so right away, but when they come into contact with the pathogen they were meant to attack, you get attacked too.

Something similar was noted with the Dengue Fever "vaccine," where the triggered immune response actually killed people because the response was overwhelming. Again, in military terms, it is like trying to take out a small army of insurgents hiding in some trees, but you use napalm to burn down the entire forest. You kill the unit, but also everything else. It's an exaggerated immune response. All previous attempts at coronavirus "vaccines" in animals have resulted in this problem occurring.

The rhetorical question this generates is: Wouldn't it have made sense to exclude antibody-dependent enhancement using the current mRNA "vaccines" prior to deploying them and recommending their use to seven billion people? I believe that was not done deliberately because they knew exactly what it would do.

So, part of the damage of the "vaccines" for this coronavirus comes from it causing antibody-dependent enhancement, or the upregulation of the humoral immune system or an exaggerated antibody reaction, when coming into contact with the antigen or the pathogen that it's designed to take out. That's long-term problem number one.

The innate immune system is made up of T-cells; natural killer cells with different mechanisms of taking out a threat. Nothing needs to be produced; they are already there, waiting like assassins to eliminate pathogens. Now, the problem there is that if that innate immune system gets damaged, you develop immune deficiency. So, for example, a Human Immunodeficiency Virus affects the T-cells and destroys them. That then leads to the destruction of the innate immune system, which leads to something called Acquired Immune Deficiency Syndrome (AIDS), and people die. People don't die from HIV; they die from the destruction of the immune system caused by HIV.

It turns out that there is a slew of evidence behind this, that these "vaccines" destroy the innate immune system. What we are seeing is the actual inhibition of the natural killer T-cells. This has led to a new syndrome called "Vaccine" Acquired Immune Deficiency Syndrome. I prefer to use the word AIDS because it has more shock value. It gets people to think when I use the term AIDS, because they immediately think of HIV. That's because HIV does cause AIDS, but it's not the only thing that causes AIDS. If you inject someone with a liquid that damages their innate immune system and inhibits their natural killer T-cells, you have given them an immune deficiency syndrome. You've given them AIDS, just not HIV.

What these mRNA "vaccines" do is cause both a dysregulation of the immune system (turning the humoral system into a zombie apocalypse of antibodies attacking without discernment), and a downregulation of the system (attacking and weakening your body's own innate defenses). This means that people who have received this "vaccine" now are at risk from their immune system's over or under-reaction to any future threat.

What does this mean long term? We can't be sure. Neither can the experts who have told us to "trust the science."

Why?

In this chapter, I have tried to illustrate how these "vaccines" operate, how the risks they posed were known before their release, and how those risks have all materialized in "injuring" or killing recipients ever since the rollout in December 2020. The most troubling component is that there is evidence they should have seen regarding the outcomes. That leads you to wonder, were they evil or just ignorant?

I'm inclined to believe they are the former.

Why did they need to release a second bioweapon?

Arguing that these false G-ds created a lethal "vaccine" to fight a lethal disease that they already deliberately engineered could appear contradictory. If, as I firmly believe the evidence suggests, this particular coronavirus was engineered to be intentionally lethal, why then would you need a "vaccine" that is also lethal to control it? Why would you want to control it? After all, you made it.

The answer to that question poses a possibly far more sinister plan than one of just infecting the world with a manmade virus.

Let's start by saying that in the psychology of men, the word "vaccine" has traditionally been associated with goodness, life preservation, and general illness prevention. We start taking vaccines in childhood, and our parents and doctors assure us they are to protect us. Unfortunately, we now have to define vaccines with adjectives. There are vaccines that do exactly what I just said and help people prevent disease. Those are good vaccines. Then there are harmful "vaccines" and killer "vaccines." I am a strong advocate of vaccines that help people. Under any pretense or excuse of pandemic, I do not support "vaccines" that, by design, kill people.

My supposition is that the current "vaccines" that are being marketed as vaccines for COVID-19 and other variants of it are bad "vaccines." They kill people, and I believe they have been developed for nefarious purposes. I'm going to do a simple three-category breakdown analysis of these mRNA "vaccines" to try to make crystal clear why they should be avoided at all cost.

They are intended to reduce world population: I mince no words in saying that these "vaccines" have been developed by homicidal, genocidal maniacs. They are tools of eugenics, the kind about which Margaret Sanger and Oliver Wendall Holmes could not have even hoped to imagine. There are four separate categories of effect associated with the "vaccines" and their use as a population-reducing weapon:

1. Acute Death: By this, I mean death within approximately three months of receiving the "vaccine." The deaths are most typically associated with blood clots, induced strokes, and heart attacks. Myocarditis also gets an honorable mention.

2. Long-term health impact: This comes from the development of cancers, hepatitis, meningitis, autoimmune disease, AIDS, and the complications from antibody-dependent enhancement mentioned earlier. These complications can take years to manifest and play out but still lead to shorter life expectancy and population reduction.

3. Infertility: You will recall that spike protein migration is found particularly in the ovaries.

4. Miscarriages: See infertility. Also, according to the DOD whistleblowers, miscarriages are 300 percent in the first trimester.

So you have an acute reduction in lifespan-death, a long-term reduction of lifespan-infertility, and miscarriages, all of which serve the same function of reducing the world population.

They are a means to monitor and control us: There is patent evidence that indicates that technology has been developed that can be injected into human tissue and used to monitor the host. This is not some wild conspiracy theory. World Economic Forum guru Yuval Noah Harari, a truly evil man, is on record saying that this COVID-19 crisis is an inflection point and will be remembered as the moment in history where 24/7 surveillance was brought to the world and digitized under the skin.

There is plenty of patent evidence to corroborate what he said. This refers to nanoscale technology that allows for the measurement of biometrics and its transmission, with the location, to a third party. As the world migrates toward cryptocurrency in general, and perhaps to one universal, or near universal, form of cryptocurrency, having biometric data transmitted will allow those heading the "new world order," (which I say is truly the oldest world order of idolatry, paganism, and child sacrifice), to control your access to funds simply by flipping a switch.

You don't need to arrest, imprison, and execute people to make them slaves. You simply have to be able to starve them or feed them through the capricious act of swiping right or left on their "citizen profile."

Recently I learned of Dr. Naomi Wolf's perspective on this slavery through her newly released book *The Bodies of Others: The New Authoritarians, COVID-19 and The War Against the Human*. Dr. Wolf details her isolation from family and friends, even being unable to work in a library because of a disability that does not allow her to wear masks over her face. In a chapter called "Cruelty, Cults, Coercion," Dr. Wolf points out that verbal attacks against the "unvaccinated" have permeated our culture, encouraging division and further isolation of both the "vaccinated" and "unvaccinated."

"*Verbal attacks on the unvaccinated continued to escalate. Many went so far as to denying them medical care. I invited an old friend over. We had shared an office in D.C. when we were young idealistic activists. We'd share thai food with another college friend. And back in our shabby attic office space, Paul would make me fall off the furniture with laughter. When a partner left me two decades later, Paul would walk beside me through the streets of his quiet suburban neighborhood, listening patiently. He told me about his love life, and I told him about crushes and heartbreaks of my own. We were fast friends. He called me Wolfie. We always understsood each other. Now he was an important public official. 'I don't sit inside with unvaccinated people,' he said. He said it smugly, as if saying it were gratifying in some way. Hoping to forgive all craziness in general, and that of my friends and loved ones, I said I would sit outside with him. On the day we were to meet it rained. I called him. 'It's raining,' he said with finality, as if the meaning was self-evident. 'Seriously?' I asked. 'We can't go have lunch in a restaurant?' 'I don't sit inside with unvaccinated people,' he repeated. An ice cold mission statement. 'So our plans won't work.' In forty years of friendship, I had never been subjected to that streak of sheer unmediated meanness in his makeup. I had not even known it existed.'*

They Contain Gene Editing Technology

According to the words of Klaus Schwab, Bill Gates, Yuval Hariri, and the other perpetrators of these "vaccines," these "vaccines" contain gene editing technology, specifically mRNA-delivered CRISPR (DNA fragments used to edit the base pairs of a gene) technology that are associated with gene editing, which changes what it means to be a human being through the manipulation of genetic code.

That code, in my opinion, is the image of G-d imprinted upon Man. Man, acting in his self-appointed role as a G-d, has now been able to decode G-d's coding. We now know what we are doing when manipulating human genome sequencing and tinkering with genes in chromosomes to potentially produce specific traits; the color of eyes, for example. We have developed a sort of cut-and-paste capability with regard to genetic coding. You can highlight an area of genetic "text."

Just like in Bill Gates' Microsoft Word, we can select a genetic sequence and delete, insert, or alter the text. That is precisely what CRISPR does. It gives false G-ds the ability to cut and paste G-d's given genetic sequence at their will. They can choose to take out what they want and put in what they want. Essentially, they are writing the genetic code. So in a kind of metaphysical framework, if you define the original genetic code, the Human 1.0 version, as being the G-d version and the one where we are actually made in the image of G-d, then the Human 2.0 version is the one derived from manipulation that makes us in the image of Klaus Schwab or Bill Gates or Yuval Noah Harari.

If and when they choose, these people are able to cut out vital gene information and put in anything they want. They can put in the DNA of a horse. They could cut out or disrupt tumor suppressor genes, which make proteins that prevent cancer. They could look for specific genes that research links to certain types of behavior, like the warrior gene, the explorer gene, or the name of your least-favorite-behavior gene, and start to try to edit selectively. If permitted, they will try to use genetic modification to create the kind of person that a false G-d would desire in Human 2.0. This is what I call transhumanism.

You might say, "Zev, I'm willing to live in a Human 2.0 world if it means that the threat from this coronavirus and all its mutations is forever vanquished because of the "good" elements of these mRNA "vaccines." To this, I would reply, "Unfortunately, that isn't a viable trade-off because not only is this a bad "vaccine," it also most definitely is not a good "vaccine.""

In a study conducted in Vietnam[14] and published in September 2021, sixty-two considered vaccinated healthcare workers were diagnosed with the

14 | Chau, N., Ngoc, N. M., Nguyet, L. A., Quang, V. M., Ny, N., Khoa, D. B., Phong, N. T., Toan, L. M., Hong, N., Tuyen, N., Phat, V. V., Nhu, L., Truc, N., That, B., Thao, H. P., Thao, T., Vuong, V. T., Tam, T., Tai, N. T., Bao, H. T., ... Tan, L. V. (2021). An observational study of breakthrough SARS-CoV-2 Delta variant infections among vaccinated healthcare workers in Vietnam. *EClinicalMedicine*, *41*, 101143. https://doi.org/10.1016/j.eclinm.2021.101143

Delta variant of the virus. The study published this brief paragraph as an interpretation of its findings:

Breakthrough Delta variant infections following Oxford-AstraZeneca vaccination may cause asymptomatic or mild disease, but are associated with high viral loads, prolonged PCR positivity and low levels of "vaccine"-induced neutralizing antibodies. Epidemiological and sequence data suggested ongoing transmission had occurred between fully vaccinated individuals.

Moving to Israel, a country with a very high vaccination rate among its population, people have been dying at such an alarming rate that morticians are unable to keep up the pace. This has been reported publicly and confirmed to me privately through anecdotal contacts. In a story published at the end of January 2022 in *The Yeshiva World*, it was reported in a headline that the Chevra Kadisha (the group of men in Israel who see to the proper ritualistic internment of Jewish deceased) were "...On Verge Of Collapse & Haven't Reached Peak Of Deaths."[15]

The article read, in part:

"It's extremely difficult to deal with the situation right now," Rav Avraham Mendla, the director of the Chevros Kadisha Forum and head of the Chevra Kadisha in Tel Aviv, told Yisrael Hayom. "We're almost completely out of manpower. We're recruiting more volunteers. We barely survived the previous wave with similar numbers but now we still aren't even close to the peak of fatalities. What will happen if there will be another 50% of the fatalities that we have today? I daven [pray] that we won't reach such a situation."

Why would it be that in a country with a very high percentage of its people vaccinated, those same people are dying at a record pace? Why do we have all of the unexplained deaths in the United States that nobody seems

---

15 | https://www.theyeshivaworld.com/news/headlines-breaking-stories/2055758/israels-chevrei-kadisha-were-on-verge-of-collapse-havent-reached-peak-of-deaths.html

to be talking about? It seems likely to me that these people have been more than "injured" by the "vaccine"; they have been mortally wounded by it.

My supposition here is that fifty percent of the Israeli public has AIDS; "vaccine" induced Acquired Immune Deficiency Syndrome. Their immune systems are so destroyed, and their killer cells and T-cells are so damaged that they are ineffective in managing common infections like a cold or Omicron. I'm not conspiratorial, but I can think critically, and I can deduce hypotheses and truths from actual facts.

Why, why, why? Why would the leaders of our nation allow this to happen? If I'm right about the objectives and consequences of the "vaccine" rollout I identified above, why would United States leaders be a party to such misadventures? Why would any Western leader become a party to it, for that matter?

Let's shave with Occam's Razor and search for the simplest explanation. This all comes back to the World Economic Forum and the evil people who run and participate therein. They are intent on seeing a new world order that has the United States no longer being a superpower and where a handful of very enlightened men and women make decisions for all of us that serve their notion of the greater good. In their minds, the greater good means them casting themselves in the role of G-d and choosing the winners and losers on behalf of what they see as a pathetic, overpopulated, and unworthy remainder of the human race. The "vaccine" process is a tool for them to use, and the death of millions is but a means to an end.

In the broadest of summaries, what these bad "vaccines" don't do is prevent disease. What they actually do is facilitate or expedite death, enslave the global community, and alter the code that graces us for being made in the image of G-d.

I hope that is clear enough.

Some Final Thoughts

People ask me, "Zev, I already had the 'vaccine.' I regret it. What should I do?" The first thing I would share as a physician is that I do not recommend you get a booster. In terms of reassurance, we know from hacked records that there was no uniformity amongst the various "vaccine" lots that were produced, meaning each lot had a different composition of ingredients compared to other labs. The obvious concern here is that one of the jobs of the FDA is to ensure that someone in one part of the world or country is getting the same exact substance as anyone else would get. Someone in New York should get the same thing as their cousin in California. That hasn't been the case.

Some lots experience significant discrepancies in ingredients and end up being fifty times, or 5,000 percent, more lethal than others. We can conjecture as to why that happened, but it might explain one of the reasons we're seeing a whole spectrum of different kinds of phenomena or results amongst people who have taken the shots. Some people have no effects, while some people have catastrophic consequences. In part, that might be because everyone's getting something different. I believe that was done to confuse the public intentionally. But the good part of that, in a sense, is if you're not yet experiencing any known side effects, you might have gotten the milder, less toxic version. There are still a lot of unknowns, but the main point is don't take it again.

People also ask me what to do about their children.

In my opinion, any parent that chooses to vaccinate their child with these COVID-19 "vaccines" at this point is committing not just child abuse but child sacrifice. I say that because when we do something medically, there has to be a reason in support of the action. Let's say you come to my office with a cold, and I tell you I'm going to amputate your hand. You may well raise the question, "Where is the medical necessity to amputate my hand when all I have is a runny nose?" A "vaccine" supporting physician-type would give an answer: "Because I know how to amputate a hand."

If, according to the CDC, the coronavirus has a 99.998 percent recovery rate without treatment in children under eighteen, meaning it's significantly safer than the influenza virus, where is the medical necessity to inject them with anything? The question is rhetorical. There is no need. There is only want, want on the part of a medical community well-trained in amputating hands.

People then ask, "But doctor, it's the fact that while my children might not die, might they not bring it home to grandma if they are not vaccinated?" In normal societies, ones that are typically G-d-centered, the adults will sacrifice for their children to survive and thrive. In G-dless or pagan societies, like the one envisioned by the WEF, children are sacrificed for the benefit of the adults. My answer to the "what about grandma" question is if you are such a believer in the "vaccine," then immunize grandma and leave your children alone. And as noted in the Vietnam study mentioned earlier, the vaccinated can carry a higher viral load, so even the "save grandma" argument doesn't really hold.

This couldn't be simpler. The case against these "vaccines" is really the case for the sanctity of our life given to us by G-d. The two are mutually exclusive.

Epilogue

Reflections on Today and How to Reach a Better Tomorrow

May 22, 2022

Our final interview for the book took place in late May. At this moment, Zev had just over a month left to live. These were both retrospective and forward-looking thoughts shared at the end of the book-writing process. They are presented here with minimal edits or annotations.

The moment we are in today is very "high voltage," and how we got to this point has been a journey that I have experienced both privately and publicly. I'll start with my own personal world by recapping what I have been through. Today, I am still fighting cancer, and I'm running out of natural paths to find a cure. There are still some available, but most of the approaches, the routes I've taken, have not, up to this point, led to a cure. They have prolonged my life, for sure. The fact that I am here more than four years after having been diagnosed with a terminal disease is beyond defying the odds. When I say terminal, I mean one hundred percent of people diagnosed with this disease are already dead. It's pretty terminal. It's diagnosed in an autopsy in most cases.

In my case, my cancer was initially thought to be a blood clot. I had an open-heart procedure to remove the clot, and it ended up being a tumor instead. This brought me into a sort of medically uncharted territory type. After heroic surgery that included removing my right lung and reconstruction of my pulmonary artery, I was spared, at least temporarily. Following that, with my own kind of G-d-given inspiration, I could come up with a chemotherapy approach that gave me two years of disease-free living.

When COVID-19 was first known, I was still kind of in remission, if you can call it that; disease-free to the best of my knowledge. When in the summer of 2020, I was diagnosed again with recurrence, it was in the midst of the crisis and my developing and perfecting my protocol. I remember I didn't sleep; I was working 21 hours a day, six days a week, for four straight months. This habit, I believe, saved me. With the recurrence of cancer came another open-heart surgery with a heart valve replacement. I needed radiation for my hip where the cancer had spread, and then I went on a difficult chemo regimen that, this time around, almost killed me. I went into congestive heart failure and developed cardiomyopathy, leaving my heart functioning as if it had a massive heart attack. I ended up in the hospital.

Eventually I stabilized and started a new chemo protocol, but that suppressed my immune system and led to me contracting COVID-19 and its attendant pneumonia in my remaining lung. I had been taking my protocol as a prophylactic, and I treated myself at home aggressively, but I still ended up in the hospital. I was pretty convinced I was going to die, but with steroids and good care, I survived.

I couldn't take any more chemo and decided to adopt a "wait and see" approach. Then, in the second half of 2021, I underwent another routine screening and showed yet another recurrence of the disease, this time in my pulmonary artery, in a place where it was too dangerous to operate. Doctors told me there was a more than 50 percent chance I would die during the operation. Surgery wasn't an option at all, and chemo just wasn't an option for me. I chose radiation into the pulmonary artery, and after completing it, I went to Europe for two months for immunotherapy.

When I came back, I felt okay and did another image, and interestingly enough, the tumor in my chest was stable, but it had spread to my hip and my L-3 vertebrae. That brings me to where I am today. I'm in quite a bit of pain with numerous procedures, either needed, wanted, or both. I'm trying to understand what my objective is at this point. Is it still to find a cure, or is it palliative care, controlling pain, decreasing symptoms, prolonging life, or improving quality of life? Whatever it is, it isn't really about trying to "cure" anymore.

Regardless, I'm optimistic. I'm hopeful that there's still hope. But one thing I find is that there is a constant state wherein G-d keeps me at the precipice between life and death. He doesn't give me a reprieve, and I have no complaints about that. While I'm not complaining, I am aware that it has brought me to a certain level of consciousness that I believe everyone should be able to reach because it reflects reality. That reality is that no one knows when their last day will come, that we all live by the grace of G-d and that we all are on that precipice between life and death all the time.

Because it's psychologically disconcerting and uncomfortable living in that place, most people tend to suppress it and try not to think about it unless they are forced to think about it. But I've been at that address between life and death now for almost four years. There's a lesson there. G-d is teaching me something, and it's becoming clear, but I can't be sure of what it all is. But one thing is for sure; He is teaching me to appreciate every moment, every instant of time. He wants me to treat each day as if it's potentially my last. He wants me to be grateful for consciousness, free choice, and the ability to just be. He has sensitized me to the sanctity of life. All of these things have been central and relevant to my life mission in the last few years.

I have been called upon to be the focal point, the tip of the spear, the epicenter, choose whatever term you like, in the fight against tyranny; in the fight against forces that are trying to destroy life, enslave humanity, and alter what it means to be human. In *Metamorphosis*, my first autobiography, which I wrote in 2018, well before the pandemic, I had a bit of a premonition when I wrote on the last page, "Just the beginning. Not the end." At that time, I felt there was more; there was just something more to come. I wasn't sure, but I was certain there was something. I don't know if I feel that same degree of certainty where I find myself now with regard to there being more for me to do. I may be coming to the end of G-d's calling.

But I am at peace with that because, in a very real sense, I don't actually exist. A concept from my faith says, "There is nothing but G-d." If you take all of creation and subtract from it all that was, is, and what will be, what is your remainder? It is G-d. Everything, the entire expanse of creation, Metaverse, or however you conceptualize the physical and spiritual realms, time, space, and everything that ever was, is, and will be in relation to the essence of the Creator, is absolutely zero. That's what it means to say there's nothing but G-d. "I am G-d, I have not changed."

That concept is super-rational, but it's not logical. It's impossible to use logic to try to figure out the source of reason. It's as if, by way of example, you create an imaginary man in your head and think that the man you've just conjured up in your imagination will figure out your essence. This is where faith steps into its own vehicle, pulls away from reason, and waves goodbye through the rear window, saddened in knowing that reason simply cannot come along for the rest of the journey.

Now, I feel that I'm being brought to a particular place. I have a visceral understanding that I'm entirely in G-d's hands at this point. I have surrendered, not in the sense of giving up, but surrendered in terms of realizing that I'm His and what He wills will be. I have not given up the exercise of using my free will and reason that He gave to me, but I realize that I have tried everything that I think I could, and to this point, it just hasn't been sufficient, at least to the extent of finding the cure for which I was looking and hoping. I'm still alive, and I do believe in miracles. Whether or not they'll happen to me is completely unknown and not in my control, but they are in G-d's control.

So, I surrender. Again, I'm not giving up. They are going to have to take my body off the battlefield. But when it comes to a point where there's nothing else for me to try, then I will just continue the fight for as long as I can. That is where I find myself medically, theologically, emotionally, and spiritually. Obviously, my love for my children and my concern for their development and well-being weighs on me. Likewise, my love and concern for my wife having to carry on possibly without me there to love her and protect her, the thought of that is a tremendous burden.

My parents are also both still very much alive. There is a certain natural pattern, let's say, in the cycle of life, where the children bury the parents, not the parents burying the children. Seeing the angst and, I don't even know the right adjective to describe the pain on my parents' faces is excruciating. I also have one brother who told me he would donate a lung if it would make a difference. While it wouldn't help in my case, just to have someone offer the lung… well, there are no words. It is so heavy and emotionally serious. It's real.

Then comes the process of pondering, knowing we all die. We begin to die from the day we're born. Most people assume it's going to be later in life. They get to retire and do all the things they always wanted to do into their seventies and eighties. But I'm forty-eight, and I am very aware that the future likely doesn't await me. That said, in some way, I'm very privileged. Why do I say that? Because many people die suddenly or unexpectedly. I have been given a kind of insight into when I may die, at least approximately. It could be six months, two years, or whatever if something miraculous doesn't happen. The reason that makes me fortunate is that it gives me time to prepare for the transition. I believe in G-d, and I believe that this is not the end of consciousness. Whatever that next stage of being is, it will be different than here, but at the same time, potentially could be a higher level of consciousness, closeness, and perception of truth.

From that perspective, it's intriguing for me. If I take away the emotional component and just think of it intellectually, it is quite interesting. I'm interested to find out what it's like in the next stage of being. Before that, however, I need to fix a few things. One thing that I believe very much regarding the next stage of being is that it's about the exposure of truth to oneself, truth that you can't hide through psychological defense mechanisms. You will see the truth of how you've chosen to live; the good and the bad. Whatever is the sum of your actions, your speech, and your thoughts, they will be exposed. G-d knows them already, but they'll be exposed to you in a way that you can't hide from them. That is a very uncomfortable feeling for me at this point, and it is where I am focused in my preparation.

I haven't lived the perfect life. It is interesting to me; people tell me that I've saved millions of lives and that they envy my reward in the world to come. I hear that, but I feel empty. I have very little recollection of what I've done or haven't done. I don't necessarily understand their certainty about my eternal salvation. I read the comments that people on social media send me, and it reminds me, "Oh, wow, I did something that really made it better. I benefited this person, or this community, or this country." Then it gets brought into my consciousness, but as a baseline, I don't remember it. I don't feel it. What I do feel is more inadequacy. It is not an inadequacy born of comparing myself to others or what they have done. It is me saying *I know I have not lived up to what Zev could have been.*

I struggle with that dynamic, and I struggle with the concept of repentance. I am getting some spiritual guidance in that area, and one of the ideas I've been drawn to is from the 12th Century Jewish philosopher Maimonides and his Laws of Repentance. He writes that one of the dimensions of repentance is when you say to G-d, "I have sinned," it's important not to qualify it with, "You know, because I had a bad day, or because someone irritated me, or because I wasn't feeling well, or because, because, because." There can be no qualification. It needs to be more like, "I have sinned. I knew better. I take full responsibility. I rebelled against your will. I have no mitigating factors. I did it volitionally and on purpose. I let my impulse for self-indulgence and evil inclination take hold of me. And with all that, I'm sorry. I have sinned. Please forgive me."

An interesting element in Judaism is that you are not allowed to make a blessing in vain. For example, if I'm going to eat something, an apple, I make a blessing, but then I don't eat the apple. That's a desecration of G-d's name. And another example of that is when we make a blessing and ask for forgiveness. If you don't believe in that completely, you're making a blessing in vain. If you are going to say it, you better believe it. That is why I struggle with the notion of repentance and seeking forgiveness for my sins from G-d. If I'm going to ask, I better really mean it, and I had best use that gift of His forgiveness. To stay with my example and turn it into a metaphor, unlike in Eden, I had better make sure I eat the apple!

Very soon, the nature of my existence is going to change. I'm going to be in the Heavenly Court, naked and exposed. I'm glad I have time to prepare for this one.

That's where I am as a human being. As I have mentioned elsewhere in this book, I have been living with the knowledge that I am already dead for the past few years. I understand that has been a non-literal use of the term "dead," even though I truly have tried to embrace that mentality. Now, as I get closer to the literal notion of death, I am at peace with G-d and getting closer to being at peace with myself.

The Fall of Freedom

As I take a look today at the pandemic that was, biomedically speaking, a product of China, I know that future strains of it, if properly managed, are easily treated and with minimal collateral damage. The problem is that the tyrannical forces behind the "vaccine," those that govern through misinformation, create false narratives, and have made all the carnage and fear used as a false justification for this gene-altering weapon of mass murder and enslavement, those folks are still in charge. If they weren't an outright Serpent, the Primordial Serpent, or the distilled product of pure evil, then there would not have been any crisis: No lockdowns, no need for "vaccines."

Unfortunately, that's not the case. Carl Jung said that people get the leadership they deserve. He says that the collective German consciousness, the German people gave birth to a force called Hitler who was, let's say, a byproduct of the nation's character at that point in time. I actually believe that. Our leaders have been using the citizenry as a means to an end, and we have allowed them, indeed aided them, in doing so.

What is happening now in society is exactly the same. Our desecration of life, marriage, gender, and the codification of the debauchery and immorality into the laws of our society, has created a vacuum and a G-dlessness. This G-dless vacuum is in the form of a Serpent, a hydra with many heads. Those heads are the well-known international suspects; The Rockefellers, the du Ponts, the Carnegies, the Orsini, the Vatican, the Rothschilds, the American Bush family, and the British Royal Family. They represent old money. They have been joined by the new field marshals like Klaus Schwab, Bill Gates, Mark Zuckerberg, Yuval Noah Harari, Barack Obama, Emmanuel Macron, Justin Trudeau, and so on. Finally, they bring along with them the ilk of degenerate foot soldiers like Anthony Fauci, Ralph Baric, and Letitia James.

Biden, who is likely just a puppet for Obama, once said in an interview that if he had a chance for a third term, he would essentially rather be in his basement in his pajamas and controlling someone in the White House who would basically be his puppet. I paraphrased, but an interview expresses that exact sentiment, and I believe that's what we have now. Now, I can't tell you for sure if it's Obama doing this, but what's the difference? We have a seriously demented leader of the Free World who needs to be in a diaper in a nursing home and not being elder abused. Regardless of the leader, they are all heads of the Serpent who have committed the highest treason against their citizens.

They are not looking out for the best interests of their own country. They have sold out their country and their people in lieu of some globalist tyrannical slave movement, and each one is vying to see who will have a higher position within the hierarchy of slave masters. We are witnessing (I hope I'm wrong, but I don't think I am) the fall of the greatest empire in the history of humanity and the greatest experiment in democracy. I am referring to the United States. We are simultaneously seeing the complete neutering of our military and our financial destruction. Our economy has been decimated and will essentially crater in a few years. This fall is due to the nearly unserviceable national debt, theft from the middle class by closing over a million small businesses, inflation completely devaluing the dollar, and then the collapse of Medicare as predicted in 2026, according to the Congressional Budget Office.

We are living through the fall of the only real force for goodness and potential freedom. The parasites and the demons are no longer knocking at the door of the United States; they are running the place.

That is my "facts on the ground" situation assessment of the way I see things going naturally. I believe that there is an opportunity for something else, and this is part of my remaining mission; to bring human consciousness to a state of awareness that is needed to reconcile humanity's heart en masse with their Creator and, in so doing, reject false G-ds. In basic terms, we need to not curse G-d, not blaspheme His name, not steal from each other, not murder each other, and not desecrate marriage through acts of immorality. We need to understand the importance of preserving the boundaries of America. We need our courts to re-establish the critical virtue of justice and show they are interested in the rule of law, not in ruling for show.

We then have a general overarching need to respect all of G-d's creation. We need to not torture animals, respect the world environment, and just generally be good caretakers of G-d's beautiful creation. We must shift from our current self-centered, egotistical existence. We spend too much time worshiping the G-ds of science, technology, money, power, politics, and lust. We must shift away from that and reconcile our hearts with our Creator. If we can do that, I believe we'll cross a certain threshold that I can't define but that I believe exists, and in crossing it, we will usher in a supernatural intervention. To be very specific, I mean the Messianic redemption.

Now, people can insert their own opinions of what that actually means. Some people will say that Jesus already came, so now I guess Zev means we are waiting for the Second Coming. If you take the Jewish approach, then we are waiting for the First Coming. There is a joke that goes: Jesus arrives on Earth and makes his way to Jerusalem. As he is about to enter, an Israeli security officer stops him, saying, "Welcome, Messiah. Tell me, is this your first or second visit to our city?"

To me, Jesus' answer to the question within the joke doesn't honestly matter. Truth is truth. When He comes, I think He will resolve all those issues. I keep using "He" because I don't truly know G-d's pronouns or how He will identify. So, "He" is not intended to offend anyone reading this who feels G-d is non-binary (if even a single person who focuses on G-d's potential gender identification is reading this book, then I have reached a demographic I had thought to be unreachable). I was talking to my daughter recently, age four, and her perception of G-d is that He's a male, authoritarian, and a strong figure. Because I'm very loving to her and I'm the male role model in her life, she feels that G-d is also a loving male. I introduced the idea that G-d is also a mother, and she cracked up. "G-d is a mother? Mommy?" Her mind couldn't process that G-d has a feminine component! She laughed for ten minutes contemplating the idea that G-d may have a feminine component.

As dark as our moment is, there is a real chance for humanity to find light, and there is no greater nation in which people have that chance than the United States. Whatever our country has become, it is a country built on the bedrock of Judeo-Christian ethics, and that has attempted to embrace the classic virtues of prudence, temperance, justice, and courage. Those elements are within our national DNA, and we need to hope that at our national cellular level, we have not been irreversibly altered, just as we need to hope that this deadly mRNA "vaccine" has not permanently changed the physiology of those who have been injected.

Sacrifice

People will have to embrace a very unpleasant-sounding word if they want to advance to a more satisfying and fulfilling existence, and that word is "sacrifice." People must be ready to sacrifice so that their children will have the freedom and the opportunity to live in a society where G-d's consciousness is still relevant and where they can choose to discover and develop a relationship with the Creator. I think it's reasonable to say that whatever freedom we've enjoyed in the last fifty years was the direct result of the sacrifice of the previous generations. They are the ones that stood up to fascism and the ones that stormed the beaches of Normandy. They are the people that really gave everything they had because they knew that freedom isn't free.

What I see in this generation is the exact opposite, a perversion of nature. I see parents ready to sacrifice their own children for their personal benefit. This is backward. Throughout history, it has been common for parents to sacrifice themselves for the benefit and protection of their children. People today are ready to sacrifice their future for a few moments of comfort in the present instead of sacrificing the present to have a future. This is short-sightedness, small-mindedness, and selfishness. It has been allowed to flourish within our culture because of relentless indoctrination on the part of those who want to control us. It has led to the death of reason, analytical thought, and skepticism. People just seem to react to immediate stimuli like a Pavlovian dog.

That needs to change, and people need to learn how to reason, think, and be ready to sacrifice their own lives if need be, for the true greater good, which is not to serve collectivist, globalist masters. The greater good is served by allowing the individual to seek his own good freely but in accordance with G-d's clear teachings on living with and loving our neighbor as ourselves. The stakes here are much greater than any one individual. I believe we live at a very privileged point in human history, at an inflection point, where we have an opportunity, which probably has never existed before, to change society permanently. We have a chance to firmly reassert the values and the ethical principles that transcend time and space, those which come from G-d. If we do not seize the opportunity, we are going to sink into Churchill's abyss, and we are going to succumb to moral relativism and the hierarchy of values to be based on survival of the fittest. We will move from social Darwinism to its fully metastasized stage four level of "unsocial Darwinism." In that stage, the vulnerable and the decent people will be eaten up like in a food processor by the Serpent and its tentacles.

I believe this is World War Three, and we must stop bullshitting and deluding ourselves. Just because the bombs are invisible, it doesn't mean they're not dropping. And it's time to create an alternate society, create cities of refuge amongst continents of tyranny. Practically speaking, take your kids out of the public school system where the raison d'etre has been to demoralize them and to have them be morally destroyed and misguided by the State to fulfill their perverse goals. Take your kids out of spiritual and physical harm's way. Become more self-sufficient, both when it comes to energy and food. Coalesce together with like-minded people and create small, tribal-like environments where you not only support each other but share a common principle: that there's a power greater than you and that you are trying to serve Him and not the Serpent.

Let me make things very concrete. In the Bible, when the snake came to Eve, he said, "Eat from the fruit of the tree, the Tree of Knowledge."

She said, "I can't. G-d doesn't want me to," and so, the Serpent answered her, "The reason why he doesn't want you to is that He knows that on that day, you will become like G-d, knowing the difference between good and bad."

Suppose you listen to Yuval Noah Harari, the degenerate prophet of Klaus Schwab, Mark Zuckerberg, Bill Gates, and Obama. He, and I quote, said: "Humans are hackable animals. If you can hack them, you could engineer them with intelligent design, but not with some divine intelligent design, but rather by intelligent human design. So, we are now G-ds."

To Harari and those like him, there is no such thing as a soul. There's no such thing as free will. And the Chinese-originated coronavirus will be marked as the inflection point in history when 24/7 digital surveillance went under the skin. These are the words and ideas of some of the most powerful people in the world. How, I ask, is that different from what the snake said to Eve? I see a full circle. The world is more like the Garden of Eden now than it's ever been before. In the Garden of Eden, before Sin, there was good and evil. How do we know? Well, there was a tree of the knowledge of good and evil. So, what happened after the Sin?

Well, the problem then was that good and bad got mixed up, and that mix-up became part of the essence of what it means to be a human being. It became internalized. So, G-d said, "Let's evict the couple from the Garden of Eden, lest they eat from the Tree of Life and live forever." You could ask the question: they were supposed to live forever, so why not let them repent and live forever anyway? The answer is that since they ate from the tree of life, evil itself would live forever because it was internalized in them. This means, from my vantage point, the existence of death serves the purpose of making sure that evil itself does not live forever.

Man and his wife were evicted from the Garden of Eden and told to get to work, a sort of metaphysical work. Every physical act in which we engage, every thought we ponder, and every word we speak needs to be focused on the Divine. We are charged with extricating or separating the good from the bad. The goal for the sum total of all labors of all humanity, the end game, is to bring the world back into a state where good and bad are clearly delineated. Like it was before the Sin.

Having lived through this pandemic, for the first time in my life, I can clearly tell you where good and bad are. Granted, it's mostly bad. I'm not in denial of that. At least I know what it is. I also know what good is. It is actually very simple. Bad is whenever someone increases fear, panic, isolation, and dehumanization. With a high degree of confidence, you could say that the motives of those in power during the pandemic were bad and that the force behind them is the Serpent: True evil. The opposite is true, also. When someone is trying to give hope, encourage integration with loved ones, to fight for the sanctity of human life and the value of each individual who has been made in the image of G-d, then I can easily say, with a high degree of confidence, that is good. From that perspective, and being deliberately narrow, I see the world today like the Garden of Eden before the Sin.

Despite all of the above warnings of the existential crisis we are facing as joined-together humanity, I am still hopeful and not without optimism. To borrow from prophetic verses, I do believe there is hope that: The spirit of iniquity will be removed from the world; death will be swallowed up forever; the world will be filled with the knowledge of G-d as the waters cover the seas, and we will see eye to eye with G-d.

Whether this happens in our lifetime (yours at least... hoping for it in mine might be just a bit too optimistic given my health situation) depends on the rate at which humanity, or the figurative human heart, will do the necessary work and reconcile with the Creator. If we don't learn our lessons quickly and we continue our course of debauchery and the desecration of life, it will take longer. If we wake up soon and our level of consciousness is raised, there is a chance to reverse course a bit faster. That has been what I try to allay by constantly attempting to point six months into the future when either warning others or calling them to action. What usually happens is that whatever narrative I push initially leads to my denigration, and then, after a while, it becomes accepted as the truth because the truth reveals itself. I have tried to keep pushing the boundaries of human consciousness. That is a big part of why I wanted to write this book.

If we look at consciousness on a scale from one to ten, with one being the lowest, I think at the beginning of this crisis, we were somewhere between one and two on the scale as a species. I think that what's happened on a global scale is that tens of millions, maybe hundreds of millions, or perhaps even billions, of people have realized that they have placed their faith in the wrong places and false G-ds. They realize now that the government has betrayed them. Science and technology have been used as a tool, not for truth, but to help create, distribute, extend, and manipulate information to support the governmental narrative. This narrative has led to enslavement.

It is an overwhelming and sobering thing to come to realize that you have been worshiping false G-ds for your entire life and placing your very existence into their cold, chilled-with-the-iciness of death hands. This collective realization creates a billion or so personal crises that eventually lead to a collective crisis, where a person, and society itself, do not know what to believe anymore. People are lost, but they are awake, and they are searching. I think the world is ripe for true divine awakening. Whether or not that happens depends on the exercise of free will through informed and hopefully G-d-directed choice. I don't have a timetable. All I can tell you is that the length of time, or how long it will take, depends on how quickly we are willing to learn and to sacrifice.

It is my most sincere hope that you have found this book to be not just one thing but many things. I have shared with you my experience, strength, and hope and have tried to combine a mixture of facts and interpretation so that there are things to help you "know" and things to help you "think." What you do with it is your choice, as it is your choice to decide how you will move forward in the human battle of evil versus good, G-d versus the Primordial Serpent.

Since I am a doctor, I feel compelled to leave you with a prescription. It might well be the last one I will ever write. For this, I draw from the words of King David. These are words that have been translated many times and paraphrased in many forms. From me, Zev Zelenko, to you, my brother and sister with G-d, I simply prescribe: Turn away from bad, do good, and live.

From the Dissident's Desk

A Hat Tip to Vladimir Zelenko, The Most Extraordinary Dissident

Being chosen as the coauthor for this book is a truly humbling privilege. There has been a limitation insofar as the book has been written in Zev's voice and based on sixty-plus hours of interviews. A curious person might wonder, "What does the coauthor think about the man who was Zev Zelenko?"

Fortunately for me, I had the chance to answer that question before Zev's passing in the following piece that was published by Human Events.

Upon reading, Zev phoned me in what turned out to be an emotional call. He expressed his sincere appreciation for the words and the sentiment.

This is the only gift, outside of friendship, that I was able to give to the man who has given so much to me, including the chance to have dinner in his home, read a bedtime story to his children, and even an ampule of sand that he brought from the beaches of Normandy.

This is what I thought about Dr. Vladimir Zelenko.
May 3, 2022

I was not born to be forced. I will breathe after my own fashion. Let us see who is the strongest.

– Henry David Thoreau

As Elon Musk's takeover of Twitter migrates from announcement to closing, Dr. Vladimir Zelenko, who had been initially banned from Twitter in 2020, then recently reinstated only to be banned last week and then again reinstated, has just been banned for a third time. If someone is charged with keeping records of the macabre, they might want to check to see if three banishments qualify for the Guinness Book of Censorship. Here is his simply outrageous post that got him banned this time around:

According to the CDC, healthy children have a 99.998% recovery rate from COVID-19 with NO treatment. What is the rationale for vaccinating this demographic?

While curious as to their reasons for issuing a suspension over such benign content, I find it pointless to speculate on the possible motives for the inner machinations of hateful people making capricious choices. Instead, I'm using the Doctor's suspension as an opportunity to reflect upon how I first came to know him and how my life has been profoundly and permanently impacted since.

Zev, as he likes to be called, had been banned from Twitter in late 2020 for a tweet in which he wished President Trump well in his recovery from the Chinese coronavirus. This banning drew the ire of those in the American dissident movement because we knew that he had been a voice of truth and courage throughout the pandemic. Twitter's de-platforming of him was yet another indication of the arbitrary power of big tech. It was a foreshadowing of just how bold the platform was yet to become in censoring the voices of anyone who dared challenge their collectivist, globalist orthodoxy.

My dear friend and broadcast partner at the time, Tamara Leigh[16], was able to connect with Zev and invite him to be a guest[17] on our weekly

---

16 | https://rumble.com/user/TamaraLeigh?date=this-month

17 | https://rumble.com/vqtv1b-looking-forward-zelenko-on-tamara-leighs-trend-on.html

YouTube show, Trend On (ultimately de-platformed by Alphabet for having candid Chinese coronavirus conversations). It was in that setting that we first met. Little did I realize that it was at that moment that my life would change irrevocably.

Following that appearance with Tamara and me, I went on to interview Zev for a piece[18] at *Human Events* titled, *Twitter Silenced Dr. Zelenko: Here is What They Don't Want You to Know*.[19] The story was widely read, but the real "story" for me was that it launched us on a path to friendship, one that has grown and bloomed over these past months, much as might a healthy Jewish tree of life.

Twitter's closing of Zev's account forced him to migrate to other platforms in order to maintain contact with his loyal followers all over the world. Rumble, Telegram, and GETTR have all benefited from Twitter's loss prior to his recent return.

It was on GETTR and Telegram that, back in early April, Zev posted news that his cancer, an affliction with which he had suffered well before the pandemic, had reemerged with a vengeance. The outpouring of love and support from his followers was spontaneous, genuine, and help-offering. Everyone who thought they had access to a cancer-curing treatment or remedy wanted to share. In my small world alone, where very few know of my friendship with Zev, several people reached out asking me to please share information with him, something which I did dutifully in each instance.

We had been prepared at *Human Events* to run a news story of Zev's most recent Twitter ban, but before we could set the type, the decision was reversed. At that moment, I decided to write a Zev piece still, but as opinion, not as news. It is not about Twitter, censorship, or the Chinese coronavirus. It is about the man himself.

---

18 | https://humanevents.com/2021/01/04/twitter-silenced-dr-zelenko-here-is-what-they-do-not-want-you-to-know/

19 | [1] https://humanevents.com/2021/01/04/twitter-silenced-dr-zelenko-here-is-what-they-do-not-want-you-to-know/

Here and There, and Now and Then, G-d Makes a Giant Among Men

Nearly 35 years ago, I had the chance to meet the most remarkable woman. Dr. Patricia Scherer was a former Northwestern University professor with expertise in working with the deaf. She had done research that showed, believe it or not, that music and the arts could activate and improve various cognitive functions for the deaf (the music works through vibrations).

The "wise" people at Northwestern rejected her ideas, so she left and went on her own and formed what became the International Center on Deafness & the Arts. Generations later, her research has been vindicated, and deaf children and adults worldwide have been living fuller and richer lives as a result of her courageous and pioneering work.

I mention the late Dr. Scherer because when I first glimpsed her as she walked into a conference room for a meeting, despite her under-five-foot frame, I could instantly sense I was in the presence of a giant. I have shared that experience many times over the years and had assumed it would be singular. It had remained such until I had the opportunity to meet Zev in person.

Vladimir Zelenko is perhaps the exact antithesis of an intimidating physical figure. What his rather modest physical presence belies is a man of such great spiritual and intellectual stature that were he to be confronted by Goliath, it might take little more than the rise of an eyebrow to send the behemoth running. No slingshot and stone needed, just the invincible combination of faith and reason.

When we did first meet in three dimensions (after many calls and video meetings) my Objectivist self immediately went to war with my Christian self in trying to deny what we both could plainly see; a remarkable man with almost an aura about him of peace and love; a truly transcendent presence. After a full day spent sharing conversation and breaking bread, I recall talking to friends and telling them that I wasn't sure what had happened to me, but I was certain I would never be the same.

I haven't been.

To travel in public with Zev is to experience something quite special. I've had the occasion in my career to be around many famous people. You get used to having fans coming up, acting as though you are not there, while shamelessly fawning over the celebrity. "I love your movies. You're my favorite player. Can we take a selfie? Can I have your autograph?"

When people approach Zev, as they do almost everywhere he goes, the reaction is very different. Their heads are bowed. Their voices are soft. Their words always vary on the theme of "G-d bless you. Thank you for what you have done. Your work saved my mother's life. It is so wonderful to be able to meet you. Thank you. Thank you. Thank you."

Zev's response, in turn, is always a variation of his own humble and immutable manner. "G-d bless you. That is very kind. Thank you so much." He engages everyone. He treats each person as if they are the first to have ever approached him. They weren't, and they won't be the last. What is special is that their place in the sequence is indistinguishable, one from another. Each is treated as an only.

ICYMI-Why We've Come to Know This Man

It does surprise me that every once in a while, I mention Zev's name, even to a fellow dissident, and they are not familiar with him or his work. The short version is that Dr. Zelenko was a family medical practitioner in upstate New York when the pandemic began. Recognizing quickly that this was no ordinary flu strain, he did what doctors used to do in the days before algorithms; he started to try things.

Through a bit of luck, research, and divine providence, he discovered that zinc, the natural enemy of coronavirus, could stop the disease in its tracks if administered early and with the assistance of hydroxychloroquine (later ivermectin) to help it reach the target. He began to treat patients, and they began to not die. He has since overseen the treatment of over seven thousand patients with only three deaths. His hospitalization rate for "high-risk" patients is 84 percent better than that of the general population.

Do you wonder how many people needed to die from the Chinese coronavirus? Start by multiplying the total number of deaths by .16. See what result that yields. For those who get headaches from math, I'll help. If one million people died, that number might have only been one hundred and sixty thousand if they had been treated early with what has come to be called the "Zelenko Protocol."

For his groundbreaking clinical work and breakthrough in lifesaving treatment, Dr. Zelenko was recognized as an international hero and appeared on the cover of every magazine in the country, from *Time* to *Popular Mechanics*.

Wait! That was in an alternate universe where politicians, corporate chiefs, and doctors wanted people to live. In this universe, he was vilified by politicians who wanted to maintain control, CEOs who wanted to make money, and doctors who, well, who can really understand the response of doctors. G-d will have to sort that with them, one refused-to-treat-patient case at a time when their own day of reckoning arrives.

But this is not a story about the pandemic. It is about a man who did good, was vilified for doing good, and then refused to stop doing good at a tremendous personal cost. Beneath that aura of peace and love, you can also sense fatigue, the fatigue of a man who has done so much against such resistance that he just needs a moment to put his hands on his knees and breathe.

He has since been vindicated. Proper research, using HCQ or ivermectin as an early intervention along with zinc and other medications, has been proven to effectively combat the Chinese coronavirus. This fact brings only tempered pleasure to my friend Zev who knows that people all over the world died because those in power denied science under the false façade of "following science."

You Are Unrepeatable. There Is A Magic About You That Is All Your Own– David Dellinger

I used to be confused when I was younger at how whenever someone passed away, there would be a piece published about their life in minutes, sometimes thousands of words long. I naively thought, *how do they write so fast?* I learned, of course, that these pieces are not written in moments; they are written in advance and then held in a sort of journalist's cryonic storage container, only to have the words brought to life when the subject's life ends.

While I understand the practice, it seems a bit of a shame; such kind things written and said absent the eyes and the ears of the person remembered. No harm in that, my Christian self says. They will experience them upon arrival in G-d's kingdom. Ah, but my Objectivist voice says nonsense! There is no such place. And so, conflicted within myself, I hedge. I share my tribute to my friend in this moment, in this space, so that it's certain he sees it.

Zev Zelenko is the most resilient person I have ever met, a man who counts his cancer as a blessing because it prepared him for the battle he has had to fight in order to treat patients with the Chinese coronavirus. To him, he is G-d's tool, and he will be here so long as G-d wants him to continue His work. That could yet be, and I hope it to be, for a very long time.

There is no certainty. Little is certain in this life, but I am certain of one thing. We are all familiar with how we will come across someone on occasion, and after chatting for a few moments, we say, "You know, you remind me of someone I once knew." I'm certain that regardless of how much time I might have left on this Earth, I will never utter that phrase to someone with Zev in mind.

That's because we also all know the old expression, "When G-d made you, He threw away the mold." We say that to someone to express that we find them to be quite unique. In Zev's case, however, the notion that G-d used some sort of special one-time, not-to-be-replicated mold doesn't quite do justice. Having had the chance to meet him, work with him, and become his friend, I've learned that G-d actually sat down and took the time to make Vladimir Zelenko by hand. He is G-d's personal work–His best work.

Love between men who are more comfortable and accustomed to invoking the term when it pertains to women is a rare and special thing. In considering my friend Zev and his current plight, I am led to borrow from the late Gale Sayers and simply say, "I love Vladimir Zelenko, and I'd like all of you to love him too. Tonight, when you hit your knees, please ask G-d to love him."

Best hurry. G-d's inbox is rapidly filling.

The Roundtable

By the time this manuscript was completed in the middle of August, 2022, Zev had passed away approximately forty-five days earlier. Everyone involved with the project was left to answer the question, "How do we bring closure to Zev's life within these pages?" It seemed both impossible and inappropriate to not acknowledge the fact that this life for him had ended and that the next one in which he so strongly believed had begun.

The transcript that follows is our attempt to answer the "closure" question. Four people who knew Zev well and whose lives he impacted profoundly got together to discuss Zev and share stories of his life, lessons, laughter, and legacy.

Brent: Hi, everyone. I'm Brent Hamachek, and I am the person fortunate enough to have been selected to be the co-author, along with Vladimir Zelenko, for his final book: *Zelenko: How to Decapitate the Snake*. The book will be out shortly as we sit down and record this in late August, and one of the things that we talked about as a group when we were working on this since Zev passed away before the completion of the book is: What do we do to acknowledge the fact that he, in fact, had passed away? It seemed wrong to issue a book without some acknowledgment of that. Then also, late in his life, right before the end, he started a Foundation that really isn't part of the book that's being written because it was something that came to light a little bit late in the game.

So, our idea was to bring together four people who were very close to Zev, who worked with him, and who had their lives impacted by him, and to share some thoughts and reflections on the man who was, what his life meant, and what his legacy could well turn out to be and what we hope it to be.

So, I am joined here by Ann Vandersteel, Menashe Amitay, Dave Lopez, and Moshe Knobel. Thanks all for joining us, I'd like to start by having each one of you just briefly introduce yourself to the audience and share who you are and how you came to know Zev, and we'll ask some questions.

Ann, why don't you start?

Ann: Thank you, Brent. Yes, as you said, I'm Ann Vandersteel. I am one of the co-Chairs of the Zelenko Freedom Foundation. My partner Kevin Jenkins and I were handpicked by Dr. Zelenko to carry on the mission and vision and his legacy of establishing truth and everything, from media across medical freedom and, of course, just respecting our One True G-d and what He has put us here on the planet to do. I feel very blessed, very honored. I had the opportunity to meet Dr. Zelenko back in March of 2020 when I heard President Trump talk about a small country doctor in New York lauding the efficacy of hydroxychloroquine, azithromycin, and zinc while standing at the podium during a coronavirus press conference one afternoon. I sought out Dr. Zelenko, introduced myself, and did one of his very first interviews that really helped put him on the map. We became fast friends. I found the humor in the man to be one of good, dry, sarcastic wit. But also, the level of intellect and the depth of his understanding of the problem, the magnitude of what we were being challenged with as humanity by evil powers - by that "Primordial Snake," as he quite often referenced - really rang true and opened my eyes even more as to what we're going to be challenged with, not only even today but what we're still staring down the barrel for tomorrow. So, with that responsibility, I take the co-Chair position of the Zelenko Freedom Foundation very seriously, and it's an honor to carry forward his legacy.

Brent: Thanks Ann. Dave Lopez, introduce yourself to our audience, please.

Dave: Hi! Yeah, I'm Dave Lopez. I'm a former Navy SEAL. I got out of the SEAL teams in 2013. After that, for about seven years, I focused on combating human trafficking, and I did that with the largest non-profits. I was the central hub where they would go whenever they wanted veterans and operations to actually happen on the ground somewhere. They would contract through a separate entity, and that would be my entity. I did that for a number of years and then decided I'd be better suited in business to help fuel those initiatives long-term. So, I became a serial entrepreneur of sorts, and right around that time, as I was starting a number of different businesses, some blockchain-related, some in the development space, the pandemic was starting. I ran into Dr. Zev Zelenko, and I was just so moved with number one: his courage. You know, the moment you meet Zev, you can tell he just doesn't care what anyone thinks. For me, I had the ability to triangulate off of intelligence, friends, and people I knew in China at the time, so I was getting a lot of information that a lot of people weren't getting, and because of that, I was a little bit ahead of the narrative, and I saw Zev just completely shattering this whole argument and using complete logic.

So, I reached out to him, and we became quick friends. I helped him with some security issues and needs at the time, and that's initially how we met. After a while, he asked me to help him start his company. I told him, "Zev, I would have done it either way, had you asked me or not." But I was happy to join and happy to lock arms with him, and I'm just proud and honored to be able to be by his side for a significant period of his life.

Brent: Thank you, Dave. Menashe Amitay, please share who you are and how you came to know Zev.

Menashe: Hi! So, I'm Menashe Amitay. I got to know Zev initially, say, 15-20 years ago. I met him in the same rabbinical school in Israel, and at that time, I didn't really know him on a personal level. He was a good friend of my brother-in-law that helped him to move to upstate New York, where he lived. My brother-in-law connected us, and he came here. I initially helped him only with his housing needs. Quickly, he asked me about my experience with manufacturing and helping out with running his company, and this is how I joined the company. Initially, I didn't know exactly who Zev was, but as I met him, I was really, I would say, inspired, and felt privileged that he asked me to help him out with this venture. I felt like it was a divine providence that we met each other, and we worked together. It was really a beautiful, beautiful relationship together, and the children miss Zev, someone that was a blessing to many, many people.

I think one of the first things that inspired me the most is when I traveled with him a few times in the car, and the multiple phone calls that I would hear from women and husbands calling and saying, "Thank you. Thank you for saving my husband. Thank you for saving my wife." I said to myself, "This guy, whatever he asks me, I'm going to help him out with after hearing this." So, it was really an honor and privilege to work with Zev, and we're continuing to do his work on many different levels. G-d willing, we should continue to be very successful in doing that.

Brent: Thank you so much. Moshe Knobel, tell us who you are and share how you came to know Zev Zelenko.

Moshe: I had the opportunity to be introduced by a mutual friend. At the time that I met him, I was a full-time life coach, and I started working with Zev. Over time, he asked if I would consider assisting him as his Chief of Staff in the company, and that was an enormous leap of faith, to say the

least, because I essentially turned all my attention to him. As time went on…
it's hard to really express this, but… he was a great, great mind, to say the
least. To being around somebody and having the opportunity to peer into
the intensity and the acuity - and literally the genius of his way of thinking,
and how he would put things together and bring diverse facts into a unified
whole - to watch that and to experience it, and help to collaborate to some
degree - whether it be in the writing of this book, or the writing of an email.
Or framing up a meeting that we're about to go into, or business idea, or
business problem, or business opportunity, a new formulation, or a new
quest of some type or another, whether it be in medicine or otherwise.

And somewhat similar to what Menashe just said, I also can't tell you,
not only how many times I would overhear the same phone calls because
he and I spent a lot of time together in the car. He was always taking phone
calls, and he was exceedingly generous with his time. He called himself a
simple country doctor. Dr. Zelenko was the farthest thing from a simple
country doctor, but if he insisted, and Donald Trump insisted, then okay.
That he was able to help so many people on an individual level while
simultaneously helping people on a broader level and on a global level was
quite awe-inspiring. It is an enormous honor, and a privilege, to be so close
to somebody with so much to give and so little time to give it.

Brent: Thanks—and for those that are reading, listening, watching, depending
upon how you take this in, I can tell you that Moshe was invaluable in the
process of putting the book together because he was more than just Chief
of Staff; he was the organizer of all things Zev, including his calendar.
Suffice it to say; I don't think the book would have gotten done, especially
on time, without your assistance. So, a great big thank you for that.

Dave, I want to turn to you and ask you a big, giant, open-ended
question: Tell us about Zev Zelenko as a man. How would you characterize
him? And what impression did he leave on you in that regard?

Dave: Well, he redefined for me bravery—something that I felt like I had a pretty good definition of because of my time in the military. But, as the world began to change, I think a big portion of people knew there was something wrong, but there was a stigma behind discussing that, right? No one wants to be alienated from friends, society. Zev—he didn't care. He didn't care about the fallout; he didn't care, even from people among his own religious sect—even people close to him. All of us went through this period of reorganizing a little bit and prioritizing certain things, and Zev was the one I would accredit to causing a consciousness shift. Not just with people like myself, but with the nucleus of the medical apparatus, the doctors, and the scientists inside the medical community that weren't as loud as Zev, but Zev was their hero. I got to spend numerous times on the phone with Zev, with people who, if I were to go through a list of all these names, you probably wouldn't believe. They're some of the most brilliant scientists on the planet, and they would quietly call Zev and say how much they appreciated him for taking the stance that he had, but they would never come out publicly and say.

I think that's just the difference right there. And I'm not taking anything away from those amazing doctors and scientists, but Zev was the one that everyone else was inspired by, and he's caused a massive consciousness shift. As a man, he was always trying to balance this new life with his family life. There's nothing easy when your time gets taken into this world and you're basically under siege: Everything changes, and home life changes. Zev weathered the storm, and he was just an absolute rock throughout it.

And even in the last days, he's sitting there, literally a week before he passed, working on ways and treatments for me, my family, and all my friends to make sure that we're prepared against the next pandemic. He's already calling people and making sure everyone has what they need in case things get worse, and I guess that's the best way to describe him. I mean, no matter what stage of life he was at, even till the end, he was always focused on patients. Even when he had a missing lung; even when he was probably one of the most at-risk people. Completely fearless.

He redefined it for me, because even in the military… guys that I know, everyone, took positions that were safe. I think in this new world that's forming, if we don't learn the lesson of being a bulldog and a fighter like Zev - and we don't have more of them - I think our future and Western civilization as we know it is pretty much over. So, that's the lesson. You've got to stand; it doesn't matter. You know who's with you, who's against you. You stand for what you believe in, and that's why I have this burden now to mimic that and be that in my own life, in the same way he was.

Brent: Thank you. Menashe, describe for folks your perception of Zev Zelenko as a man.

Menashe: I totally aligned with everything Dave said. I felt in many ways the same way, and many times I feel bad that I tried to tone him down. In many ways, I would say to Zev, "You know, we don't have to say it so out loud. You don't have to say it so drastically." But he kept on telling me, "This is what I believe in. This is what I see."

He was a very gentle person in in his own life. You could see it with the way he treated people, the way he interacted with people; it was extremely gentle. But when he felt that someone was spreading lies, he would just stand out there, and suddenly it was a totally different Zev. He would put up a fight, and he would make sure that the truth was heard. I saw it time after time.

He was an extremely caring person, but he had this dichotomy. On the one hand, he would fight for the truth. But on the other hand, he would feel the pain of another person. And like Dave just said, I saw him in times where he was literally suffering, coughing his lungs out, but he was still on the ball. He came to the office; he did the interviews. When he came to Florida, he didn't even have an office, so he would come to my office and conduct the interviews from here. I saw him sometimes go days without sleep; he would sleep on the couch that I'm sitting on here.

And he just continued to work. He worked non-stop. It's not that he was a workaholic or anything like that. He just really felt that he came to the world for this mission. He said, "This is my mission." He could have been a rabbi; he was offered to be a rabbi. But his rabbi told him, "Your mission is to be a doctor; to help out. So, there are enough Jewish leaders that are big rabbis, but your job is to be a great Jewish doctor," and that's what he did until this very day. In the community in upstate New York, where he served for most of his life, they are very thankful. We saw it in his passing and still see it with letters that we are getting to the office. But to me personally, I think that what impressed me the most is that - besides having this great responsibility of being this doctor for so many people and being a father and a businessman, all the other responsibilities that he had - he always had this time for laughter, time to be gentle, kind, and playful.

And he liked the little toys he used to keep... he brought some of my youth back in many ways. It's like, "Leave it!" And still, we are in our 40s, in our 50s, and we're pushing, and we have all these responsibilities, but let's not forget to be a kid from time to time. Personally, it impressed me a lot. Besides his learning and the depth of his intellect, he could talk to you about cabalistic things, but at the same time, he had this joy. He really enjoyed every day of his life. According to Jewish teachings, one of the things that you're being asked after 120, that G-d would ask you, "Did you enjoy my world? I put you here, did you enjoy my world?" I think Zev can answer, "I definitely attempted to enjoy this world."

Brent: I think that's probably true, and we're going to talk a little bit about his sense of humor in a few minutes. Ann, as you share what your perceptions were of him as a man, I must tell our readership and audience that you held a special place in Zev's heart. There was a moment when I was sitting with him in person, and we were going through a list of people that he said would be willing to promote the book on social media, and he was looking down at his phone and scrolling through a list. As he looked down, he said, "Ann Vandersteel," and then he looked down, and again he looked back up at me and said, "I really like her." Then he looked back down again, and he looked back up at me and said, "She's very pretty." Then he went back to naming names. So, from the lady that Zev thought was very pretty and who he felt very close to, tell us what your thoughts were of him as a man.

Ann: He was an incredible father. I mean, this is a man who put his family first, in addition to the battles he waged for all of us. If you take it back to the beginning, when his name was first put on the international stage, he was standing in the gap and the breach for all of us. He was taking slings and arrows because he had truly shined a very bright light into the abyss of the Deep State, pharmaceutical Big Pharma, and the medical-industrial complex conspiracy to collude with the government against the people.

Just the mere fact that he uttered the words hydroxychloroquine drove me to learn very quickly that hydroxychloroquine had been studied by Fauci at the NIH in 2003 and was approved to treat coronavirus very safely and effectively. Right then, I knew that he had exposed Big Pharma and the medical-industrial complex and their collusion with big government.

But he had a real sense of humor because he always jokingly said, "Well, you know, they're gonna get me. They don't like what I'm saying; they're gonna get me." He used his G-d-given courage like nobody I've ever known before. He was fearless, as many of you, or all of you have said here, and because he was so fearless, he understood the importance of his family. He knew he had few hours, days, weeks, months left between the battle of Big Pharma and the medical-industrial complex and the battle against this demon called cancer, so he fought bravely, very bravely, and never let it slow him down to which you've heard testimonials about already.

I have to say he made sure, no matter where he was, he was always home for Shabbat on Friday nights. That was the most important thing, to be with his family for the weekend, turn everything off, disconnect from the electronic world, and focus on his family. That was his priority, and that's why I and so many others admired him. He would fly to the end of the Earth to speak to whomever, but he was home Friday by sundown. He never missed it.

I really admired that because so many of us have, unfortunately, forsaken our families in this battle because we see this battle as saving our family's future. But we forget that we need to set time aside, too. So, he led by example for me, to remind me I need to turn things off, turn my electronics off, decompress and spend time with my family on the weekend. It's utterly important that I do because, at the end, that's who you want around you when you're taking your last breath here before you go and meet our One True G-d. So, I really admire that.

But his sense of humor was like none other, Brent. I have a couple of examples. One time I was driving home from work. I'd been working in the studio all day, and a reminder popped up on my phone that Pete Santilli, a colleague and friend of mine, was live on the show at that moment. I thought, "let me see who Pete's got on." It was Zev! Zev was doing a live with Pete Santilli at the time, and they were talking about the National Guard being deployed to deliver the, as Dr. Zelenko called it, "the poison death shot" in our arms, going door to door, as they were doing in Australia. Zev turned around live on camera and said, "If someone shows up at my door to give me a shot…" He grabbed his gun from his desk, brandished a weapon on live TV, and said, "Someone's gonna get shot." I screenshotted that, and I texted it to Zev. As soon as he got off the air, he called me. We were laughing, and I said, "I cannot believe you just did that on live television! I love you so much!"

He was grounded. He knew exactly what his life meant and the battle he was waging, and I'll never forget that particular moment, like many others with him, but we'll talk about more. That's one that just jumps out to me, Brent, for sure.

Brent: Yeah, he was very proud of that story, by the way; he shared that regularly. Moshe, you could make an argument, and I might be the one to make it, that nobody was closer to him and knew him better over the last part of his life than you. You were inseparable. Share as a real true subject matter expert here. Describe Zev as a man from your perspective

Moshe: Sure. So, at first, I would say that I would take exception and say that I think his wife has that position and knew him better than anyone.

Brent: Next to his wife—in a different way than the wives know their husbands.

Moshe: Of course. But you know, to tell you that many of the things that have already been said about Zev, his biggest frustration in the world was that he did not have enough time with his wife, his family, and his children. It was such a central part and so central to who he was. And every Friday afternoon, it didn't matter where we were that week - we spent a good couple of months out of the country seeking treatment in Europe - every Friday, no matter what, he would always make sure to not only just call the children and, of course, his wife, but also to send flowers for the Sabbath. As a man, if we were to come back to us, I would say that he would tell us that among the thing he misses the most, the biggest would be the love of his family. He would also tell us about his frustration at not being able to spend more time with them and more time -not only just while he was alive - but more time with them as a father, watching his children grow into the various different stages of life.

Talking about his humor, one of his favorite jokes has got to be the following: Do you know the difference between G-d and a doctor? He would wait for the pause and say, "G-d knows he's not a doctor." He loved that joke in particular because he was very aware and sensitive to the fact that doctors are sometimes put in these unusual positions that test their pride and their humility, which can be at odds from time to time. If there's one thing that makes him distinct, more than anything that I could separate out - other than what everybody has said so far - it is his constant willingness and passion to grow as a person on a personal level. What could he do better?

How could he change? He was very open to hearing other perspectives, diverse opinions, and things that people found problematic. Now, we're not talking about his desire to behead the Primordial Snake, which is something maybe we'll talk about later.

But, when it came to him fighting the fight, there was no backing down. He did not back down. As Menashe said, maybe there is regret in trying to hold him back a little bit more than he did. And Dave, I know you can also weigh in on that, but when it came to his personal persona, he just wanted to grow and be the best person he could be, to be the best husband he could be, the best father he could be, the best doctor he could be, and the best leader of the very, very unique position that G-d put him into educate us and bring the truth to the surface.

Brent: Thank you. So, Ann and Moshe have shared a couple of humorous stories. Menashe, Zev had such a dry wit, and a keen sense of humor. It seems everybody that knows him has a favorite. Do you have a humorous anecdote to share about Zev?

Menashe: Really, there are so many. Somehow, he could make laughter out of many things in a positive way. I remember when Zev was away, just to enforce what Moshe said, I would get a phone call from the guard: The delivery of flowers. That is something that I would hear every Friday. The delivery of flowers. It was very important for him to have this stronger relationship with his family. I saw it time after time, despite all the craziness that was going on. The family was really important to him.

Another thing that impressed me a lot is that he set time for learning. He had a time that he would dedicate for learning, and learning Torah was something very precious to him because there's a book that he wrote in *Essence to Essence*. And there's another book that he wrote in *Metamorphosis*. He came to my house a few times for the weekend when his wife and family had not yet moved to Florida. He was just such a personality that the whole community gravitated to him. So, I thought I was just having Zev in my house, but it ended up with a Friday afternoon - sorry, Saturday afternoon - the entire community was at my house just sitting there and listening to Zev. Part of it was because of his humor, which is very interesting because he said very serious things, and he would say things that made people stop for a moment, and sometimes more than a moment, but then he would somehow be able to break it down.

I can't think of a specific joke that he would say because he did not repeat himself too many times. He said it once, and that was it. But overall, I could tell you that his personality was one of a kind. It was really one of a kind. Just being such an intellect, having a depth of intellect, but at the same time being such a nice person who could speak to anyone. I had people who came into the office and just asked him such simple questions, and he would respond. He would respond to workers if anybody had anything in the office that didn't feel good. He helped them and said, "Actually, I miss the family practice." Despite the fact that he was now doing much, much bigger things, he helped employees that had a sore throat and things like that, he would help them with prescriptions, and he would say, "I miss family practice."

Brent: So, his sense of humor was so dry that, on occasion, when we were working on the book, he would pause and say to me, "That was a joke." He did this because I'd be so focused and serious that I'd be trying to take seriously everything he was saying, and he would have to alert me that it was a joke! We would play the tape in my head and then laugh because I'd missed it.

Dave, share a humorous Zev story with us, please.

Dave: I was thinking of what would be the best one to tell. Shortly before his passing, he was down in Dallas. He's in bed, and there's not much he can do at this point; he's just waiting for his procedure. We had one of our security guys there with him the whole time, one of his best friends named Tommy. He was talking to Tommy, joking around with him the whole time.

Eventually, he convinces him to watch *Saving Private Ryan* with him. This was at two in the morning, and almost everyone was gone from the hospital. Suddenly, he says, "Hey, let's go take a walk." He's totally not supposed to be out of bed, and he's just like, "Let's go!" And he just started walking. He just got up and started acting like he was in the military, peeking around corners and stuff with Tommy, and… that's him. That's that childlike way that he had about him. He was living his best life, even when most people would have already thrown in the towel. And you know, nothing, nothing broke his spirits, nothing. The only thing that would really cut him up as he was processing the reality of his situation was leaving his family, his girls, and his eldest, his kids, and how we would stay up late at night talking and… but everything else… yeah, he was fearless. He didn't care at all about personally dying. That's something he did not care about. In many ways, I think he was ready. He was more than ready for that transition if family wasn't involved.

Brent: So, Ann, I want to turn to you. We've talked about the lighthearted here, but I think that everybody who knew Zev and spent time with him had a story that was perhaps a bit more poignant, touching, and impactful. I know that in my own case, some of the conversations I had that I felt were forever life-changing for me, and forced you to make certain confrontations, if you will, within yourself. Share, if you would, with the folks that are reading a special way that he may have impacted you in what I'll call a "moment," for lack of a better term.

Ann: Well, that, to me, is very clear-cut. I spent a lot of time with him on the phone, talking about personal family matters, and about things going on in my life, in my kids' lives. I have a stepson that was in the military; he's not anymore. I have a son who's currently still in the military. And, of course, I was gravely concerned about the mandates that were going around in the military and our "woke" DoD forcing these poison death shots on our kids. And I had a daughter also in college; she's in the aerospace industry, she's got her senior year left, she's got a great job when she gets out of school, working in the Mars Mission Program in the nuclear rocket division. She's brilliant, but they were mandating this stuff for our kids, and because of the work I'm doing and that everybody who's reading this book is well aware of, nobody wanted this shot. And if you got it, you're trying to figure out how to detoxify it.

So, I called Dr. Zelenko on a number of occasions, and we talked it through. We would do what we called "game theory," where if he had a meeting with somebody, he would call me, and I'm sure others, for an opinion on how that meeting was going to go with whomever it might be the time. It could have been somebody in the White House, or it could have been a close friend of the President's, or what have you. And so, I called him and said, "You know, Dr. Z, I need to game theory this out here because I've got a son who's sworn an oath to defend the Constitution. But he's being told by his superiors that he has to get these jabs or he's out, and this kid wants to go into buds." I mean, he really wants to be a SEAL. He's trained his whole life for this; he's made for this. We're talking about a kid who was a top-ten international golfer; he's got a mind of steel and a body to match. And he's driven. And I really can't get into the specifics of the conversation, but I will tell you this much. He instilled the courage in me to have a conversation I needed to have with my son and basically help him formulate a plan of action on how to move through that whole process of the mandate and dealing with the jab.

If it were not for him in that instance, as well as then for my daughter, who was attending school, writing her a medical exemption letter because she was vaccine-injured from the HPV shots, I'm not sure that we're going to be able to help what injury she has from the shot. We've switched her to ivermectin, but she was taking daily hydroxychloroquine for rheumatoid arthritis, which became a serious issue, in addition to other issues and concerns.

She had a bad reaction to the HPV shot, so, she really couldn't take another jab, especially this one. So, he wrote her the medical exemption letter. And it was funny, the university knew who he was, and it first denied her exemption letter. So, I called him, and he advised, he said, "Just have her go back in and find somebody else." So, she did, and the next person she spoke to at the university level, they accepted her exemption letter, because they didn't know who he was, thank G-d. But, this is the kind of stuff he put his life on the line, his name, his reputation, his license, to guide me to help me save my own kids through this process. And you know, I personally have worked with Dr. Zelenko and other doctors, and freedom fighters to do medical rescues out of hospitals, where hospitals are putting people on ventilators, and putting them on Remdesivir, and executing them based on the Fauci protocols. Dr. Zelenko taught us how to do this, how to save people's lives. And he didn't just teach us, HE DID IT. He did it by holding your hand, personally. So, what he did for me is what has driven me to do it for others, and I've had probably a couple hundred people whose lives I've touched personally that were medical rescues in hospitals working with teams of people, including Dr. Zelenko. So, when I talk about someone who had an impact, and made an impact, he impacted me personally in ways that I'll never be able to repay. And this is the reason that drives me with what I'm doing in the Foundation. When the call came in, it was, "I'll drop everything, and let's go get this done, because we've got to continue on in his work."

Brent: Wonderful. Menashe, a story from you. Something special about a moment you remember was Zev.

Menashe: It's really hard to pick one moment because, thank G-d, we had a lot of moments that I truly cherish. I would say that Zev was a follower of the Lubavitcher Rebbe – the Lubavitcher Rebbe is the founder of the Hasidic Chabad movement - and so am I, so we come from the same sect. One of the teachings that I think Zev carried that came originally from the Lubavitcher Rebbe was that you don't make followers. You make leaders. Zev inspired me a lot when I saw that every time he spoke and tried to convince people to do the right thing, he really encouraged them to study, encouraged them to know the information.

He said, "Don't just listen to me. I want you to doubt what I'm saying. I want you to go and check. Check. Go over here, go over there." He directed them where to go, and by doing so, I think he accomplished two things. Number one, he was able to convince them, and number two, he now made them messengers. He made them people that could carry his message by doing so. So, I think to me personally, not just on the leader level, but also on the business level, it was a very smart, inspiring thing that he did because he really believed in it.

You mentioned a humorous remark: He always said that Noah was a conspiracy theorist until it started raining, right? He used to say it a lot. It makes you think that we hear all these things, and the media immediately combated with saying this one word: "conspiracy," but he knew how to react to that.

He said, "You know what? We already had precedents to this. Look at the Bible. Everyone laughed at Noah, but one day it started raining, and they figured out he was right." Now, I see it so much, even at the synagogue, at the close circles where people are saying, "You know what? Zelenko was right. Dr. Zelenko was right."

Brent: Wonderful, thank you. Moshe. Please give us a story. You must have many, but give us one special story that people can really hold on to from your relationship with him.

Moshe: So, when I went with him to Europe, it was very, very difficult for my daughter. She and I are very close. I have a son and a daughter. He has four daughters and four sons, but my daughter was very, very… it was very hard for her for me to be away for one week, let alone for close to two months. So, she couldn't make it. She just couldn't accept it. We were together all the time.

So, I'm calling home, and he's sitting in the car. We were sitting together wherever we were at the time, either in Budapest or Vienna, and he could hear that my daughter was sad. My daughter wasn't aware that Zev was listening, and she was saying that she was my little baby. She's a 21-year-old, so she's a mature young lady.

She said, "I've never been away from you for this long. When are you coming back?" So, at one point, he jumps in, he says, "Shayna, I want you to know how much it means to me." He was always grateful to her, my wife, and my son because I was away with him.

"Since you think there's something that you want that I can do for you, and I'm gonna do it," he said, and she was like, "What?"

"No, you just… you think of something. Okay? And just call me, it doesn't matter what it is. Call me." Sure enough, somehow, he followed up. They talked, and I noticed at the time that she shared with him, "I want this particular handbag." It was a very fancy, expensive designer handbag.

She literally got that handbag in the mail from him. one day, it just shows up, and she couldn't believe it. She goes, "I can't believe he really did this." She was so taken, and she wore that bag; she had never had such a fancy thing before in her life. She wore it with pride, so much more than if it was like a trinket or something. It was like Zev's way of saying, "I got it that it hurt you, and I want to do something special for you."

Brent: It's a great story. Dave, you're up. Give us a special moment story from your perspective, your experience.

Dave: Well, the normal thing that would happen, kind of like what Ann was explaining, is people were getting trapped in hospital care with very ineffective protocols and things that were really reducing their chances for survival. So, we would undergo many rescue attempts, which would include Zev basically coaching the patient on how to deal with that specific hospital system: What to say, who to say it to, and how to really turn the advantage. Zev had become a master at this because of how many times he had to do it.

I remember there was a SEAL buddy of mine in his 70s, an older guy, that had been in there for over a month. After four or five coaching conversations, Zev could finally get this guy out and get him proper treatment. It ended up saving his life. But this is the story. This was like a normal Tuesday for Zev. That's what he did. Most people don't realize that he was not just actually treating people with his protocol, which obviously affected the world.

Let me give you an example of what I mean by his protocol affecting the world. In El Salvador, the whole health ministry brought all of their physicians, over a thousand physicians, to learn Zev's exact protocol. They implemented it nationwide and completely eradicated COVID from their country. No one has any idea. And this is the kind of stuff he would do, and I would be a part of it. I would listen and just help. I'm watching this guy going… how is this such a black market? It was so strange the way we had to go through all these procedures and how he had to coach people on what kind of things they could and shouldn't say to the hospital system in order to save their life from the hospital. So, it was definitely the most bizarre time of my life. To sum it all up, that was living with Zev and being wrapped in his world. This is what I saw almost every week, some issue just like this, a new one, and he was there for all of them. He never once said no.

Brent: So, let's talk a little about legacy and the Foundation that was started just right toward the end of Zev's life. Ann, you were selected to be the co-Chair of that Foundation, and you were kind enough to invite me to be on the board, which is a real privilege, and very humbling. Talk about Zev's legacy and then the Foundation's work, and how you see the Foundation preparing and creating that legacy for him, building upon what he's done already himself.

Ann: Sure. Zev was very much a futurist. He understood how the past related directly to the future—like a looking glass, if you will. He was such a perfect vessel for the word of G-d that if you listened to him, you felt as if G-d was directing you in what to do next. Part of Zev's foundation, or I should say Zev's legacy, which will be carried out through the work of the Foundation, is engaging with our future, and our future is our children.

We have got to put our arms around our kids today. Zev was the course correction for humanity by exposing the evil collaboration between Big Pharma, the medical-industrial complex, and our government. We've got to collaborate with the youth because they are our future tomorrow. The "woke" generation today could potentially be facilitating us in our elderly years of tomorrow, and I can tell you right now, based on how they value life and Zev recognized how the "woke" did not value life, I certainly don't want them rendering me care when I'm in my golden years. So, the Foundation's work will embrace the youth through the Zelenko Fellow Program, where we will work with these students and academia. We will work with these kids in other initiatives of the work of the Foundation, including media, which Zev talked about.

He wants the truth out there, like a mantra. He wants it everywhere. So, by having truth in media, we can show these young minds today what true New Media is, which should reflect back on old media when you presented the facts and let people draw their own conclusions. Give them the information. Don't put it in their face and sway them one way or the other, as we see with the lies that are told over and over because they're compensated by the collaboration of Big Pharma and our overgrown bureaucratic government that doesn't represent We, the People.

Other initiatives include community development. We are looking around at the institutions that have destroyed communities. We can go in, and we can rebuild. We can rebuild with far less expensive materials than what you see on the markets today, with hurricane impact ratings of over two hundred miles an hour. You've got fireproof, water-resistant, and mold-proof infrastructure, in addition to investing and incubating new technologies, creating jobs, manufacturing, and bringing those incubated companies into those communities that we're developing so we can provide sustainable jobs and housing for people in which to live and thrive. We're talking to companies that have true organic farming and bringing in the necessary food supply for those communities, which can also include areas for community development, community service, and community engagement, if you will: Education, and homeschooling, all under one umbrella. So, you can build back these communities not in the image of the World Economic Forum, which I believe the Zelenko Foundation is really squaring off with on other sides of the of the ring, but in the true essence of what G-d would want. He would want us to be free. Zev was very clear about that. He believed that we are all G-d's children, are meant to be free, and answer to our Divine Creator. What we are being subjected to today is anything but all of that.

So, the legacy of the Foundation will include that, in addition to working with the brightest minds in the medical world and in public policy, so that we can really work in terms of creating a government of the people, by the people, for the people, and generating the right public policy to address what the needs of the people are. Not the needs of the few, not what Bill Gates and Melinda Gates want, not what Klaus Schwab from the World Economic Forum wants, and certainly not what Fauci, the FDA, CDC, and NIH want, or any of these big medical-industrial complex corporations want. What we want.

We can do it all in G-d's image while glorifying Him at the same time. This is how Zev lived his life: Bold, strong, and outspoken, and the Foundation will represent all of that. But most importantly, it will serve the people; through that service, we glorify G-d, which Zev truly believed in. So, I'm humbled to be able to play a role in that and work with incredible minds to deliver that.

Brent: Thank you, Ann. Dave, talk a little bit about what you see as Zev's legacy and how the Foundation might play into that.

Dave: Well, Zev always wanted to start what he called the "Z army." I wish we had thought about starting this earlier. This is about empowering the people that have been so affected by Zev to continue forward and to continue in the knowledge, and really the continuation of this thought process, which is thinking for yourself and not just taking whatever anyone says as gospel.

I think there has been a fractured sense of trust in the major medical establishment, and I don't think that trust will be repaired anytime soon. There is a strong sense of trust that has been created by Zev and the doctors that have really rallied around Zev in the aftermath. This is all about: how do we organize? How do we formalize? What this thought process... I mean, we're very fractured. The one thing that the World Economic Forum has that we don't have is that they're extremely organized. They're able to work all over the world very effectively. There are really things that need to be emulated on that side, not on the actual goals they're implementing, but just how organized and strategic they are. We have to have the same type of resolve, if not more because we're severely outgunned in many ways.

But when I think of the Foundation and everything Ann just said, I think of resilience. I think the key to this new kind of way of life is that people wonder, *what's the future gonna look like for my kids?* Are there going to be these mandates every time they travel? This new world is changing, and I think for us to learn to slowly adjust our lives to live in a way that makes us resilient and able to not care who's in office anymore, you know? Or care a little bit less, because its not that we don't stop caring about that, but we stop caring about it in a way where we think our life is going to fall apart because of it. We want to live in a way where we can feel confident, regardless of the times that come ahead. And so, that's what I think of the Foundation; it's about resilience.

Brent: Good, thank you. Menashe, speak to your ideas about Zev's legacy, the Foundation, and the role it might play.

Menashe: I think it comes to Zev's legacy. It's a legacy of redemptive thinking—to believe that things can change for the positive, constantly believing in questioning but not disrespecting. He believed in bringing knowledge while running away from arrogance and that it shouldn't sound arrogant in any way. To be humble, but at the same time to question.

Thinking about legacy and what Zev would like, I think he would like the knowledge. People are looking for the knowledge of G-d and looking for truth in all areas. If it's medicine, if it's politics... whatever it is, that it's the truth. Zev was not, I would say, afraid to be disputed or debated. He was willing to debate even those with more experience and maybe even more knowledge, but he believed in what he was doing. So, I think his legacy is to bring that consciousness, that knowledge, that questioning that he had to the younger population—to everyone, but specifically, to those that can lead, to those that can pass on the information to others. So, his legacy is the legacy of passing truth, of questioning, and not being afraid to say, "I didn't know this," or "I was wrong over here," but constantly continuing to seek the truth.

Brent: Thank you. Moshe, I want to ask the same question to you, and then we're going to conclude this by giving you each thirty seconds to make one final, nice, tight statement that summarizes your thoughts on the man that was Zev Zelenko. But, Moshe, please share your thoughts on his legacy and the Foundation's role.

Moshe: Thank you. The greatest piece of his legacy would encourage all of us to fear G-d and not man. To see the frailties and the evil designs that are in the world that can be expressed on so many different levels, especially with media being such a pervasive part of our life and our consciousness. It was his continuous mastery of interweaving. He could interweave science, medicine, politics, and spirituality all in the same sentence. It's what made him, I think, so effective in being able to bring people into what the true narrative was.

And he was very G-d-centric in his life, speech, and how he would conduct himself. Remember, as I said earlier, he was always seeking to grow, always wanting to know: what can I do more? It didn't matter that he was nominated for this or that. I would be remiss to say, having had hundreds of lunches with him and being all over the world in the most diverse places, it was almost impossible to go anywhere where somebody didn't recognize him and thank him for saving some person. It was incredible seeing people saving themselves and his legacy will be for us to redirect any form of man-based fear, whether it be in any of the organizations that were raised today in any of the political appendages of the world. Regardless of what country you live in, he would call scripture, quote the Psalms of David, and say, "Don't put your fear in men. Put your faith in G-d." That, to me, is the greatest tribute to his legacy.

Brent: All right, good. So, each of you will wrap this up for thirty seconds. Just a final quick thought, an exclamation mark, if you will, on this wonderful session. I thank you all for joining us. I think this has been what we wanted it to be: A wonderful way to acknowledge the man, the totality of his life, and share some final thoughts since he's no longer with us, to share them. Ann, let's start with you. Zev was a big believer in chivalry, so ladies first.

Ann: Zev was a gentle lion. He absolutely stood up to tyranny. He never bowed down to tyrants, and I believe his G-d courage was infectious. He gave people the drive to ask the hard questions, zero in on the answers, and then deliver solutions. He wasn't afraid of anything.

I think Moshe said it beautifully when he said, "Don't fear man, fear G-d." And man is making mistakes left and right. But again, man can also decipher when you're using the word, what is right and what is wrong, and Zev was unequivocal about that. So, I love that man like a brother to me. He was incredibly important in my life, and I will forever cherish our friendship. It's because of that love of who he is and what he represented to all of humanity, his selfless acts, and everything he did, but because he put his family and G-d first, he will always be forever the hero for humanity. I think he needs to be remembered that way and I think that's how history will record him: that he saved humanity because he stood up to the tyrants. I think that's how we need to record him. Very simply put.

Brent: Thank you. Dave, thirty seconds, put an exclamation mark on our session for us here.

Dave: The thing I'll miss the most about Dr. Zelenko is our late-night conversations. I've never in my life experienced someone that was so self-aware and so willing to discuss their own failings. He was a guy that even was aware of any type of small, proud thought. He would analyze, and he was a guy that was totally aware and at peace with himself, and that translated into him because he put G-d first in his life. Nothing else mattered to him. Nothing. That's, I think, why he was able to be so transparent and so brutally honest. You very rarely find that. He caused me to be more honest about myself. Seeing the peace that he lived with and died with has shown me a clear direction forward of what I want to emulate.

Brent: Thank you. Menashe, your final thought?

Menashe: I think to me Zev is… the first thing is a kind-hearted person, not just someone who said it, but actually someone who practiced it on a day to day, every moment of his life. Someone that maximizes time to the fullest. If there was no one there at lunch, he would have to compete with someone, with chess or something like that. There was always something, and he was always busy. Someone that put his family first. Someone that had the ability to see ahead. As written in scripture, who is the wise man? Someone who can see the future, someone who can look ahead and see what's coming.

To me, Zev is not just a giant of intellect, of brilliance, but someone that was really humble, and I believe that reading now his intellectual book, his cabalistic book, I can even appreciate the depth of his knowledge that he had. So, it's someone to emulate on so many levels. But I would say the one thing that sticks the most is the honesty. Honesty and humility.

Brent: Thank you. Moshe, your final thought. It's appropriate that we conclude with you after all the time you spent right up until the end, and you will end our session today.

Moshe: Thank you. I first want to say that when his children have the opportunity to read this, or listen to this, to please never think for a moment that he did not love you or want the world for you. He may not have been able to execute everything as perfectly as he would have liked, but as I said, he constantly wanted to grow, do better, and improve himself. But all eight of you should know that you're the central point of his life, and you should all feel good that you had someone that all of you made such a big impression on.

In closing, I would say the following: he insisted that the subtitle of the book be "cutting off the head of the Primordial Snake." This is a very, very deep conversation and a very, very long and detailed study, but each one of us has within us the potential to choose good or evil. To the effect that we can choose good, seek forgiveness, rend our ways for whatever evil we might have done, and take up the arms against the evil that others may do to ourselves, our children… That would be the greatest joy that Dr. Vladimir "Zev" Zelenko could have in heaven. To see that we will continue that fight for truth, for fear of G-d over any other, and for bringing forth the hope that always burned inside of him.

I'll leave you with this one last thing. He said to me, "I'm not afraid to die." We were in Europe. He said to me, "I'm not afraid to die, but I want to live." So don't think that he was a fatalist and was ready to just transition. He accepted G-d's will; he knew there was a purpose to it. But we have inside of ourselves the ability to burn, internally and externally, the desire to emulate a person who loved life, loved G-d, loved his children and his family, and really wants the best for all of us. Maybe we should all be able to say that we were very blessed to be part of someone who had such an impact on the world and on our lives personally. May that impact continue for eternity.

Brent: Thank you so much. So, thanks to all of you for joining us. Ann, David, Menashe, Moshe. I hope that those of you who read this or listened to it, or watched it -or perhaps all three - I hope that it did for you what it did for us, which was to try to bring a sense of closure and perspective. We're grateful for your taking the time to read the book and read through this and what we've done here. So, I think it's safe to say that I'm thinking of the line from the song in the show *Wicked*: because we all knew him, we have been changed for good. With that, thank you very much to everyone. I'm Brent Hamachek, co-author of this book. Very humbled and grateful to have had a chance to lead this conversation. Thank you.

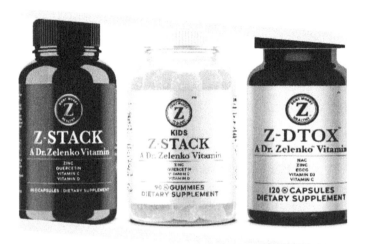

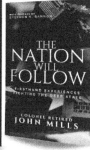

Made in the USA
Monee, IL
17 December 2022

22395315R00193